GEOMETRIC
TRANSFORMATIONS III

NEW MATHEMATICAL LIBRARY

published by

Random House/Singer School Division

for the Monograph Project *of the*

SCHOOL MATHEMATICS STUDY GROUP†

EDITORIAL PANEL

Basil Gordon, Chairman (1968–)
University of California, L. A.

Anneli Lax, Technical Editor
New York University

E. G. Begle	*Stanford University*
M. Bell (1962–68)	*University of Chicago*
L. Bers (1958–62)	*Columbia University*
B. Bold (1963–66)	*Stuyvesant High School, N. Y.*
W. G. Chinn (1961–67)	*San Francisco Public Schools*
H. S. M. Coxeter (1958–61)	*University of Toronto*
P. J. Davis (1961–64)	*Brown University*
E. C. Douglas (1966–69)	*The Taft School, Conn.*
E. Dyer (1963–66)	*City University of New York*
H. J. Greenberg (1964–67)	*University of Denver*
P. R. Halmos (1958–63)	*University of Indiana*
J. H. Hlavaty (1958–63)	*DeWitt Clinton High School, N. Y.*
N. Jacobson (1958–61)	*Yale University*
M. Kac (1961–65)	*Rockefeller University*
M. Klamkin (1965–68)	*The Ford Motor Company*
J. Landin (1966–69)	*University of Illinois, Chicago*
I. Niven (1962–68)	*University of Oregon*
R. S. Pieters (1958–62)	*Phillips Academy*
H. O. Pollak (1958–61)	*Bell Telephone Laboratories, Inc.*
G. Pólya (1958–61)	*Stanford University*
W. Prenowitz (1962–65)	*Brooklyn College*
D. Richmond (1965–68)	*Williams College*
A. Y. Rickey (1965–68)	*Dade County, Fla., Public Schools*
H. E. Robbins (1958–61)	*Columbia University*
W. W. Sawyer (1958–60)	*University of Toronto*
D. S. Scott (1963–66)	*Oxford University*
N. E. Steenrod (1958–62)	*Princeton University*
J. J. Stoker (1958–61)	*New York University*
H. Swain (1967–70)	*New Trier Township H. S., Ill.*
M. Zelinka (1962–65)	*Weston High School, Mass.*
L. Zippin (1958–61)	*City University of New York*

† The School Mathematics Study Group represented all parts of the mathematical profession and all parts of the country. Its activities were aimed at the improvement of teaching of mathematics in our schools.

QA
601
I 313
v.3

GEOMETRIC TRANSFORMATIONS III

by

[I. M. Yaglom]

translated from the Russian by

A. Shenitzer

York University, Toronto

82855

24

RANDOM HOUSE/SINGER School Division

RANDOM HOUSE, INC.

NEW YORK

Illustrated by George H. Buehler

First Printing

© Copyright, 1973, by Yale University
All rights reserved under International and Pan-American Copyright
Conventions. Published in New York by Random House, Inc., and
simultaneously in Toronto, Canada, by Random House of Canada, Limited.

Library of Congress Catalog Card Number: 72–5702

Manufactured in the United States of America

Note to the Reader

This book is one of a series written by professional mathematicians in order to make some important mathematical ideas interesting and understandable to a large audience of high school students and laymen. Most of the volumes in the *New Mathematical Library* cover topics not usually included in the high school curriculum; they vary in difficulty, and, even within a single book, some parts require a greater degree of concentration than others. Thus, while the reader needs little technical knowledge to understand most of these books, he will have to make an intellectual effort.

If the reader has so far encountered mathematics only in classroom work, he should keep in mind that a book on mathematics cannot be read quickly. Nor must he expect to understand all parts of the book on first reading. He should feel free to skip complicated parts and return to them later; often an argument will be clarified by a subsequent remark. On the other hand, sections containing thoroughly familiar material may be read very quickly.

The best way to learn mathematics is to *do* mathematics, and each book includes problems, some of which may require considerable thought. The reader is urged to acquire the habit of reading with paper and pencil in hand; in this way mathematics will become increasingly meaningful to him.

For the authors and editors this is a new venture. They wish to acknowledge the generous help given them by the many high school teachers and students who assisted in the preparation of these monographs. The editors are interested in reactions to the books in this series and hope that readers will write to: Editorial Committee of the NML series, NEW YORK UNIVERSITY, THE COURANT INSTITUTE OF MATHEMATICAL SCIENCES, 251 Mercer Street, New York, N. Y. 10012.

The Editors

v

NEW MATHEMATICAL LIBRARY

Other titles will be announced when ready

1. NUMBERS: RATIONAL AND IRRATIONAL by Ivan Niven
2. WHAT IS CALCULUS ABOUT? by W. W. Sawyer
3. INTRODUCTION TO INEQUALITIES by E. Beckenbach and R. Bellman
4. GEOMETRIC INEQUALITIES by N. D. Kazarinoff
5. THE CONTEST PROBLEM BOOK I, Annual High School Contests of the Mathematical Association of America, 1950–1960, compiled and with solutions by Charles T. Salkind
6. THE LORE OF LARGE NUMBERS by P. J. Davis
7. USES OF INFINITY by Leo Zippin
8. GEOMETRIC TRANSFORMATIONS I by I. M. Yaglom, translated from the Russian by Allen Shields
9. CONTINUED FRACTIONS by C. D. Olds
10. GRAPHS AND THEIR USES by Oystein Ore
11. HUNGARIAN PROBLEM BOOK I, based on the Eötvös Competitions, 1894–1905
12. HUNGARIAN PROBLEM BOOK II, based on the Eötvös Competitions, 1906–1928
13. EPISODES FROM THE EARLY HISTORY OF MATHE-MATICS by Asger Aaboe
14. GROUPS AND THEIR GRAPHS by I. Grossman and W. Magnus
15. MATHEMATICS OF CHOICE by Ivan Niven
16. FROM PYTHAGORAS TO EINSTEIN by K. O. Friedrichs
17. THE MAA PROBLEM BOOK II, Annual High School Contests of the Mathematical Association of America, 1961–1965, compiled and with solutions by Charles T. Salkind
18. FIRST CONCEPTS OF TOPOLOGY by W. G. Chinn and N. E. Steenrod
19. GEOMETRY REVISITED by H. S. M. Coxeter and S. L. Greitzer
20. INVITATION TO NUMBER THEORY by Oystein Ore
21. GEOMETRIC TRANSFORMATIONS II by I. M. Yaglom, translated from the Russian by Allen Shields
22. ELEMENTARY CRYPTANALYSIS—A MATHEMATICAL APPROACH by Abraham Sinkov
23. INGENUITY IN MATHEMATICS by Ross Honsberger
24. GEOMETRIC TRANSFORMATIONS III by I. M. Yaglom, translated from the Russian by A. Shenitzer

Contents

Translator's Preface

The present volume is a translation of the first of the two chapters that make up Part III of *Geometric Transformations* by I. M. Yaglom. Parts I and II are available in English as NML volumes 8 and 21. The second, not yet translated, chapter of Part III deals with inversions, that is, *transformations of the plane that take circles* (*including lines which may be viewed as circles of infinite radius*) *into circles*, but need not carry lines into lines; it also deals with transformations of the plane that take circles (including points which may be viewed as circles of zero radius) into circles, and lines into lines, but need not carry points into points. Like the first chapter, so too the second chapter concludes with a *Supplement* on hyperbolic geometry. For technical reasons, it was not possible to include both chapters of the Russian original Part III in a single NML volume; it is hoped that the remaining untranslated chapter will, at some future time, be published in English as a separate volume.

This NML volume deals with affine and projective transformations of the plane. As in NML 8 and 21, the 112 problems interspersed throughout the text are an essential part also of this book; their detailed solutions are included.

The translator wishes to thank Professor Yaglom for his valuable assistance in preparing this American edition. He examined the draft of the translation, made several additions and corrections, and prepared a number of new problems for the translation, not present in the Russian version.

An effort was made to use similar English terminology in all parts of this translation; however, we note one exception: the composite of two transformations is called their *product* in the present volume, but was called their *sum* in NML 8 and 21 (see translator's note[T] on page 13 of NML 21).

The translator wishes to express special thanks to Dr. Basil Gordon for reading and correcting drafts of this translation, and to Dr. Anneli Lax, editor of the SMSG Monograph Project, for her assistance and patience in the preparation of the final version.

Abe Shenitzer

From the Author's Preface

This part of *Geometric Transformations* is devoted to the study of transformations of the plane which carry lines into lines. These are known as affine and projective transformations, or simply as collineations, and studied at the university in the USSR. Yet, the present work is aimed primarily at readers concerned with high school mathematics: high school students and teachers as well as prospective high school teachers and *their* teachers. Thus, the main objective of the present work is to demonstrate the close connection between affine and projective transformations (affinities and projectivities) and elementary geometry.

Considerations of space ruled out almost entirely a discussion of more advanced theories connected with geometric transformations. The one significant excursion into "higher geometry" is the *Supplement* devoted to hyperbolic geometry. But even here no effort was spared to keep the exposition elementary in the hope of making the *Supplement* accessible to the more persistent high school students.

The problems form an essential part of the book; their solutions appear in the second half of the book. While the basic text is entirely independent of the problems, the author believes that the reader's attempts to solve at least some of them is bound to deepen his understanding of the text. All the problems pertain to elementary geometry, except those in the *Supplement* which are intended to acquaint the reader with concrete theorems of hyperbolic geometry. (To keep the exposition at once concise and elementary the author refrained from introducing the concept of "conic section". This made it impossible to treat the natural question of the effects of affine and projective transformations on *circles*.) Some of the solutions include general remarks bearing on the use of the transformations discussed.

This part of *Geometric Transformations* is essentially independent of the preceding two.[T] (The few references to them can be replaced by references to a suitably detailed textbook on plane geometry.) Nevertheless there is a rather direct link between the *Introduction* and *Supplement* in this part and the *Introductions* in the two earlier parts.[T] With one significant exception noted in the Translator's Preface to the present volume, the same terminology is used in all three volumes.

The reader may initially omit the *Introduction* and *Supplement* (but the author would regret it if a reader ignored these parts altogether). A similar remark applies to the last section (Section 5) which is rather tenuously connected with the rest of the book.

I. M. Yaglom

[T] The translations of the preceding two parts of *Geometric Transformations* appeared as NML volumes 8 and 21.

What is Geometry? (Final Essay)

In the introduction to NML 8 we defined geometry as a discipline concerned with those properties of figures which remain invariant under motions. In the introduction to NML 21 we gave a new definition of geometry as a discipline concerned with those properties of figures which remain invariant under similarities. It is natural to ask whether or not these definitions are fully equivalent, that is, whether they are different definitions of the same discipline, or whether there exist two different geometries: the one discussed in the introduction to NML 8, and the other discussed in the introduction to NML 21. We shall show that the second alternative is the correct one, that is, that these two geometries are different (though closely related), and in fact, there exist many different geometries. One of the most interesting is the non-Euclidean geometry of Lobachevski-Bolyai, also called hyperbolic geometry; it differs radically from the usual geometry and is discussed in the *Supplement* at the end of this book.†

In the introduction to NML 21 we pointed out that our earlier definition of geometry as the study of those properties of figures which are invariant under motions was inexpedient. We supported this claim as follows: Motions are transformations of the plane that preserve the distance between any two points. However, the number expressing distance depends on the choice of a unit of measurement. Since a geometric proposition cannot depend on the choice of a unit of length, it follows that geometric theorems must refer to ratios of lengths of segments rather than to lengths of segments. Another way of saying this is that in geometry we do not distinguish between similar figures. Briefly, *if a theorem is true for a certain configuration, it is true also for any similar configuration.*

† See also I. M. Yaglom, *Complex Numbers in Geometry* (Academic Press, N.Y., 1968) Appendix, where the 8 non-Euclidean geometries of the plane, including hyperbolic geometry, are discussed.

2

While this argument is valid for all *theorems* of elementary geometry, it is not valid, for example, for all geometric *constructions*. If in a geometric construction we are given the length of a segment, then this length is given not by means of a number, but by means of a given segment. For example, if we are required to construct a triangle ABC given the lengths of two of its sides, AC and AB, and the length of the median CD, this means that we are given segments congruent to AC, AB and CD (Fig. 1). What is involved here is lengths of segments rather than ratios of such lengths, and this means that not all similar triangles can be regarded as acceptable solutions; if one of these triangles is a solution of our problem then the others (not congruent to it) are not. We see that, while the definition of geometry given in the introduction to NML 21 covers all theorems of elementary geometry, the same cannot be said of all construction problems (based, in an essential way, on the definition of geometry given earlier, in the introduction to NML 8). That is why the exposition in Kiselyov's textbook[T] is based on the earlier definition and opens, accordingly, with theorems dealing with the congruence of triangles; such theorems would be devoid of content if we did not distinguish between similar triangles since, in that case, the very notion of congruence would be vacuous.

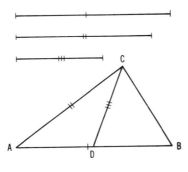

Figure 1

We are thus led to the conclusion that the geometries defined in the introductions to NML 8 and NML 21 are different. Furthermore, all properties of figures in the second geometry (conveniently called the *geometry of similarities*) are also properties of figures in the first geometry (the *geometry of motions*); indeed, every property of a figure preserved under similarities is certainly preserved under motions. The converse of this assertion is false; there are more properties in the geometry of motions than in the geometry of similarities. (In the geometry of motions the distance between two points of a figure is one of its geometric properties, whereas in the geometry of similarities only ratios of distances have

---

[T] This is the standard Russian textbook of geometry.

significance.) This explains why there are far fewer construction problems in the geometry of similarities than in the geometry of motions.†

Recall how we arrived at our two definitions. We defined the geometry of motions as the study of those properties of figures that are preserved under motions. To put it differently, in this geometry we regard two figures which can be carried into each other by a motion, that is, two congruent figures, as indistinguishable. We defined the geometry of similarities as the study of those properties of figures which are preserved under similarities. To put it differently, in this geometry we regard two figures which can be carried into each other by a similarity as indistinguishable; briefly, here "congruent" is replaced by "similar". Following this approach, *we define two figures to be equivalent relative to a definite class of transformations if they can be carried into each other by a transformation of the class.‡ The geometry associated with the class of transformations in question is defined as the study of those properties of figures which are preserved under the transformations of that class.*

We are now close to a final answer to the question of what is geometry. To give a complete definition of geometry (more accurately, of the totality of different geometries) we must still explain what restrictions, if any, should be imposed on the class of transformations underlying a particular geometry.

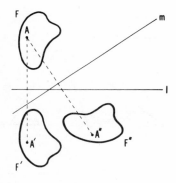

Figure 2

---

† In the geometry of similarities the only geometric properties of a figure are angles and ratios of distances. So in that geometry the only possible construction problems involve certain angles between lines of the figure and ratios of distances between its points. For example: Construct a triangle ABC given the angle A and the ratio of the lengths of the angle bisector and the altitude from the vertex B. To solve this problem is to find any of the similar triangles with a given angle at one vertex and a given ratio of angle bisector to altitude from another vertex.

‡ In what follows we introduce classes of transformations more general than the class of similarities.

The need for imposing some restrictions is rather obvious. Suppose, for example, we tried to define a "geometry of reflections" as the study of those *and only those* properties of figures which are preserved under reflection in a line. In this hypothetical geometry, the two figures F and F' (Fig. 2), symmetric with respect to the line l would belong to the same class, and since F'' is symmetric to F with respect to the line m, F and F'' would belong to the same class; yet F' and F'' are not symmetric with respect to any line.† Thus we have not introduced a useful set of equivalence classes into our hypothetical geometry; F' and F'' are not in the same class, although both belong to the same class as F!

To see what restrictions must be imposed on a class of transformations which is to serve as a basis for a geometry, we consider more closely the relation of equivalence of figures.

Our experience with equivalence relations in mathematics, in other disciplines and in daily life indicates that equivalence of figures must satisfy the following requirements:

1. *Every figure is equivalent to itself.*
2. *If a figure F is equivalent to a figure F', then, conversely, F' is equivalent to F.*
3. *If a figure F is equivalent to a figure F_1 and F_1 is equivalent to the figure F', then F is equivalent to F'.*

These requirements will certainly be satisfied if our class G of transformations has the following properties:

1. *G contains the identity transformation* (the transformation which leaves each figure pointwise fixed).
2. *If G contains a transformation* Π *which carries a figure F into a figure F', then it must also contain a transformation P (the inverse of* Π*) which carries F' into F* (Fig. 3a).

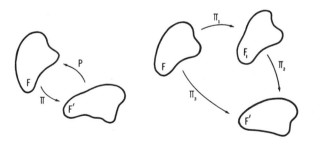

Figure 3a   Figure 3b

† This follows, for example, from the fact that two figures symmetric with respect to a line are always oppositely congruent, whereas the figures F' and F'' are directly congruent (cf. NML 8).

3. *If G contains a transformation Π_1 which carries a figure F into a figure F_1 and a transformation Π_2 which carries F_1 into F', then it must also contain a transformation Π_3 (the "product"[T] of the two transformations) which carries F into F'* (Fig. 3b).

A class G of transformations with properties 1–3 is called a *group of transformations*. Thus, for example, all motions form a group, and the same is true of all similarities. All rotations of the plane about a fixed point O also form a group. Indeed,

1. The identity transformation is the rotation about O through $0°$ (or any multiple of 360°);

2. The inverse of a rotation about O through an angle α is the rotation about O through the same angle α in the opposite direction;

3. The product of a rotation about O through an angle α and a rotation about O through an angle β is the rotation about O through the angle $\alpha + \beta$.

In contrast to the rotations about a point, the class of *all* rotations of a plane does not form a group; the product of two rotations may turn out to be a translation and not a rotation (cf. Ch. 1, §2 of NML 8). The totality of reflections of a plane in all of its lines likewise fails to form a group; here neither condition 3 nor 1 of the definition of a group is met (the product of two reflections is generally not a reflection in a line, cf. Ch. 2, §1 of NML 8; the identity transformation cannot be represented as a reflection in a line).

We can now state the definition of a geometry as follows: *A geometry is a discipline concerned with those properties of figures which do not change under the transformations of a group of transformations.* This definition emphasizes that there are many geometries, not just one, and that to obtain a geometry we need only select a group of transformations. Two instances are the geometry of motions and the geometry of similarities studied in school. In the *Supplement* to this book we shall show that hyperbolic geometry can also be regarded as a geometry in this new sense.

The definition of a geometry as a study of those properties of figures which are not affected by transformations belonging to a particular group is due to the German mathematician F. Klein. Although this is not the most general definition (it does not include certain important areas of geometry), it has proved to be very useful and has played an important role in the development of science. In particular, the concept of a group

---

[T] The composite $\Pi_3 = \Pi_2 \cdot \Pi_1$ of Π_1 and Π_2, $\Pi_3(F) = \Pi_2[\Pi_1(F)]$, is usually called the "product" of Π_1 and Π_2, but it was called the "sum" in Parts I and II of *Geometric Transformations*, see NML vol. 8 and vol. 21. Cf. footnote [T] on p. 13 of NML 21.

of transformations is now one of the most important concepts of modern mathematics.†

Elementary plane geometry concerns itself largely with figures made up of lines and circles. It can be shown (cf. NML 21, p. 57) that *similarities can be defined as transformations of the plane which carry lines into lines and circles into circles*. The transformations of the plane that preserve lines (i.e., carry lines into lines) without necessarily preserving circles are known as *affine transformations* or *affinities* and form a group‡ which is the basis of *affine geometry*. The transformations of the *projective plane* (cf. p. 41) that preserve lines (cf. footnote † on p. 52) without necessarily preserving circles are known as *projective transformations* or *projectivities* and form a group which is the basis of *projective geometry*.¶ The transformations of the plane that preserve circles (with lines viewed as circles of infinite radius) are known as *circular transformations* and form a group which is the basis of *inversive geometry*.||

While the present book deals with affine and projective transformations, it is not meant to serve as an introduction to the important and interesting geometries associated with these groups of transformations; its aim, rather, is to demonstrate that the existence of various geometries can be very helpful even if we do not go beyond elementary geometry. If we realize that a particular theorem is essentially a theorem of, say, projective geometry (that is, the theorem deals with properties unchanged under projective transformations), then we can frequently simplify its proof. For example, suppose that we are required to prove that three lines l_1, l_2 and l_3 are concurrent. If we apply a projective transformation to the diagram of our theorem, then the lines l_1, l_2, l_3 go over into lines l_1', l_2', l_3' which are concurrent if and only if l_1, l_2, l_3 are concurrent.

---

† Two excellent elementary introductions to the theory of groups are: P. S. Alexandroff, *An Introduction to the Theory of Groups*, Hafner Publishing Co., New York, 1959, and I. Grossman and W. Magnus, *Groups and Their Graphs*, Random House, New York, 1964, NML 14 of this series.

‡ Clearly, if a transformation Π carries lines into lines then so does its inverse; if two transformations Π₁ and Π₂ carry lines into lines, then so does their product Π₃; and the identity transformation preserves lines. So, the line preserving transformations of the plane form a group.

¶ Projective geometry is commonly taught in college. Two introductions to the subject (in English) are: H. S. M. Coxeter, *Projective Geometry*, Blaisdell Publ. Co., New York, 1964, and A. Seidenberg, *Lectures in Projective Geometry*, D. Van Nostrand Co., Inc., Princeton, N. J., 1962.

|| Cf. Ch. 8 of A. Tuller, *A Modern Introduction to Geometries*, D. Van Nostrand Co., Inc., Princeton, N.J., 1967.

Now it may happen that a clever choice of the projective transformation results in lines l_1', l_2', l_3' whose concurrency is easier to demonstrate than that of the original lines l_1, l_2, l_3. This method of proof is illustrated in this book by many varied examples.

We note that the techniques the reader will encounter for solving problems in the present book differ somewhat from those in NML 8 and NML 21. There we applied motions and similarities to transform a definite *part* of the diagram of a problem, whereas in the present book we shall very frequently transform the *whole* diagram of a problem. The reason for this difference in approach is clear. A motion applied to a diagram as a whole leaves the diagram unchanged (in elementary geometry we do not distinguish between figures which differ in position alone) and consequently unsimplified. On the other hand, in proving a theorem of elementary geometry, which is essentially a theorem of projective geometry or inversive geometry, we may find that a transformation of the complete diagram of the theorem offers considerable advantages.

Just as the techniques used to solve problems in the present book differ somewhat from those used in NML 8 and NML 21 so does the character of the problems. Whereas in NML 8 and NML 21 the reader is mostly asked to carry out various constructions, in the present book he is usually asked to prove theorems. However, it should be pointed out that projective transformations or inversions can sometimes be of help even in the solution of construction problems, as shown by the following three interesting problems:

(a) Inscribe in a given circle an n-gon whose sides pass through n given points in the plane (cf. Problem 84(a) in §5, p. 97).

(b) Circumscribe about a given circle an n-gon whose vertices lie on n given lines (cf. Problem 84(b), §5, p. 97).

(c) Inscribe in a given n-gon another n-gon whose sides pass through n given points in the plane (cf. Problem 90, §5, p. 99).

The solution of the first of these problems without the use of projective or circular transformations is very complicated.† As for the second and third problems, no simple solution which does not employ such transformations is known.

We note, finally, that the use of projective and circular transformations enables us to answer the question of possible straightedge constructions (cf. §5) and possible compass constructions (cf. Ch. 2^T).

---

† See, for example, L. I. Golovina and I. M. Yaglom, *Induction in Geometry*, D. C. Heath and Co., Boston, 1963, pp. 49–52.

T Reference to untranslated Russian material.

CHAPTER ONE

Affine and Projective Transformations (Affinities and Projectivities)

1. Parallel projection of a plane onto a plane
Affine transformations of the plane

Let π and π' be two distinct (parallel or intersecting) planes. By a *parallel projection of π onto π' in a direction a* we mean a mapping of π onto π' that associates with each point P in the plane π the point P' in the plane π' which lies on the line through P parallel to the given line a (Fig. 4a, b).† Such a mapping takes every figure F in the plane π into some figure F' in the plane π'. The image of a window produced by the sun on a floor (Fig. 5) can be thought of as the result of a parallel projection.‡

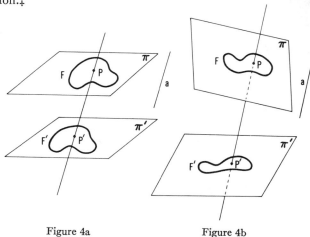

Figure 4a   Figure 4b

† It is clear that the line a which determines a parallel projection of the plane π onto the plane π' must not be parallel to π or to π'. In the sequel we take it for granted that this requirement is satisfied.

‡ In view of the great distance to the sun we may suppose its rays parallel.

Figure 5

If the planes π and π' are parallel, then a parallel projection takes a figure in π into a congruent figure in π' (in this case a parallel projection reduces to a translation in space in the direction of the line a; cf. Fig. 4a†). If π and π' are not parallel, then a parallel projection distorts the form of figures (cf. Fig. 4b; recall how strongly the shadows of objects are distorted in the morning and in the late afternoon).

It is sometimes possible to simplify the solution of geometric problems by considering not a given configuration, but rather its image under a suitable parallel projection. The present section is devoted to this technique of solving problems. First, however, we must study fundamental properties of parallel projections.

† Translation in space is defined in a manner similar to that of translation in the plane (cf. NML 8, p. 15).

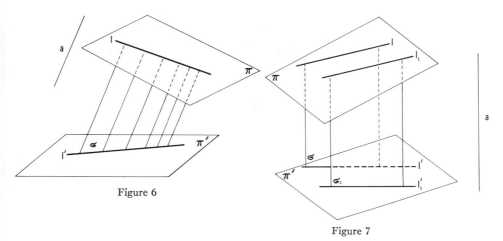

Figure 6

Figure 7

A. *A parallel projection maps lines in π onto lines in π'.* Indeed, the lines parallel to a and passing through the points of a line l in the plane π form a plane σ (passing through l and parallel to a). It follows that the image of l under our parallel projection is the line l' in which the plane σ intersects π' (Fig. 6). Conversely, every line in π' is the image of some line in π.

B. *A parallel projection takes parallel lines into parallel lines.* Indeed, if the lines l and l_1 in π are parallel, then the planes σ and σ_1, parallel to a and passing through l and l_1, are parallel. It follows that the lines l' and l_1' where the planes σ and σ_1 intersect π' are parallel (Fig. 7).

C. *A parallel projection preserves the ratio of the lengths of two collinear segments.* This is an immediate consequence of the theorem: parallel lines intersecting the sides of an angle cut off proportional segments on these sides (cf. Fig. 8a, where $AB/BC = A'B'/B'C'$).

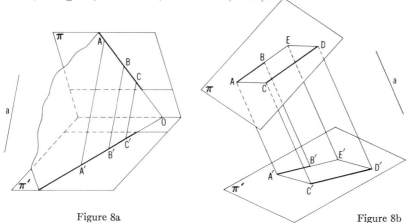

Figure 8a

Figure 8b

A *parallel projection also preserves the ratio of the lengths of two segments on parallel lines.* Indeed, let AB and CD be two segments in the plane π such that $AB \parallel CD$, and let E be the point on the line AB such that $ED \parallel AC$ (Fig. 8b). A parallel projection takes the parallelogram $ACDE$ into the parallelogram $A'C'D'E'$ (since the segment AB goes over into the segment $A'B'$, and parallel lines go over into parallel lines). Hence (bearing in mind that a parallel projection preserves the ratio of the lengths of two collinear segments) we see that

$$\frac{CD}{AB} = \frac{AE}{AB} = \frac{A'E'}{A'B'} = \frac{C'D'}{A'B'}.$$

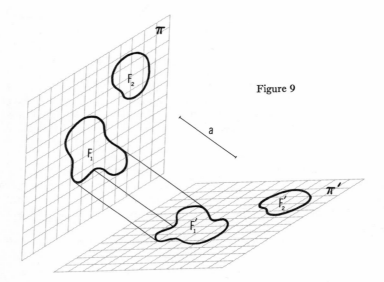

Figure 9

D. *A parallel projection preserves the ratio of the areas of two figures in the plane.* To prove this assertion draw in the plane π a network of congruent squares. Properties B and C imply that a parallel projection will map this network of squares into a network of congruent parallelograms in π' (Fig. 9). Let F_1 and F_2 be two figures in π, and let F_1' and F_2' denote their images in π' under a parallel projection. If the network of squares is sufficiently fine, then the ratio of the number of squares in the interior of F_1 to the number of squares in the interior of F_2 will differ by arbitrarily little from the ratio S_1/S_2 of the areas of the figures F_1 and F_2,[†] and, similarly, the ratio of the number of parallelograms in the interior of F_1' to the number of parallelograms in the interior of F_2' differs by arbitrarily little from the ratio S_1'/S_2' of the areas of F_1' and F_2'.

† S_1/S_2 is the limit of the ratio of the number of squares in F_1 to the number of squares in F_2 as the side of a square in the network decreases indefinitely.

Since the number of squares in F_1 is equal to the number of parallelograms in F_1', and the number of squares in F_2 is equal to the number of parallelograms in F_2', we conclude that

$$S_1/S_2 = S_1'/S_2',$$

as asserted.

We now prove the following fundamental theorem on parallel projections.

THEOREM 1. *Let* A, B, C *be three non-collinear points in a plane* π, *and let* M, N, P *be three non-collinear points in a plane* π'. *Then the planes* π *and* π' *can be so placed in space that there exists a parallel projection of* π *onto* π' *which maps* $\triangle ABC$ *onto a triangle* $A'B'C'$ *similar to* $\triangle MNP$.

We place the given planes π and π' so that they intersect along the line AB. Now we choose in the plane π' a point C' such that $\triangle ABC' \sim \triangle MNP$. Then the required parallel projection is determined by the line CC' (Fig. 10).

Figure 10

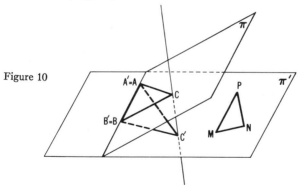

1. Prove that the three medians of a triangle are concurrent (that is, intersect in a point).

2. Prove that the line joining the point of intersection of the extensions of the nonparallel sides of a trapezoid to the point of intersection of its diagonals bisects the base of the trapezoid.

3. Let l and l_1 be two given parallel lines in a plane.
   (a) Bisect a segment AB on the line l using a straightedge alone.
   (b) Through a given point M draw a line parallel to l and l_1 using a straightedge alone.

A generalization of Problem 3 (a) is Problem 32 (b) in the next section (p. 43).

4. Let M, N and P be three points on the sides AB, BC and AC of a triangle ABC such that $AM/MB = BN/NC = CP/PA$. Show that:
(a) the point of intersection of the medians of $\triangle MNP$ coincides with the point of intersection of the medians of $\triangle ABC$;
(b) the point of intersection of the medians of the triangle formed by lines AN, BP and CM coincides with the point of intersection of the medians of $\triangle ABC$.

5. Given a triangle ABC. Find a point M in the interior of $\triangle ABC$ such that the triangles ABM, BCM and CAM have equal areas.

6. Let A_1, B_1, C_1 be points on the sides BC, CA, AB of a triangle ABC such that

$$\frac{BA_1}{A_1C} = \frac{CB_1}{B_1A} = \frac{AC_1}{C_1B} = k.$$

Furthermore, let A_2, B_2, C_2 be points on the sides B_1C_1, C_1A_1, A_1B_1 of $\triangle A_1B_1C_1$ such that

$$\frac{C_1A_2}{A_2B_1} = \frac{A_1B_2}{B_2C_1} = \frac{B_1C_2}{C_2A_1} = k.$$

Show that triangles ABC and $A_2B_2C_2$ are similar.

7. Let K, L, M be points on the sides of a triangle ABC of area 1 which divide its sides in given ratios k_1, k_2, k_3. Show that the area of triangle KLM depends only on the numbers k_1, k_2, k_3 and not on which sides are divided in what ratio.

8. Through each of the vertices of a triangle ABC we draw two lines dividing the opposite side into three equal parts. These six lines determine a hexagon (Fig. 11a). Prove that the diagonals joining opposite vertices of this hexagon meet in a point.

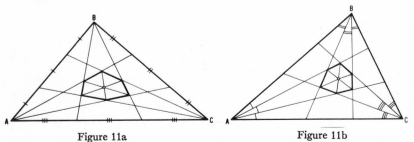

Figure 11a   Figure 11b

In Problem 8 we assumed that the two lines from each vertex of $\triangle ABC$ divided the opposite *side* into three equal parts. If, instead, we assume that these lines divide the *angle* into three equal parts we obtain an interesting variant of the theorem in Problem 8 (Fig. 11b). (A particularly simple proof may be found in Coxeter's *Introduction to Geometry*, (2nd ed.) pp. 25, 423 (Ex. 1) or in NML 19, pp. 49, 163 (Ex. 1.).

9. Let M, N, P be points on the sides[T] AB, BC, and AC of a triangle ABC. Show that

(a) if the points M_1, N_1, and P_1 are symmetric to M, N and P with respect to the midpoints of sides AB, BC, AC, respectively, (Fig. 12a), then triangles MNP and $M_1N_1P_1$ have equal areas (in particular, if the points M, N and P are collinear, the same is true of the points M_1, N_1 and P_1);

(b) if M_1, N_1 and P_1 are points on sides AC, BA and CB of $\triangle ABC$ such that $MM_1 \parallel BC$, $NN_1 \parallel CA$ and $PP_1 \parallel AB$ (Fig. 12b), then triangles MNP and $M_1N_1P_1$ have equal areas (in particular, if the points M, N and P are collinear, the same is true of the points M_1, N_1 and P_1).

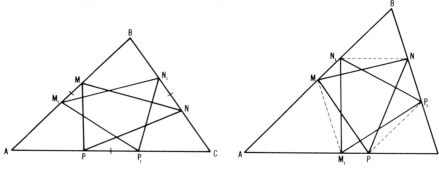

Figure 12a   Figure 12b

10. Let the points M, N, P and M_1, N_1, P_1 be chosen as in 9(a). Show that the triangle with sides AN, BP, CM has the same area as the triangle with sides AN_1, BP_1, CM_1 (in particular, if lines AN, BP, CM are concurrent, then so are lines AN_1, BP_1, CM_1).

11. (a) Let l be a line passing through the point M of intersection of the medians of a triangle ABC and intersecting its sides in points R, S, T (R and S lie on the same side of M). Show that

$$\frac{1}{MR} + \frac{1}{MS} = \frac{1}{MT}.$$

(b) Let l be a line passing through the vertex M of a parallelogram $MNPQ$ and intersecting the lines NP, PQ, NQ in points

---

[T] Here and in Problem 10, "side" of a triangle means the *entire line* through two vertices, not merely the segment joining them.

R, S, T. Show that

$$\frac{1}{MR} + \frac{1}{MS} = \frac{1}{MT}.$$

12. Inscribe a rectangle of given area σ in a given triangle ABC so that two of its vertices lie on the side AB and the remaining vertices lie on the sides CA and CB.

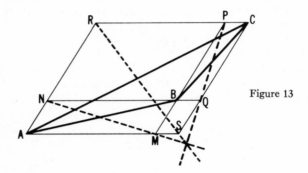

Figure 13

13. The sides of a triangle ABC are diagonals of three parallelograms whose sides have the same directions (Fig. 13). Show that the other diagonals of these parallelograms are concurrent.

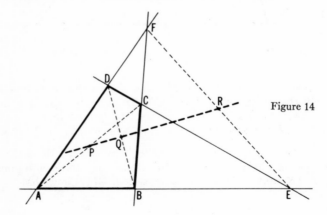

Figure 14

14. Show that the line joining the midpoints of the diagonals of a quadrilateral $ABCD$ bisects the segment joining the points of intersection of the opposite sides of the quadrilateral (Fig. 14). (Clearly, for opposite sides to intersect, the quadrilateral must not be a parallelogram or a trapezoid.)

The theorem in Problem 14 is frequently formulated differently. A plane figure formed by four lines no three of which are concurrent and no two of which are parallel is called a *complete quadrilateral*. The six points in which the four lines (sides of the complete quadrilateral) intersect are called its *vertices*, and the lines joining opposite vertices (i.e., vertices not on the same side) are called its diagonals. Using these terms we can state Problem 14 as follows: *The midpoints of the diagonals of a complete quadrilateral are collinear* (Theorem of Gauss or Theorem of the Complete Quadrilateral).

15. (a) Let A_1, B_1, C_1, D_1 be points on the sides CD, DA, AB, BC of a parallelogram $ABCD$ such that

$$\frac{CA_1}{CD} = \frac{DB_1}{DA} = \frac{AC_1}{AB} = \frac{BD_1}{BC} = \frac{1}{3}.$$

Show that the area of the quadrilateral formed by the lines AA_1, BB_1, CC_1, DD_1 is one thirteenth of the area of parallelogram $ABCD$.

(b) Let A_1, B_1, C_1 be points on sides BC, CA, AB of a triangle ABC such that

$$\frac{BA_1}{BC} = \frac{CB_1}{CA} = \frac{AC_1}{AB} = \frac{1}{3}.$$

Show that the area of the triangle determined by lines AA_1, BB_1, CC_1 is one seventh of the area of $\triangle ABC$.

16. Prove the *theorem of Ceva:* If M, N, P are points on the sides AB, BC and CA of a triangle ABC (but not on their extensions), and if

$$\frac{AM}{MB} \cdot \frac{BN}{NC} \cdot \frac{CP}{PA} = 1,$$

then the lines AN, BP and CM are concurrent.

Problem 27(b) in Ch. 1, §1 (see NML 21, p. 34) and Problem 34(b) in §2 of the present work yield a proof of a more complete version of Ceva's Theorem; also, §2 contains many applications of this important theorem.

— · —

So far we have always assumed that the planes π and π' are distinct. That is why, in this section, we spoke of mappings of a plane π onto a plane π' rather than of transformations of a plane onto itself (exemplified by the isometries and similarities studied in NML 8 and NML 21).

We shall now consider a transformation of a plane π onto itself which results when π is moved about in space and subsequently mapped onto its original position by a parallel projection. We shall call such a transformation a *parallel projection of the plane onto itself*. Every isometry is a special case of such a transformation of the plane; a parallel projection of the plane onto itself is an isometry provided the plane's new position in space is parallel to its original position.

Property A of a parallel projection implies that *under a parallel projection of a plane onto itself lines go over into lines*. A one-to-one transformation of a plane onto itself that takes lines into lines will be called an *affinity*. Isometries and similarities of a plane are the simplest examples of affinities. A parallel projection of a plane onto itself is a more general affinity than isometries and similarities, since it need not preserve ratios of lengths of segments and thus, in general, alters the shape of a figure.

It turns out that *every* affinity of a plane is essentially a parallel projection of the plane onto itself. In fact, the following theorem holds:

THEOREM 2. *Every affinity of a plane can be realized by means of ·a parallel projection of the plane onto itself followed by a similarity.*

This theorem shows that the study of properties of affine transformations is synonymous with the study of properties common to parallel projections of a plane onto itself and similarities;† in particular it implies that affinities of a plane have properties B, C, and D (cf. pp. 17–18), as these are shared by parallel projections of a plane onto itself and similarities. Theorem 2 also clarifies the nature of the product of two or more parallel projections of a plane onto itself; namely, it shows that such a product is again a parallel projection of the plane onto itself, followed, possibly, by a similarity (for such a product is, clearly, an affinity of the plane).

Theorem 2 is a consequence of Theorem 1 and the following theorem:

THEOREM 3. *There exists a unique affinity of the plane which takes three non-collinear points A, B, C into three non-collinear points A', B', C'.*

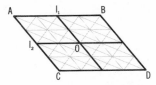

Figure 15a

If we suppose Theorem 3 proved, then Theorem 2 follows readily. Indeed, since there is only one affinity which takes a given triangle ABC into a given triangle

† Theorem 2 implies that an affine transformation can be *defined* as a parallel projection of a plane onto itself followed by a similarity (cf. NML 8, pp. 68–70).

$A'B'C'$, this transformation must coincide with the parallel projection of the plane onto itself and subsequent similarity that take the triangle ABC into the triangle $A'B'C'$ (that such a parallel projection and similarity exist follows from Theorem 1). It remains to prove Theorem 3.†

The idea of the proof is as follows. Suppose that an affinity takes three points A, B, C into three given points A', B', C'. We must show that this determines the image M' of every point M in the plane. We shall first find a number of points whose images we can determine; then we shall find more such points, still more such points, etc. In this way we shall obtain in the plane an arbitrarily dense set of points whose images under the considered affinity we shall be able to construct. Thus for each point M in the plane there will be points of the set arbitrarily close to M. Moreover, we shall be able to include any point M in the interior of an arbitrarily small polygon whose vertices belong to the set of points whose images are determined. Consequently, every such polygon goes over into a definite polygon, and it follows that the image M' of a point M is also determined;‡ this is what we set out to show.

We shall now show how to construct the set of points discussed above. We make use of the following property of an affinity: *An affinity takes parallel lines into parallel lines.* If, to the contrary, the images of two parallel lines l and m were two intersecting lines, then the preimage of their point of intersection would belong to each of the parallel lines l and m, which is impossible.¶

Let l_1 denote the line AB and l_2 the line AC. Our transformation takes l_1 into l_1' passing through the points A' and B', and the line l_2 into l_2' passing through the points A' and C'. Let CD be the line through C parallel to l_1 and BD the line through B parallel to l_2 (Fig. 15a). Since an affinity takes parallel lines into parallel lines, CD is taken into the line through C' parallel to l_1', BD into the line through B' parallel to l_2', and D into the point of intersection D' of these two lines. Thus parallelogram $ABCD$ in Fig. 15a goes over into the parallelogram $A'B'C'D'$ and the point O of intersection of diagonals AD and BC of $ABCD$ into the point O' of intersection of diagonals $A'D'$ and $B'C'$ of $A'B'C'D'$. Now consider the midlines

---

† Strictly speaking, Theorems 3 and 1 imply only that every affinity of a plane taking at least one triple of *non-collinear* points A, B, C into a triple of *non-collinear* points A', B', C' can be realized as a product of a parallel projection of the plane onto itself and a similarity. However, it is easy to see that we cannot have an affinity which takes every triple of points into a collinear triple of points. In fact, if every triple of points A, B, M with A, B fixed and M arbitrary, were to go over into a collinear triple of image points A', B', M', then *all* points in the plane would go over into points of the line $A'B'$, contrary to the definition of an affinity of the plane (cf. p. 18).

‡ While these considerations make Theorem 3 plausible, they do not constitute a rigorous proof; the mere fact that we have an arbitrarily dense set of points whose images we know does not imply that every point is included in the set (for example, no set of rational points on the x-axis, however dense, will include the point with coordinate $x = \sqrt{2}$). Thus there may exist a point M whose image we do not know in spite of the fact that we know the images of points arbitrarily close to M. To make the above argument into a rigorous proof of Theorem 3 it is necessary to use additional considerations into which we do not enter here. In this connection see, for example, H. S. M. Coxeter, *Introduction to Geometry*, J. Wiley and Sons, Inc., New York 1961.

¶ Note that an affinity carries intersecting lines into intersecting lines.

of *ABCD*, i.e., the lines through *O* parallel to l_1 and l_2. Their images are lines through *O'* parallel to l_1' and l_2', i.e., the midlines of *A'B'C'D'*, in other words, the points of intersection of the midlines of *ABCD* with l_1 and l_2 are taken into the midpoints of the sides of *A'B'C'D'*.

Next we treat each of the four parallelograms into which the midlines divide the parallelogram *ABCD* just as we treated *ABCD*, etc. (Fig. 15a). This yields a lattice (i.e. a net) of parallelograms in the interior of *ABCD* which our affine transformation takes into a lattice of parallelograms in the interior of *A'B'C'D'*, with lattice points in *ABCD* going into corresponding lattice points in *A'B'C'D'*. By repeating this procedure sufficiently often we can make the sides of the parallelograms in our net arbitrarily small, and so make the lattice points arbitrarily dense.

Now we pass lines through *A* and *D* parallel to *BC*, and lines through *B* and *C* parallel to *AD*. Their images under our affine transformation are lines through *A'* and *D'* parallel to *B'C'* and lines through *B'* and *C'* parallel to *A'D'*. In this manner we obtain a parallelogram *KLMN* twice as large in area as *ABCD* whose image is a known parallelogram *K'L'M'N'*. Repeating this procedure, we obtain a parallelogram *PQRS* four times as large in area as *ABCD* with sides parallel to the sides of *ABCD* (Fig. 15b) whose image is the parallelogram *P'Q'R'S'*, etc.

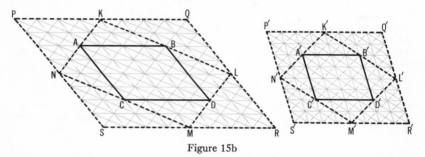

Figure 15b

By combining our two procedures (of building ever larger parallelograms with known images and ever smaller parallelograms with known images in their interiors) we can form a dense set of points in the plane with known images under our affine transformation, as we set out to do.

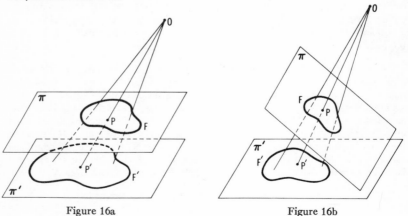

Figure 16a   Figure 16b

2. Central projection of a plane to a plane
Projective transformation of a plane

Let π and π' be two planes in space. We choose a point O not on either of them and *project the plane π to the plane π' from the point O,* i.e., we associate with a point P in π the point P' in π' which lies on the line OP (Fig. 16a, b).

The mapping just defined is called a *central projection* (from π to π') with center O. The image of a figure F in π under a central projection is some figure F' in π' (think, for example, of the shadow in the street cast at night by a window frame in a brightly lit room; Fig. 17).

If the planes π and π' are parallel, then a central projection from π to π' takes every figure F in π into a similar figure F' in π' (in this case yielding a central similarity in space with center O;† cf. Fig. 16a.) In the sequel we shall be primarily concerned with the case when π and π' are not parallel (Fig. 16b).

Figure 17

† Cf. the second footnote on page 30 in NML 21.

We observe that in the latter case there is a line in π whose points have *no images* in π', namely the line x of intersection of π with the plane through O parallel to π' (Fig. 18a). Similarly, there is a line in π' whose points have *no preimages* in the plane π, namely the line y' of intersection of π' with the plane through O parallel to π (Fig. 18b).

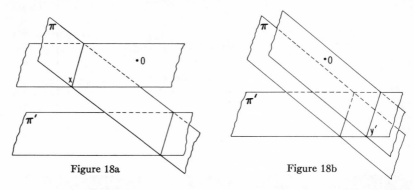

Figure 18a   Figure 18b

Thus, in a central projection from a plane π to a plane π' there are two lines (one in π, the other in π') in exceptional positions to which we shall refer as the *special lines* in the planes π and π'.†

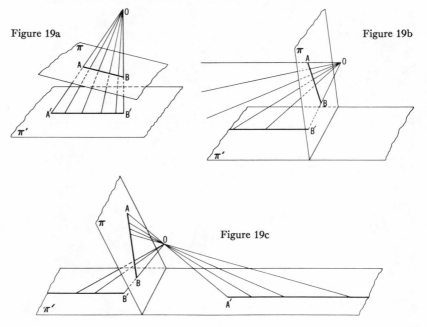

Figure 19a   Figure 19b

Figure 19c

† Clearly, x is parallel to y', both lines being parallel to the line of intersection of the planes π and π'.

A central projection deforms figures to a much greater extent than a parallel projection. The image of a segment under a central projection may be a segment, a ray or two rays (Fig. 19), and the image of a triangle may be any one of the figures depicted in Fig. 20a–e.

It is sometimes possible to simplify a complicated diagram by means of a suitable central projection and thus make it easier to solve some problem connected with the diagram. In such cases we make use of the following properties of central projections.

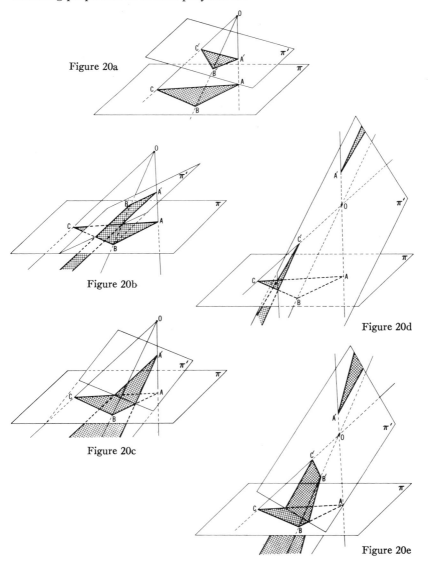

Figure 20a

Figure 20b

Figure 20c

Figure 20d

Figure 20e

A. *A central projection carries lines in* π *into lines in* π′ (an exception is the special line *x* in π whose points, as already noted, are not carried into any points in π′).

Indeed, the lines joining the points on a line *l* in π to the point *O* fill a plane σ. The projection with center *O* carries *l* into the line *l′* where σ intersects π′ (Fig. 21).

Conversely, *every line l′ in the plane* π′ (except the special line *y′*) *is the image of a line l in the plane* π.

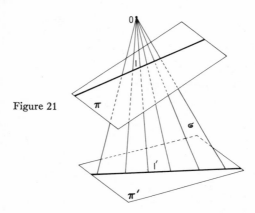

Figure 21

B. *Let* l_1 *and* l_2 *in the plane* π *intersect in a point M on the special line x. Then their images under a central projection are two parallel lines* $l_1′$ *and* $l_2′$ *in* π′.

Indeed, in this case the planes σ_1 and σ_2 determined by the point *O* and the lines l_1 and l_2, respectively, intersect in the line *OM* parallel to π′. It follows that the projections $l_1′$ and $l_2′$ of l_1 and l_2 are parallel lines in π′ (Fig. 22a).

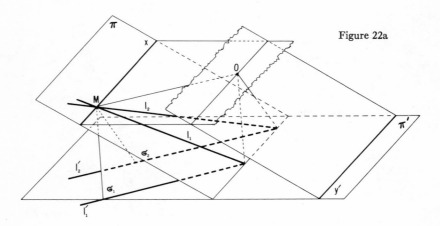

Figure 22a

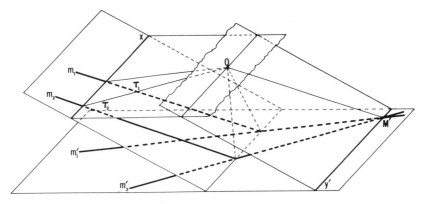

Figure 22b

A central projection carries two parallel lines m_1 and m_2 in π into two lines m_1' and m_2' in π' whose point of intersection M' is on the special line y'. This follows from the fact that the planes τ_1 and τ_2 determined by the point O and the lines m_1 and m_2, respectively, intersect in a line OM' parallel to π and meeting π' in a point M' on the special line y' (Fig. 22b). *Exceptions to this rule are lines parallel to x; these lines are mapped onto lines parallel to y'* (Fig. 23).

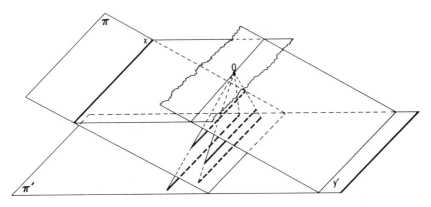

Figure 23

Using properties A and B of a central projection, we can prove a number of interesting results. (We observe that the statements of some of these theorems contain certain inaccuracies that are dealt with later (cf. p. 37 ff.).)

17. (a) In a plane let two lines l_1 and l_2 and a point P not on either
of them be given. Pass two lines through P, one intersecting l_1 and
l_2 in points A and B and the other in points C and D (Fig. 24a).
Show that

(i) the locus of points of intersection of lines AD and BC (for
all pairs of lines passing through P) is a line p,

(ii) for l_1 not parallel to l_2, p passes through the point of intersection Q of l_1 and l_2, and

(iii) p does not change if we replace P by a point P_1 on the
line PQ.

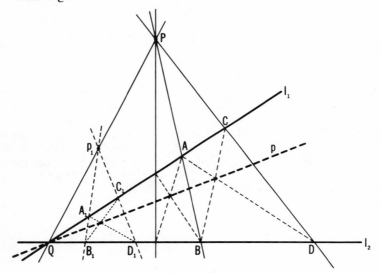

Figure 24a

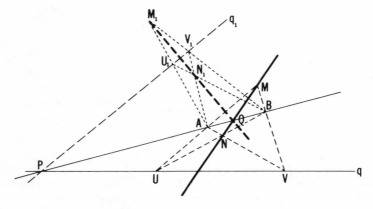

Figure 24b

(b) Let a line q and two points A and B not on q be given in a plane. Let U, V be a pair of points on q, M the point of intersection of the lines UA and VB, and N the point of intersection of the lines UB and VA (Fig. 24b). Every choice of points U, V on q yields a corresponding line MN. Show that all these lines intersect in a point Q on the line AB; also show that the point Q does not change if we replace q by a line q_1 passing through the point of intersection P of q and AB.

The line p in Problem 17(a) is called the *polar of the point P with respect to the pair of lines* l_1, l_2 (compare this concept with that of a polar of a point with respect to a circle in §4 of this book). The point Q in Problem 17(b) is called *the pole of the line q with respect to the pair of points A and B.*

18. (a) Let M be a point in a plane, and let l_1 and l_2 be two lines in that plane which intersect in an inaccessible point (cf. NML 21, pp. 24–25). Using a straightedge (but no compasses), draw a line through M which passes through the point of intersection of l_1 and l_2 (Fig. 25a).

(b) An inaccessible line l in a plane is determined by two pairs of lines p_1, p_2 and q_1, q_2 which intersect in points P, Q on l (Fig. 25b). Let m be a given line and M a given point. Using a straightedge alone, draw a line through M which passes through the point of intersection of m and l.

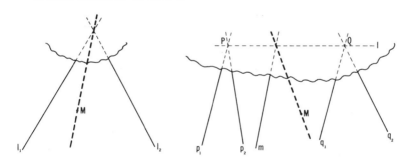

Figure 25a   Figure 25b

(c) Using straightedge alone, draw the line l through the inaccessible points P and Q determined by the pairs of lines p_1, p_2 and q_1, q_2 (Fig. 25c).

(d) Each of two inaccessible lines l_1 and l_2 in a plane (Fig. 25d) is determined by two pairs of lines in the manner of the line l in Problem 18(b) above. Using straightedge alone draw a line through a given point M passing through the point of intersection L of l_1 and l_2.

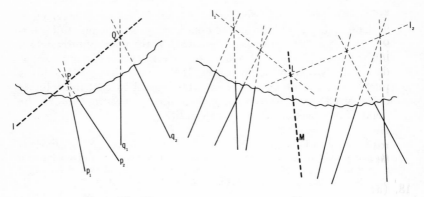

Figure 25c   Figure 25d

In NML 21 where we first encountered constructions involving inaccessible elements ("constructions in a bounded portion of the plane") we noted their importance in the practice of geodesy (cf. footnote on p. 24 in NML 21). In this connection it should be pointed out that, since geodesic practice precludes the use of compasses, constructions by means of straightedge alone have particular value.† Problems 18(a)–(d) are precisely of this type.

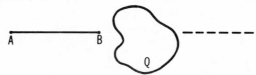

Figure 26

19. Consider a segment AB and a region Q coplanar with it (Fig. 26). How, using only a straightedge, can one extend the segment AB to the right of the region Q without drawing any lines in the interior of Q? (This problem admits the interpretation: Extend a line on the ground beyond a wood, say, from which the given direction cannot be viewed.)

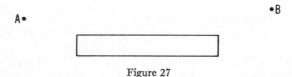

Figure 27

† Strictly speaking, the geometric counterpart of geodesic constructions is constructions with straightedge and protractor; indeed, geodesic instruments enable one to draw lines and to lay off a given angle at a given point of a given line. Constructions with straightedge alone are the simplest constructions of practical geodesy.

20. Consider two points A and B in a plane. How can we connect them by a line if we have at our disposal only a straightedge shorter than the distance AB (Fig. 27)?

In solving construction problems one usually assumes that any two points can be joined by a line, i.e., that the person solving the problem has at his disposal an infinitely long straightedge. Actual rulers are, of course, quite short. The value of the solution of Problem 20 is that it shows that *all constructions which can be carried out with an infinite straightedge can also be carried out with a straightedge of finite length* (in fact, with an arbitrarily short one).

We also observe in passing that the limited spread of every pair of compasses does not reduce the class of possible constructions; namely, we shall show in §5 that every construction which can be carried out by straightedge and compasses can also be carried out by straightedge and compasses of fixed spread (and, furthermore, the compasses need be used at most once).

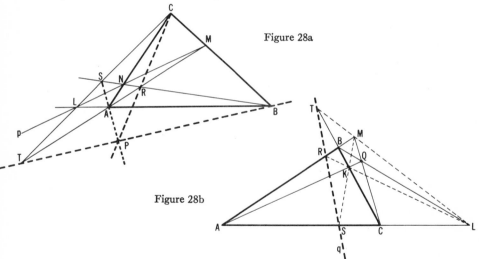

Figure 28a

Figure 28b

21. (a) A line p intersects the sides (or their extensions) AB, BC, and CA of a triangle ABC in points L, M, and N. As in Fig. 28a, denote the point of intersection of AM and BN by R, of BN and CL by S, and of AM and CL by T. Show that the lines AS, BT, and CR are concurrent.

(b) Let a triangle ABC be given together with a point Q. As in Fig. 28b, denote the points of intersection of the lines QA, QB and QC with the appropriate sides (or their extensions) of $\triangle ABC$ by K, L, and M, and the points of intersection of the pairs of lines KL and AB, KM and AC, LM and BC, by R, S, and T. Show that the points R, S, and T are collinear.

The point P in Problem 21(a) where AS, BT and CR meet is sometimes referred to as the *trilinear pole of the line p with respect to the triangle ABC*. The line q in Problem 21(b) on which R, S, and T lie, is called the *trilinear polar of the point Q with respect to the triangle ABC*.

22. *Desargues's Theorem.* Prove that if two triangles ABC and $A_1B_1C_1$ are located in a plane so that lines AA_1, BB_1, and CC_1 are concurrent, then the points of intersection of lines AB and A_1B_1, AC and A_1C_1, BC and B_1C_1 are collinear (Fig. 29). Conversely, if the points of intersection of lines AB and A_1B_1, AC and A_1C_1, BC and B_1C_1 are collinear, then lines AA_1, BB_1, and CC_1 are concurrent.

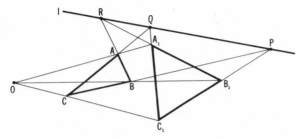

Figure 29

Triangles satisfying the assumptions of Desargues's Theorem are said to be *perspective*. The point O common to the lines joining corresponding vertices of the triangles is called the *center of perspectivity*, and the line containing the points of intersection of the pairs of corresponding sides is called the *axis of perspectivity*.

Observe that Desargues's Theorem expresses a common property of lines and points in a plane not necessarily tied to a pair of triangles. The emphasis given to certain elements in Fig. 29 makes it easier to remember the theorem but obscures its symmetry, since it conceals the fact that all lines and points in Desargues's Theorem are of equal weight. Thus, for example, in Fig. 29 line OCC_1 may be viewed as an axis of perspectivity (for triangles PBB_1 and QAA_1), and point B may be viewed as a center of perspectivity (for triangles PRB_1 and CAO). Similar remarks can be made concerning Problems 21(a), (b), 25, 26, 27, 28; in this connection see Ch. III of the very interesting book by D. Hilbert and S. Cohn-Vossen, *Geometry and the Imagination*, Chelsea New York, 1952.

The Theorems in Problems 21(a) and (b) are special cases of Desargues's Theorem; in Fig. 28a, triangles STR and ABC are perspective with axis p, and in Fig. 28b, triangles KLM and ABC are perspective with center Q.

23. A quadrilateral $EFGH$ is inscribed in a quadrilateral $ABCD$ (with E on AB, F on BC, etc.). Show that if the point of intersection of sides EF and HG is on the diagonal AC of $ABCD$, then the point of intersection of EH and FG is on the diagonal BD.

24. (a) Given a triangle ABC and three collinear points P, Q, R; inscribe in $\triangle ABC$ a triangle XYZ whose sides pass through the points P, Q and R, respectively.†
(b) In a given n-gon $A_1A_2 \cdots A_n$ inscribe another n-gon so that its sides pass through n given collinear points.‡
(c) Let three concurrent lines l_1, l_2 and l_3 and three points A, B and C be given in a plane. Construct a triangle XYZ whose sides pass through the points A, B, C, and whose vertices lie on the lines l_1, l_2, l_3.

Note that Problem 24(a) is a special case of Problem 24(b), Problem 24(c) is a special case of Problem 61 (p. 81), and all four problems are special cases of Problem 90 (p. 99).

25. *Theorem on doubly perspective triangles.* Let ABC and $A_1B_1C_1$ be two given triangles such that lines AA_1, BB_1, CC_1 intersect in a point O, and lines AB_1, BC_1, CA_1 intersect in a point O_1 (Fig. 30). Prove that lines AC_1, BA_1, CB_1 also intersect in a point O_2; in other words, two doubly perspective triangles (in the sense of the statement of our problem) are in fact triply perspective.

[Granted the existence of doubly perspective triangles, the theorem in Problem 25 asserts the existence of three triangles, ABC, $A_1B_1C_1$ and OO_1O_2, any two of which are triply perspective, the three centers of perspectivity being, in each case, the vertices of the third triangle.]

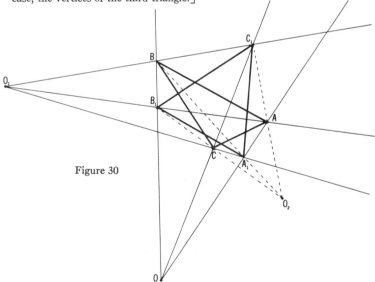

Figure 30

† This means that one is to construct a triangle XYZ whose vertices X, Y, Z lie on the sides of $\triangle ABC$ or on their extensions, and the sides of $\triangle XYZ$ or their extensions pass through the given points.

‡ Interpret the term "inscribed" in accordance with preceding footnote.

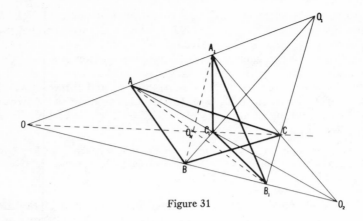

Figure 31

26. *Theorem on triply perspective triangles.* Let ABC and $A_1B_1C_1$ be two triangles such that lines AA_1, BB_1, CC_1 intersect in a point O, lines AA_1, BC_1, CB_1 intersect in a point O_1, and lines AC_1, BB_1, CA_1 intersect in a point O_2 (Fig. 31). Prove that then lines AB_1, BA_1, CC_1 intersect in a point O_3 (in other words, two triangles triply perspective in the sense of the problem are necessarily quadruply perspective).

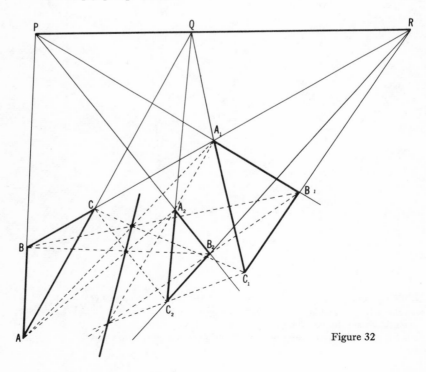

Figure 32

27. Let three triangles ABC, $A_1B_1C_1$ and $A_2B_2C_2$ be given such that lines AB, A_1B_1, A_2B_2 intersect in a point P, lines AC, A_1C_1, A_2C_2 intersect in a point Q, lines BC, B_1C_1, B_2C_2 intersect in a point R, and P, Q, R are collinear. In view of Desargues's Theorem (Problem 22), the lines in each of the triads AA_1, BB_1, CC_1; AA_2, BB_2, CC_2; A_1A_2, B_1B_2, C_1C_2; intersect in a point. Prove that these three points are collinear (Fig. 32).

[The theorem in Problem 27 can be given the following brief formulation: If the axes of perspectivity of three pairwise perspective triangles coincide, then their centers of perspectivity are collinear.]

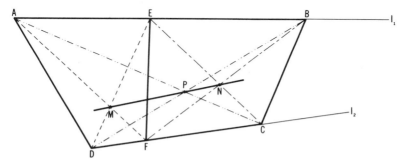

Figure 33

28. *Pappus's Theorem.* Show that if a line EF divides a quadrilateral $ABCD$ into two quadrilaterals $AEFD$ and $BCFE$ (Fig. 33), then the points of intersection of the diagonals of the three quadrilaterals $ABCD$, $AEFD$, $BCFE$ are collinear.

We note that Problem 28 can also be formulated in the following two ways (see Fig. 33):

(a) If the vertices A, E, B of a hexagon $AFBDEC$ (which may be non-convex and even self-intersecting) lie on a line l_1, and the vertices D, F, C lie on a line l_2, then the points of intersection of the opposite sides of this hexagon are collinear.

(b) If the sides AB, CN, DM of a hexagon $ABNCDM$ (which may be non-convex or even self-intersecting) pass through a point E, and its sides CD, BN, AM pass through a point F, then the diagonals AC, BD, MN of this hexagon are concurrent.

These two variants of Problem 28 resemble closely Problems 46 and 47 in §3 (cf. also the solutions of Problems 75 and 80 in §5).†

† This analogy is not accidental. To explain it fully it would be necessary to bring in the general theory of conic sections (cf. the work of D. Hilbert and S. Cohn-Vossen quoted on page 30). Because of limitations of space we decided not to present this theory in the present work.

29. Project the plane π of Fig. 33 onto a new plane π' so that

    (i) line AB is the special line of π;
    (ii) line AD is the special line of π.
What is the new form of Problem 28?

30. Let four lines be given in a plane no two of which are parallel and no three of which are concurrent. Prove that the points of inter-section of the altitudes in each of the four triangles formed by these lines are collinear.

      Problem 30 appears in another connection in NML 21 (cf. Problem 63, p. 78).

31. Project the plane π of quadrilateral $ABCD$ in Problem 23 (p. 30) to a new plane π' so that

    (i) side AB is the special line of π;
    (ii) diagonal AC is the special line of π.
What is the new form of Problem 23?

    Properties A and B of a central projection are to some extent analogues of properties A and B of a parallel projection (cf. p. 11). We shall now try to find a partial analogue of property C (cf. p. 11).

    We consider the effect of a central projection on the length of a seg-ment. Let AB be a segment in a plane π, and let $A'B'$ be its image in a plane π' under a central projection with center O (Fig. 34). We recall that the ratio of the areas of two triangles having a common angle is equal to the ratio of the products of the sides containing the common angle. (This follows, for example, from the well known formula Area $\triangle ABC = \frac{1}{2}ab \sin C$.) Therefore, denoting by h and h' the dis-tances from the point O to the lines AB and $A'B'$, we have

$$\frac{\text{Area } (\triangle OA'B')}{\text{Area } (\triangle OAB)} = \frac{h' \cdot A'B'}{h \cdot AB} = \frac{OA' \cdot OB'}{OA \cdot OB}$$

or

$$A'B' = AB \cdot \frac{OA' \cdot OB'}{OA \cdot OB} \cdot \frac{h}{h'}.$$

    Now, if A, B, C are three points on a line l in π, and A', B', C' are their images under projection to π', then the above argument yields

(*) $\dfrac{A'C'}{B'C'} = \dfrac{AC[(OA' \cdot OC')/(OA \cdot OC)](h/h')}{BC[(OB' \cdot OC')/(OB \cdot OC)](h/h')} = \dfrac{AC}{BC} \dfrac{OA'/OA}{OB'/OB}.$

This shows that here, in contra-distinction to a parallel projection, the ratios $A'C'/B'C'$ and AC/BC are, in general, unequal. However, if we form the *ratio of two ratios* resulting from the division of the segment AB by two points C and D on the line AB (Fig. 34), then, clearly,

$$\frac{A'C'}{B'C'} \bigg/ \frac{A'D'}{B'D'} = \frac{AC}{BC} \cdot \frac{OA'/OA}{OB'/OB} \bigg/ \frac{AD}{BD} \cdot \frac{OA'/OA}{OB'/OB} = \frac{AC}{BC} \bigg/ \frac{AD}{BD}.$$

The expression

$$\frac{AC}{BC} \bigg/ \frac{AD}{BD}$$

is called the *cross-ratio* of the four points A, B; C, D.

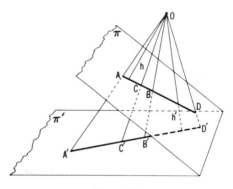

Figure 34

To sum up:

C. *A central projection preserves the cross-ratio of four points A, B; C, D on a line.*

The cross-ratio of four (collinear) points is the ratio of two simple ratios AC/BC and AD/BD. Since simple ratios can be positive or negative (cf. NML 21, p. 12), it is natural to assign a positive or negative sign to the cross-ratio of four collinear points. Obviously, the cross ratio $(AC/BC)/(AD/BD)$ of four points A, B; C, D is positive if C and D are both interior or both exterior to the segment AB (for then the simple ratios AC/BC and AD/BD have the same sign), and negative if one of the points C and D is interior, the other exterior to the segment AB (for then the ratios AC/BC and AD/BD have different signs). In other words, we may say that the cross-ratio A, B; C, D of four points is negative if the pairs A, B and C, D separate each other (Fig. 35a) and positive if they do not (Fig. 35b). It follows that a central projection preserves the sign of the cross-ratio, i.e., property C is valid even if we take into consideration the sign of the cross-ratio. To prove this assertion, note that if the pairs of points A, B and C, D separate (do not separate) each other, then the pairs of lines OA, OB and OC, OD separate (do not separate) each other; but then the pairs of image points A', B' and C', D' of A, B and C, D under a projection from O separate (do not separate) each other.†

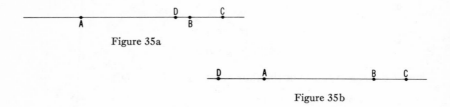

Figure 35a

Figure 35b

We note that if AB is parallel to the special line of π (i.e., if it is parallel to the line of intersection of π and π'; Fig. 36) then, clearly $AB \parallel A'B'$ and $OA'/OA = OB'/OB$. Thus, in this case formula (*) yields

$$\frac{A'C'}{B'C'} = \frac{AC}{BC};$$

in other words, *a central projection preserves the simple ratio of two segments of a line parallel to the special line of the plane.*

Property C of a central projection is relatively complicated. It will, at times, play an important part in our elementary exposition (see, in particular, the last section). It plays a crucial role in all advanced work dealing with central projections.

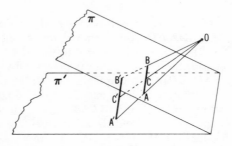

Figure 36

† Note that, similarly, a parallel projection of three collinear points A, B, C preserves not only the magnitude of the simple ratio AC/BC, but also its sign.

Consider the ratio AC/BC in which a point C divides a segment AB. The case when C is the center of AB, i.e., when AC and BC have equal magnitudes and opposite directions so that $AC/BC = -1$, is of special interest. Similarly, in considering the cross-ratio $(AC/BC)/(AD/BD)$ of four points A, B; C, D, we single out the case $(AC/BC)/(AD/BD) = -1$. Then one of the points C and D is interior to the segment AB, the other is exterior to it; also the ratios AC/BC and AD/BD are equal in absolute value (Fig. 37). To describe this situation we say that the points C, D divide the segment AB *harmonically* (or that the points C, D are *harmonic conjugates* of the points A, B).

We saw above that centers of segments figure prominently in problems involving parallel projections (cf., for example, Problems 1, 2, 3(a), 4, 9(a), 14, the solutions of Problems 3(b), 8, 9(b), the proof of Theorem 3 on pp. 19–20, where the midlines of certain parallelograms played a fundamental role, and so on). Similarly, in problems involving central projections there often occur pairs of points dividing certain segments harmonically. Thus, for example, the locus in Problem 17(a)—the polar of a point P relative to a pair of lines l_1 and l_2—can be defined as the locus of points M such that the points P, M divide harmonically the segment of line PM whose end points are on l_1, l_2; the point Q of Problem 17(b) is a point of the line AB such that Q and P divide segment AB harmonically,† and so on. All these assertions are readily proved by means of property C of a central projection.

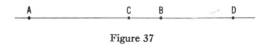

Figure 37

We shall now remedy certain inaccuracies of our exposition. We recall that when a plane π is projected into a plane π', each of the two planes contains a special line; the points of the special line in π have no images in π', and the points of the special line in π' are not the images of any points in π. Because of this, accurate formulation of propositions involving central projections invariably requires the inclusion of special cases. The inaccuracies just mentioned were due to the fact that, so far, as a rule, we ignored such special cases. Thus, for example, the statement of Desargues's Theorem (cf. Problem 22) is, strictly speaking, incorrect, for it does not consider the possibility that a central projection may carry concurrent lines (e.g., the lines AA_1, BB_1 and CC_1 or AB, A_1B_1 and PQ in Fig. 29) either into concurrent or into parallel lines. An accurate statement of Desargues's Theorem takes the following form: *If two coplanar triangles are such that the lines joining their corresponding vertices are concurrent or parallel, then either the points of intersection of corresponding sides of the triangles are collinear* (Fig. 38a, b), *or one pair of corresponding sides is parallel to the line joining the points of intersection of the*

† The fact that the points Q and P in Problem 17(b) divide segment AB harmonically is frequently stated as follows: *Any two diagonals of a complete quadrilateral divide the third diagonal harmonically* (cf. above). We leave it to the reader to prove that this theorem is equivalent to our assertion.

remaining two pairs of corresponding sides (Fig. 38c, d), *or, finally the corresponding sides of the two triangles are parallel in pairs* (Fig. 38e, f) *and conversely.* We see that, when accurately stated, the theorem is clumsy and hard to grasp. A similar remark holds for many other statements.

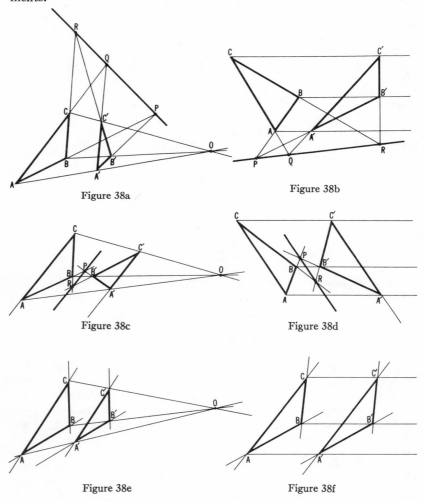

Figure 38a

Figure 38b

Figure 38c

Figure 38d

Figure 38e

Figure 38f

To remove the complications due to the exceptional character of the special lines, we shall say that the special line x in the plane π is projected to the "line at infinity" of the plane π' and that the "line at infinity" associated with π is projected to the special line y' in π'. We emphasize that this terminology is a matter of convention; the statement "the line x is projected to the line at infinity" is equivalent to the statement "the line x is not projected to anything". We shall say of every point X of the special line x that it is projected to a "point at infinity" of the plane π'. We shall say of the class of parallel lines obtained by projecting the class of lines passing through X (cf. Fig. 39) that "they intersect in a point at infinity".† Thus every line l has a point at infinity‡ which is the "point of intersection" of l with every line parallel to it. The totality of points at infinity of the lines in the plane forms its "line at infinity".

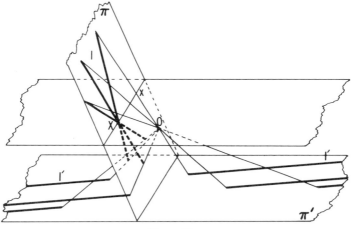

Figure 39

We now justify this terminology. If a point M on a line l approaches the point X of intersection of l and x, then its projection to the plane π' moves indefinitely far along the line l' [in a direction depending on the direction in which M approaches X (cf. Fig. 40)]. Similarly, if M moves indefinitely far in either direction on l, then its projection approaches the point Y' in which l' intersects y' (cf. Fig. 40).

Introduction of points at infinity makes it necessary to supplement the definition of the cross-ratio of four collinear points. Note that if D is the point at infinity of the line AB, then it is natural to put the ratio AD/BD equal to one (since the ratio AM/BM approaches the limit one as the

† The fact that with every point at infinity there is associated the class of parallel lines "passing through that point" enables us to identify the points at infinity with the *directions* in the plane. For example, the statement: "the line passing through the given point A and the given point at infinity B" signifies the line through A in the direction corresponding to the point at infinity B, and so on.

‡ Contrary to intuition, it turns out to be convenient to assign to a line a *single* point at infinity.

point M approaches the point at infinity D, i.e. as M moves indefinitely far in either direction along AB). Thus if D is a point at infinity,
then the cross-ratio $(AC/BC)/(AD/BD)$ coincides with the simple
ratio AC/BC. It is easy to see that property C of a central projection
still holds even if one of the points A, B, C, D is a point at infinity or
if its projection is a point at infinity.

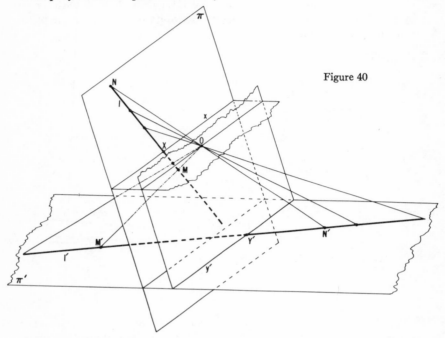

Figure 40

Introduction of the line at infinity and of points at infinity enables us
to include in a single proposition a number of special propositions, all
provable in a similar way. This is because, insofar as central projections
are concerned, the fictitious points at infinity are on an equal footing
with actual points; points of one type can be carried into points of the
other type. For example, the special cases of Desargues's Theorem listed
earlier are all included in the original statement of that theorem (Problem
22) provided the point of intersection of lines AA_1, BB_1 and CC_1, as
well as the points of intersection of the corresponding sides of triangles
ABC and $A_1B_1C_1$, are interpreted to mean ordinary points or points at
infinity.

A plane supplemented in this manner by the addition of fictitious
points at infinity and a fictitious line at infinity is called a *projective plane*.

We wish to point out a fundamental difference between the two uses
we have made of points at infinity: 1. to create a convenient terminology
for expressing certain facts connected with central projections (cf. above),
2. to create the projective plane.

The concept of the projective plane goes beyond mere terminology. It is a step on the road of mathematical abstraction leading to a new mathematical concept: a plane containing, in addition to the familiar points of school geometry, additional points, namely, the points at infinity. (Points at infinity are on a par with the other points, since central projections can carry points of one type into points of the other.) It must be stressed that a projective plane is just as legitimate as the ordinary "Euclidean" plane (or the "inversive plane" discussed in the second chapter[T]). After all, the notion of a Euclidean plane with lines that can be continued indefinitely is also just a mathematical abstraction with no counterpart in physical reality, and its adequate description is achieved by a set of axioms characterizing the geometry of the plane. Various interpretations of the term "plane" lead to different choices of axioms. For example, the following axiom, not valid in the Euclidean plane, holds in the projective plane: "Any two (distinct) lines intersect in a unique point" (in fact, two lines parallel in the Euclidean sense intersect in a point at infinity in the projective plane, and an ordinary line and the line at infinity intersect in the point at infinity of the ordinary line). Each of the different admissible ways of approaching the concept of the plane is distinguished by a particular choice of axioms. Depending on the type of problem we propose to solve we may find it convenient to interpret the term "plane" in one or another way. A case in point is the study of inversions carried out in the second chapter,[T] where we use "points at infinity" in a manner different from that employed in the projective plane. The resulting "plane" is different from both, the Euclidean and the projective planes, but is not "superior" or "inferior" to either of these.

It is relevant to point out that introducing "infinitely distant" points and lines may be helpful in problems not involving central projections. For example, it is convenient to regard a translation as a central similarity with center at the point at infinity corresponding to the direction of the translation and with coefficient one. [To see this consider the images F_1, F_2, F_3, $\cdots$ of a figure F under a sequence of central similarities that map a certain point A of F onto some point A'; then, as the centers O_i ($i = 1, 2, 3, \cdots$) of these central similarities move indefinitely far along the line AA', the figures F_i approach the figure F' obtained from F via the translation defined by the segment AA', and the coefficient

$$\frac{O_iA'}{O_iA} \qquad (i = 1, 2, 3, \cdots)$$

approaches the value one (cf. Fig. 41).] As a result of this identification it is no longer necessary to single out special cases occurring in a number of theorems involving centrally similar figures. We can now claim, for example, that any two circles are centrally similar in two ways (cf. Ch. 1, §1, NML 21). The product of two central similarities (with finite or infinite centers) is again a central similarity (with finite or

[T] Reference to untranslated Russian material.

infinite center; cf. Ch. 1, §1 of NML 8 and Ch. 1, §1 of NML 21). The theorem on three centers of similarity (p. 29, NML 21) can now be stated in the following brief form: The three centers of similarity of three pairwise centrally similar figures are collinear. This statement includes the case where one of the centers is a point at infinity (two of the three figures are congruent), the case where all three centers are points at infinity and the axis is the line at infinity (all three figures are congruent in pairs), and, finally, the case where all three centers coincide. If we adhere to our present point of view, then three circles always have six centers of similarity located in sets of three on four axes of similarity (for the special cases covered by this theorem, cf. NML 21, Ch. 1, §1). Theorem 2 of Ch. 1, §2 of NML 21 now takes a simpler form, because we can regard a glide reflection as a special case of a dilative reflection, and so the case when F is mapped onto F' by a glide reflection requires no separate consideration. From our present point of view Theorem 2 in Ch. 2, §2 in NML 8 is a special case of Theorem 2 in Ch. 1, §2 in NML 21 (which explains the close resemblance in the statements and proofs of the two theorems). Sometimes it is also convenient to regard a translation as a rotation with center at the point at infinity corresponding to the direction perpendicular to the direction of the translation in question. Then all theorems on products of direct motions (i.e., rotations and translations; cf. NML 8) can be covered by a single theorem.

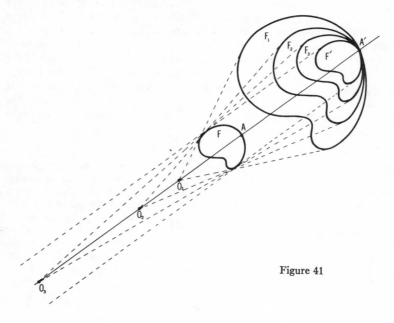

Figure 41

32. (a) Let $ABCD$ be a given parallelogram. Prove that if the line DM cuts off a segment $AM = AB/n$ from the side AB, then it cuts off a segment $AN = AC/(n+1)$ from the diagonal AC (Fig. 42 illustrates the case $n = 2$). What form will this proposition

T Reference to untranslated Russian material.

take if we project the plane of the figure to another plane so that line AB is parallel to the special line of that plane?

(b) Let two parallel lines l and l_1 and a segment AB on l be given. Divide the segment AB into n equal parts by means of straightedge alone.

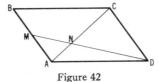

Figure 42

33. What form will the theorem on the complete quadrilateral (cf. Problem 14 and the comment which follows it) take if we project Fig. 14 so that line ABE is the special line?

34. (a) Prove the *theorem of Menelaus:* Three points M, N, P on sides AB, BC and CA of a triangle ABC (or on their extensions, see Fig. 43) are collinear if and only if

$$\frac{AM}{BM} \cdot \frac{BN}{CN} \cdot \frac{CP}{AP} = 1.$$

(b) Prove the *theorem of Ceva:* Three lines AN, BP and CM, where the points M, N, P lie on the sides AB, BC, CA of $\triangle ABC$ (or on their extensions, see Fig. 44) are concurrent or parallel if and only if

$$\frac{AM}{BM} \cdot \frac{BN}{CN} \cdot \frac{CP}{AP} = -1.$$

See also Problems 27 (a), (b) in Ch. 1, §1, NML 21 and Problem 16 in this book. For the connection between the theorems of Menelaus and Ceva, see Problem 66 in §4 of this book.

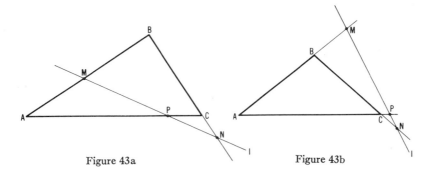

Figure 43a   Figure 43b

It is not difficult to see that if the points M, N, P are collinear then, for any triangle ABC, either two or none of these points are interior to the sides of this triangle (Fig. 43a, b). Hence, of the three ratios AM/BM, BN/CN, CP/AP, either two or none are negative, so that the product of the three ratios is necessarily positive. Similarly, if lines AN, BP and CM are concurrent or parallel (Fig. 44a, b), then of the three points M, N, P either all three are, or exactly one is, interior to the sides of the triangle. Hence, of the three ratios AM/BM, BN/CN, CP/AP, two or none are positive, so that the product of the three ratios is negative.

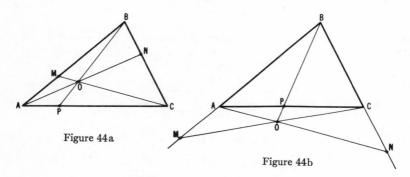

Figure 44a

Figure 44b

The theorems of Menelaus and Ceva are frequently applied when the collinearity of three points or the concurrence of three lines is to be proved. Using the theorem of Menelaus one can solve Problems 7, 16, 61 (NML 21), 14, 21(b), 22, 27, 28, 38(b), 45, 46, 68, 71, 73(a), (b) and others in this book; using the theorem of Ceva one can prove the concurrence of the medians, the altitudes, the angle bisectors, and solve Problems 43(a), (b) (NML 8), 14(b), (c) (NML 21), 8, 13, 21(a), 22, 25, 26, 38(a), 39(a), (b), 40(a), (b), 47, 50, 57, 70 and others. (Also, many of the theorems whose formulation is required in Problems 60, 62–64, 69–74 can be proved using the theorems of Ceva and Menelaus. We suggest that the reader try to prove the various results using these theorems.)

35. Show that if E and F are the points of intersection of opposite sides AB and DC, AD and BC of an (arbitrary) quadrilateral, then

$$\frac{AE \cdot CE}{BE \cdot DE} = \frac{AF \cdot CF}{BF \cdot DF}.$$

We shall now prove the following important result.

THEOREM 1. *Let* A, B, C, D *be four points in a plane* π *no three of which are collinear, and let* M, N, P, Q *be four points in a plane* π' *no three of which are collinear. Then* π *and* π' *can be placed so that there exists a central (or parallel) projection from* π *to* π' *which carries the quadrilateral* $ABCD$ *into a quadrilateral* $A'B'C'D'$ *similar to* $MNPQ$.†

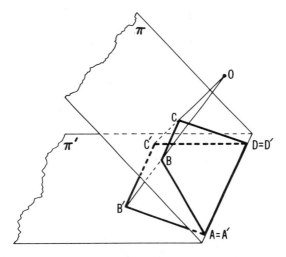

Figure 45

We first prove our theorem in the special case where quadrilaterals $ABCD$ and $MNPQ$ are trapezoids: $AD \parallel BC$, $MQ \parallel NP$. Here we introduce a trapezoid $A'B'C'D'$ in π' similar to $MNPQ$ and such that $A'D' = AD$. We then move the plane π in space so that the segments AD and $A'D'$ coincide, and the points B and C are outside the plane π' (Fig. 45). Now we join B to B' and C to C'. The lines BB' and CC' are coplanar; indeed, $BC \parallel AD$, $AD \parallel B'C'$ imply that BC and $B'C'$ are parallel and therefore coplanar. If O is the point of intersection of lines BB' and CC', then the central projection with center O carries $ABCD$ into $A'B'C'D'$; if $BB' \parallel CC'$, then the parallel projection in the direction determined by these lines carries $ABCD$ into $A'B'C'D'$.

We now show that the general case can be reduced to the special case just considered. Thus let $ABCD$ and $MNPQ$ be two quadrilaterals in π and π' (Fig. 46).‡ Assume that a certain central (or parallel) projec-

† More correctly, the vertices of the quadrilateral $ABCD$ can be mapped onto the vertices of a quadrilateral $A'B'C'D'$ similar to $MNPQ$ (cf. the footnote on p. 156).

‡ The quadrilaterals $ABCD$ and $MNPQ$ in Fig. 46 are convex. However, the argument is unchanged if one or both quadrilaterals are nonconvex.

tion of π to π' carries the quadrilateral $ABCD$ into a quadrilateral $A'B'C'D'$ similar to $MNPQ$. We shall show that $ABCD$ and $MNPQ$ determine the special line of π. To see this let E, E', R be the points of intersection of the pairs of sides AB and CD, $A'B'$ and $C'D'$, MN and PQ of the quadrilaterals $ABCD$, $A'B'C'D'$, and $MNPQ$. In view of property A of a central projection the image of the point E is E'. If X_1' is the point at infinity of $A'B'$ then, in view of property C of a central projection, it is the image of a point X_1 of AB such that

$$\frac{AE/BE}{AX_1/BX_1} = \frac{A'E'/B'E'}{A'X_1'/B'X_1'} = \frac{A'E'}{B'E'} = \frac{MR}{NR}$$

(since $A'X_1'/B'X_1' = 1$, cf. p. 39). From this relation we can determine the ratio AX_1/BX_1 (magnitude and sign!) and so find X_1. Similarly, the relation

$$\frac{CE/DE}{CX_2/DX_2} = \frac{C'E'}{D'E'} = \frac{PR}{QR}$$

determines the point X_2 of DC which is mapped on the point at infinity X_2' of $D'C'$.† The line X_1X_2 is the required special line in π. Note that X_1 and X_2 can be found from the given quadrilaterals $ABCD$ and $MNPQ$. A similar argument enables us to determine the special line $Y_1'Y_2'$ in π'; see Fig. 46. The points Y_1' and Y_2' are determined from the relations

$$\frac{AE}{BE} = \frac{A'E'/B'E'}{A'Y_1'/B'Y_1'} \quad \text{and} \quad \frac{CE}{DE} = \frac{C'E'/D'E'}{C'Y_2'/D'Y_2'}.$$

Through points A and B we now pass lines parallel to the special line X_1X_2, and denote by K and L their points of intersection with CD. In view of property B of a central projection, the parallel lines AK and BL go over into parallel lines. This means that our central projection carries the trapezoid $ABLK$ into the trapezoid $A'B'L'K'$ (where $A'K' \parallel B'L' \parallel Y_1'Y_2'$). Now we can use the quadrilaterals $ABCD$ and $MNPQ$ to find the trapezoid $ABLK$ and the trapezoid $MNTS$ similar to $A'B'L'K'$. To this end we must find on lines MN and PQ points Z_1 and Z_2 such that

† If the point E is mapped onto the point at infinity of $A'B'$ (i.e., if $A'B' \parallel C'D'$) then, instead of AB and CD, we consider AD and BC. If E and the point I in which AD and BC meet are mapped onto points at infinity (i.e., if $A'B'C'D'$ is a parallelogram), then the special line of π is EI; in this case Theorem 1 can be proved without computing ratios of segments. (It would be instructive for the reader to attempt this task.)

$$\frac{MR/NR}{MZ_1/NZ_1} = \frac{A'E'/B'E'}{A'Y_1'/B'Y_1'} = \frac{AE}{BE},$$

$$\frac{PR/QR}{PZ_2/QZ_2} = \frac{C'E'/D'E'}{C'Y_2'/D'Y_2'} = \frac{CE}{DE},$$

and draw $MS \parallel NT \parallel Z_1Z_2$.

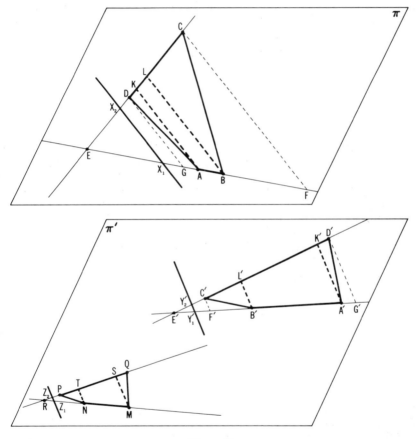

Figure 46

The special case of Theorem 1 established above guarantees the existence of a central (or parallel) projection which carries the trapezoid $ABLK$ into the trapezoid $A'B'L'K'$ similar to $MNTS$. To prove our theorem we must show that this projection carries $ABCD$ into $A'B'C'D'$, i.e., that it takes the points C, D into the points C', D'.

Observe that the special line in π relative to our projection is the line X_1X_2 found above; in fact, the special line is parallel to AK and BL (property B of a central projection†) and passes through X_1 (for the point E of intersection of AB and KL is mapped onto the point E' of intersection of $A'B'$ and $K'L'$, and the point X_1, for which $(AE/BE)/(AX_1/BX_1) = A'E'/B'E'$, is mapped onto a point at infinity). In much the same way we show that the special line of π' is $Y_1'Y_2'$. Since E, X_2 and the point at infinity of KL are mapped, respectively, onto E', a point at infinity, and the point Y_2' of $K'L'$, it follows, in view of property C of a central projection, that the image of the point C is the point $\bar{C}$ of $K'L'$ such that

$$\frac{EX_2/CX_2}{1} = \frac{1}{E'Y_2'/\bar{C}Y_2'} \, ;$$

hence

$$\bar{C}Y_2' = E'Y_2' \cdot \frac{EX_2}{CX_2} \, .$$

It remains to show that $\bar{C}$ coincides with C'. To this end we carry the trapezoid $CDGF$ depicted in Fig. 46 (with $CF \parallel DG \parallel X_2X_1$) into the trapezoid $C'D'G'F'$ (with $C'F' \parallel D'G' \parallel Y_2'Y_1'$) by means of a central (or parallel) projection followed by a similarity; this is possible in view of the partial result established above. This mapping carries E into E', the point X_2 of CD into the point at infinity X_2' of $C'D'$, and the point at infinity Y_2 of CD into the point Y_2' [since, by the definition of the points X_2 and Y_2', $(CE/DE)/(CX_2/DX_2) = C'E'/D'E'$, and $CE/DE = (C'E'/D'E')/(C'Y_2'/D'Y_2')$]. Hence, in view of property C of a central projection,

$$\frac{EX_2/CX_2}{1} = \frac{1}{E'Y_2'/C'Y_2'} \, ,$$

so that

$$C'Y_2' = E'Y_2' \cdot \frac{EX_2}{CX_2} \, .$$

It follows that $\bar{C}$ coincides with C'. We prove in much the same way that the central (or parallel) projection which carries $ABLK$ into $A'B'L'K'$ maps D onto D'. We now see that our projection carries the quadrilateral $ABCD$ into the quadrilateral $A'B'C'D'$, as asserted.

It is easy to modify the proof of Theorem 1 when some of the points A, B, C, D or A', B', C', D' are points at infinity.

† This conclusion can also be reached by noting how one constructs the central (or parallel) projection which carries a trapezoid into a trapezoid (cf. pp. 45–47).

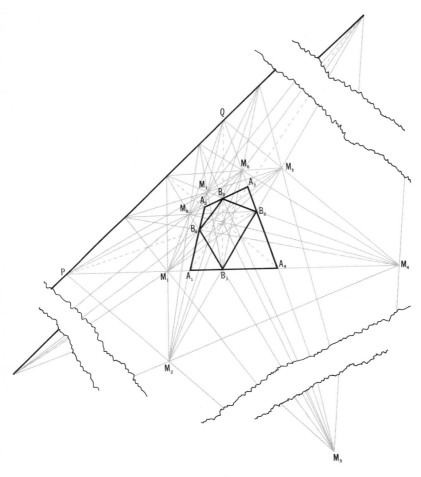

Figure 47

36. Let $A_1A_2A_3A_4$ be a quadrilateral whose diagonals intersect in N, and let pairs of opposite sides meet in P and Q; let B_1, B_2, B_3, B_4 be the points where the sides of the quadrilateral intersect the lines NP and NQ. Let the sides of $A_1A_2A_3A_4$ intersect the sides of the inscribed quadrilateral $B_1B_2B_3B_4$ in M_1, M_2, M_3, M_4, M_5, M_6, M_7, M_8, as shown in Fig. 47. Prove that:

(a) Lines M_1M_5, M_2M_6, M_3M_7 and M_4M_8 pass through N.

(b) Lines M_2M_3 and M_6M_7 pass through P; lines M_1M_8 and M_4M_5 pass through Q.

(c) Lines M_1M_2, M_3M_8, M_4M_7 and M_5M_6 pass through the point of intersection of PQ and the diagonal A_2A_4; lines M_3M_4, M_2M_5, M_1M_6 and M_7M_8 pass through the point of intersection of PQ and the diagonal A_1A_3.

(d) The lines in each of the four tetrads

M_1M_3, M_5M_7, B_4M_4, B_2M_8; M_2M_4, M_6M_8, B_4M_5, B_2M_1;

M_3M_5, M_1M_7, B_1M_6, B_3M_2; M_4M_6, M_2M_8, B_1M_7, B_3M_3;

meet in a point, and these four points lie on PQ.

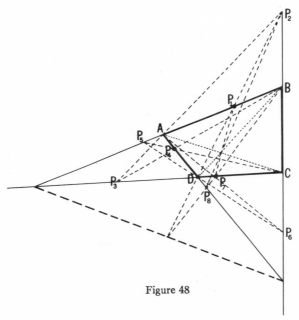

Figure 48

37. Let P_1 denote a point on the side AB of a quadrilateral $ABCD$ (Fig. 48). Let P_2 denote the projection of P_1 from the center D to the line BC; P_3 the projection of P_2 from A to the line CD; P_4, the projection of P_3 from B to the line DA; P_5, the projection of P_4 from C to the line AB, and so on. Prove that:

(a) The point P_{13} on the side AB (obtained after going around the quadrilateral three times) coincides with the given point P_1 (and, consequently, the point P_{14} coincides with P_2, point P_{15} coincides with P_3 and so on).

(b) The lines P_1P_7, P_2P_8, P_3P_9, and so on, pass through the point of intersection of the diagonals of the quadrilateral.

(c) The lines P_1P_2 and P_7P_8; P_2P_3 and P_8P_9; P_3P_4 and P_9P_{10}, and so on, intersect on the line joining the points of intersection of the opposite sides of the quadrilateral.

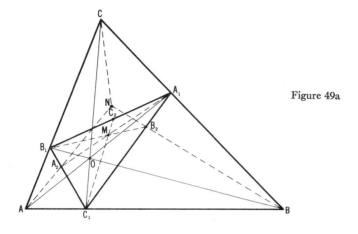

Figure 49a

Figure 49b

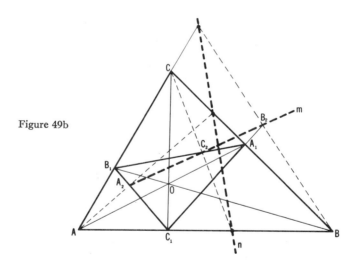

38. Let O be a point in the plane of a triangle ABC, and let A_1, B_1, C_1 be the points of intersection of the lines AO, BO, CO with the sides of the triangle opposite A, B, C (Fig. 49). Prove that:

(a) If A_2, B_2, C_2 are points on sides B_1C_1, C_1A_1, A_1B_1 of $\triangle A_1B_1C_1$ such that the three lines A_1A_2, B_1B_2, C_1C_2 are concurrent, then lines AA_2, BB_2, CC_2 are also concurrent (Fig. 49a).

(b) If the points A_2, B_2, C_2 on sides B_1C_1, C_1A_1, A_1B_1 of $\triangle A_1B_1C_1$ are collinear, then the points of intersection of the lines AA_2, BB_2, CC_2 with the opposite sides of $\triangle ABC$ are collinear (Fig. 49b).

— · —

82855

So far we have considered only mappings of a plane π to another plane π'. Now we consider a transformation which takes π into itself, defined as follows: We move the plane π in space in an arbitrary manner and then project it to its original position from some center O. We shall call this transformation a *central projection of the plane π into itself*. A special case of this transformation is a similarity; a central projection of a plane onto itself is a similarity if the new position of the plane just before projection is parallel to its original position.

The properties of central projection imply that a central projection of the plane π into itself carries lines into lines with the exception of the special line, which goes into the line at infinity. Every line in a part of the plane π not containing the special line is carried into a line.

A transformation of the plane which carries lines passing through some definite part of the plane into lines is called a *projective transformation* or *projectivity*.† Every affine transformation is a projective transformation, but the converse is not true; for example, a central projection of a plane onto itself is a projective transformation but is not, in general, affine.

The following fundamental theorem clarifies the nature of a projective transformation of the plane:

THEOREM 2. *Every projective transformation of the plane can be realized by means of a central (or parallel) projection of the plane to itself followed by a similarity.*

The proof of Theorem 2 is similar to that of Theorem 2 of §1 (cf. p. 18). We shall give a proof of Theorem 2 for the case when the part of the plane referred to in the definition of a projective transformation is a convex quadrilateral (say, a page in a notebook.‡)

Thus let a projective transformation carry the quadrilateral $ABCD$ into the quadrilateral $A'B'C'D'$ (Fig. 50). Theorem 1 tells us that it is possible to carry $ABCD$ into $A'B'C'D'$ by a central (or parallel) projection of the plane into itself followed by a similarity. Therefore, Theorem 2 will be proved if we can show that the projective transformation taking $ABCD$ into $A'B'C'D'$ is unique.

The proof that a projective transformation is determined by the images of the vertices of a quadrilateral resembles closely the proof of Theorem 3 of §1 (cf. pp. 19–20),

† A projectivity can also be defined as a one-to-one transformation of the *projective plane* π (cf. p. 40) onto itself which carries lines into lines. This definition differs from the definition of an affine transformation (cf. p. 18) in that here π denotes a projective plane rather than an ordinary plane.

‡ This assumption does not restrict the generality of the theorem: In fact, in any region G it is possible to choose a (small) quadrilateral $ABCD$. Every line intersecting $ABCD$ must pass through G. But then every transformation which carries lines passing through G into lines must carry lines intersecting the (convex) quadrilateral $ABCD$ into lines.

and so we merely sketch the required argument. Let E, F; E', F' be the points of intersection of the extensions of sides AB and CD, AD and BC; $A'B'$ and $C'D'$, $A'D'$ and $B'C'$ of quadrilaterals $ABCD$ and $A'B'C'D'$ (some of these points of intersection may be points at infinity), and let G and G' be the points of intersection of their diagonals. Since AB goes into $A'B'$ and CD into $C'D'$, it follows that E goes into E'; similarly, F goes into F' and G into G'. Hence lines EG and FG go into the lines $E'G'$ and $F'G'$.

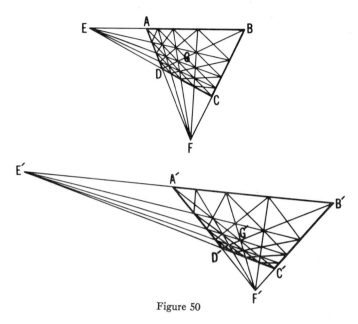

Figure 50

The lines EG and FG divide quadrilateral $ABCD$ into four smaller quadrilaterals; each is carried by our projective transformation into a known quadrilateral. By joining the intersections of the diagonals of the smaller quadrilaterals to E and F and by continuing the process we obtain a network of lines in $ABCD$ of which we know the image network in $A'B'C'D'$ under our transformation (cf. Fig. 50). This network can be made arbitrarily dense. (It is easy to see that a central projection of the plane of our figure into itself which carries EF into the line at infinity carries our network into a network of parallelograms depicted in Fig. 51 and appearing in the proof of Theorem 3, §1. Now the proof of uniqueness of the projective transformation which carries $ABCD$ into $A'B'C'D'$ follows in a manner analogous to the proof of Theorem 3, §1.)†

† We restricted ourselves to the determination of the images of the points in the interior of the quadrilateral since the very definition of a projective transformation is concerned with a portion of the plane. We note, however, that it is possible to extend our network beyond the original quadrilateral in much the same way as was done in the proof of Theorem 3, §1.

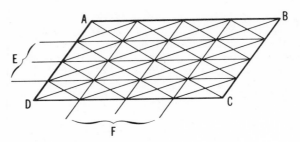

Figure 51

3. Central projections which carry a circle into a circle. Stereographic projection.

In the preceding section we stated a number of problems whose solutions were simplified by means of an appropriate projection of the plane of the figure to another plane. It is natural to consider the scope of this method. In elementary geometry one studies the properties of figures made up of lines and circles. Central projections preserve lines, but not, in general, circles. This may give rise to the impression that the use of central projections is restricted to the relatively small class of problems not involving circles (all problems in the preceding section fall in this category). This impression is incorrect; in fact, we propose to show in this section how central projections can be used to solve problems involving circles. To this end we establish the following two results.

THEOREM 1. *Let S be a circle in a plane π, and let Q be a point in the interior of S. Then there exists a central projection from π to a suitable plane π' which carries S into a circle S' in π' and Q into the center Q' of S'.*

THEOREM 1'. *Let S be a circle in a plane π, and let l be a line in π not intersecting S. Then there exists a central projection from π to a suitable plane π' which carries S into a circle S' in π' and l into the line at infinity of π'.*

There are different ways of proving these theorems. Our way is not the simplest, but it yields insights well worth the additional effort.† Our approach is based on the study of a *stereographic projection* of a sphere to a plane.

† Another proof is sketched in Ch. 26 of the book *The Enjoyment of Mathematics* by Rademacher and Toeplitz (Princeton Un. Press, 1957). See also H. Steinhaus, *Mathematical Snapshots*, second edition, Oxford, London, 1950.

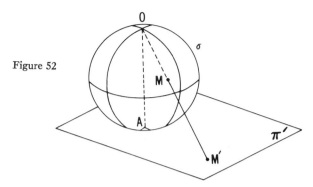

Figure 52

By a stereographic projection of a sphere σ to π', the plane tangent to σ at a point A, we mean the central projection of σ to π' with center at the endpoint $O \neq A$ of the diameter of σ through A; thus the image of a point M on σ ($M \neq O$) under the stereographic projection is the point M' where the line OM intersects π' (Fig. 52). The point O of the sphere is not carried into any point of π' by the stereographic projection.

The most important property of a stereographic projection is stated in the following theorem.

THEOREM 2. *A stereographic projection carries every circle on the sphere σ into a circle or a line in the plane π' and, conversely, the preimage of a line or a circle in π' is a circle on σ.*

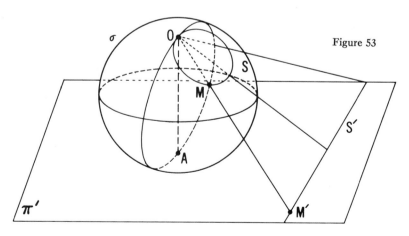

Figure 53

PROOF. It is clear that a stereographic projection carries a circle S on the sphere σ and passing through O into a line S' in the plane π' (Fig. 53) and, conversely, the preimage of a line in π' under a stereographic projection is a circle on σ passing through O. Now let S be a circle on σ not passing through O; S may be thought of as the curve

of tangency of σ with the circumscribed cone K (Fig. 54a) or with
the circumscribed cylinder Λ (Fig. 54b). Now let P' be the point where
the line through O and the vertex P of the cone K, or through O
and parallel to a generator of the cylinder Λ, intersects π'. We shall
show that the stereographic projection carries S into a circle S' in π'
with center P'.

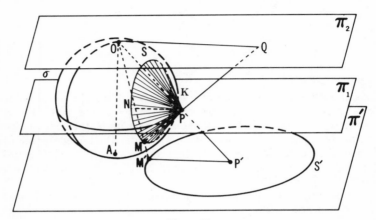

Figure 54a

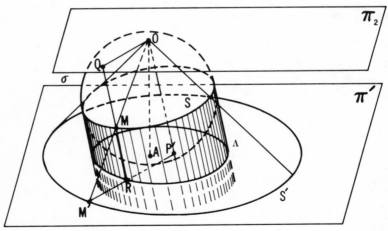

Figure 54b

Let M be a point on S, and let M' be its projection in the plane π'.
We must show that the distance $P'M'$ is independent of the choice of
the point M of S (this is equivalent to showing that the locus of M'
is a circle S' with center P'). We consider first the case where S is

the circle of tangency of a *cone* K with the sphere σ (Fig. 54a). We pass planes π_1 and π_2 parallel to π' through points P and O, denote by N the point of intersection of line OM with π_1 and by Q the point of intersection of line PM with π_2. Next we join Q to O. Lines $P'M'$, PN and QO are parallel since they are lines of intersection of the plane OPM with the parallel planes π', π_1 and π_2. It follows that $\triangle MPN \sim \triangle MQO$, and that $\triangle OPN \sim \triangle OP'M'$. The similarity of the first pair of triangles implies that $PN/PM = QO/QM$. Since QO and QM are tangents from Q to the sphere σ (QO lies in the plane π_2 tangent to σ; QM is a generator of the cone K circumscribed about σ), $QO = QM$. But then $PN = PM$. This shows that the length of the segment PM is independent of the choice of M on S (PM is constant for all M on S). Further, the similarity of the second pair of triangles implies that $P'M'/PN = OP'/OP$, so that

$$P'M' = PN \cdot \frac{OP'}{OP} = PM \cdot \frac{OP'}{OP}.$$

This means that $P'M'$ is indeed independent of the choice of M, which is what we wished to prove.

If S is the circle of tangency of the *cylinder* Λ and the sphere σ (Fig. 54b), then we pass through M a generator of the cylinder and denote its points of intersection with the planes π' and π_2 (introduced above) by R and Q. Since $MR \parallel OP'$, R lies on the segment $M'P'$. We join Q to O and conclude as before that $\triangle MRM' \sim \triangle MQO$. From this we infer that $MR = RM'$ (for $QM = QO$ as tangents from Q to σ). Now the similarity of the triangles $OP'M'$ and MRM' enables us to conclude that

$$P'M' = P'O,$$

which means that, in this case too, the length of $P'M'$ does not depend on which point M on S we choose.

Conversely, let S' be an arbitrary circle in the plane π' with center P', M' a point of S', and M the point of σ mapped by the stereographic projection onto the point M'. Let P be the point of intersection of the line OP' with the plane α tangent to σ at M (provided such a point exists). As before we prove that P is independent of the choice of the point M' on the circle S'. If the plane α is parallel to OP' for our M', then α is parallel to OP' for all points M' on S'. We conclude that the locus of points M is the circle S of tangency of the sphere σ and either the cone K of tangents to the sphere from the point P, or the cylinder Λ of tangents parallel to OP'.

Using Theorem 2 we can readily prove the fundamental Theorems 1 and 1'.

PROOF of Theorem 1'. Let S be a circle in a plane π and let l be a line in π not intersecting S. Pass a sphere σ through S and a plane α through l tangent to σ at some point O. Now let π' be the plane parallel to α and tangent to σ at the point A diametrically opposite to O (Fig. 55). The central projection from O of π to π' carries S into a circle S' in π' (in view of Theorem 2) and, obviously, carries l into the line at infinity of π'.

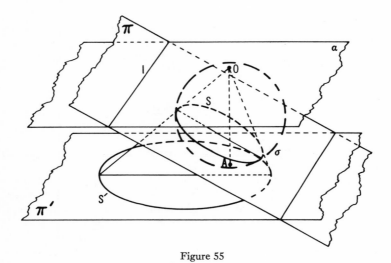

Figure 55

PROOF of Theorem 1. Let S be a circle and Q a point in the interior of S. Let AC and BD be two chords through Q, and consider the quadrilateral $ABCD$ (Fig. 56). Denote by E and F the points of intersection of its opposite sides.

All lines through E either (1) intersect S twice on arc AB, or (2) twice on arc CD,† or (3) once in arc AD and once in arc BC, or (4) they have no point in common with S. Similarly, all lines through F either (1) intersect S twice in arc AD, or (2) twice in arc BC,† or (3) once in arc AB and once in arc CD, or (4) they have no point in common with S. The line EF must belong to the fourth category because, if it belonged to one of the other three with respect to E, it would violate the conditions for being in one of the four categories with respect to F.

† If the two intersections on the same arc coalesce, the line in question is a tangent and the argument remains valid.

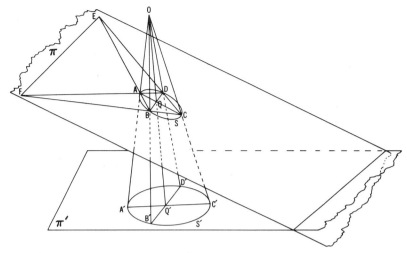

Figure 56

Now project our diagram to a plane π' so that S goes over into a circle S', and EF into the line at infinity of π' (which is possible by Theorem 1'). The image of the quadrilateral $ABCD$ is a parallelogram $A'B'C'D'$ inscribed in S', that is, a rectangle. Since Q is the point of intersection of the diagonals of $ABCD$, it follows that its image Q' is the point of intersection of the diagonals of the rectangle $A'B'C'D'$, that is, the center of S'.

Theorems 1 and 1' enable us to use central projections to solve many problems involving circles. A number of such problems follow. In solving these, it is often helpful to bear in mind the rather obvious fact that a central projection which carries a circle S into a circle S' also carries a tangent to S (that is, a line which has a *single* point in common with S) into a tangent to S'. Without the use of central projections the solution of these problems is, as a rule, very difficult.

39. (a) Prove that the lines joining the vertices of a triangle to the points at which the opposite sides touch the inscribed circle of the triangle are concurrent (cf. Fig. 63d).

(b) Let ABC be a triangle and S a circle which intersects sides AB, BC and CA in the points M and N, P and Q, R and T, respectively. Let C_1, A_1, B_1 be the points of intersection of the tangents to S at the points M and N, P and Q, R and T, respectively. Show that lines AA_1, BB_1, CC_1 are concurrent.

It is clear that Problem 39(a) is a limiting case of Problem 39(b). Specifically 39(b) goes over into 39(a) when M and N, P and Q, R and T coincide in pairs.

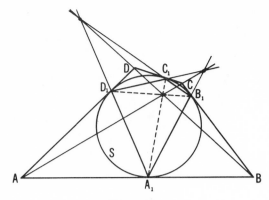

Figure 57

40. Let $ABCD$ be a quadrilateral circumscribed about a circle S, and let A_1, B_1, C_1, D_1 be the points at which its sides touch S (Fig. 57). Show that:
   (a) The points of intersection of the diagonals of the quadrilaterals $ABCD$ and $A'B'C'D'$ coincide.
   (b) The extensions of the diagonals of quadrilateral $ABCD$ pass through the points of intersection of the opposite sides of quadrilateral $A_1B_1C_1D_1$.

41. Let $ABCD$ be a quadrilateral inscribed in a circle S, let P and Q be the points of intersection of its opposite sides, and let O be the point of intersection of its diagonals. Prove that:
   (a) There exist infinitely many triangles inscribed in S whose sides (or their extensions) pass through P, Q and O (more precisely, if two sides of a triangle inscribed in S pass through two of the points P, Q and O, then the third side necessarily passes through the third point).
   (b) There exist infinitely many quadrilaterals inscribed in S such that the points of intersection of their opposite sides coincide with P and Q (more precisely, if two opposite sides of a quadrilateral inscribed in S intersect at P and a third side passes through Q, then the side opposite to it also passes through Q), and the points of intersection of the diagonals of all such quadrilaterals coincide with O.
   (c) There exist infinitely many quadrilaterals inscribed in S such that the points of intersection of their diagonals coincide with O, one point of intersection of opposite sides coincides with P (more precisely, if the point of intersection of the diagonals of a quadrilateral inscribed in S coincides with O and one side passes through P, then the side opposite to it also passes through P), and the second point of intersection of opposite sides (of all such quadrilaterals) coincides with Q.

42. Let S be a circle and P a point in the plane of S. Consider the totality of secants of S passing through P. Each of these secants determines a pair of points of S. With each of these pairs of points we associate the points of intersection of the tangents to S at the pair of points in question. Find the locus of these intersection points.

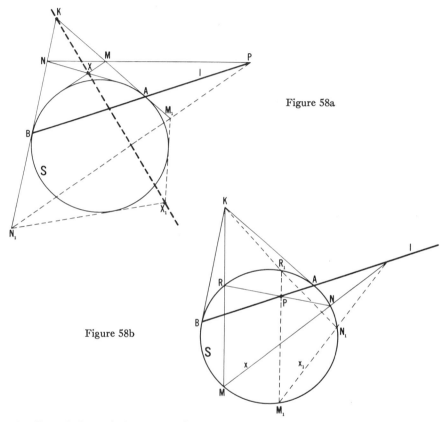

Figure 58a

Figure 58b

43. Let S be a circle, P a point, and l a line passing through P and intersecting S in points A and B. Let K denote the point of intersection of the tangents to S at A and B.

(a) A variable line through P intersects AK and BK at points M and N (Fig. 58a). Prove that the locus of points X of intersection of the second tangents to S from points M and N is a line passing through K (more precisely, the part of that line outside S).

(b) A variable point R of the circle S is joined to the points P and K (Fig. 58b). Show that the line x joining the second points of intersection M and. N of the lines RK and RP and S passes through a fixed point (independent of the choice of R!) on the line l.

44. Inscribe a quadrilateral in a given circle given:
(a) the point of intersection M of its diagonals and two points K and L lying on opposite sides.
(b) the point of intersection of two opposite sides and one point on each of the remaining sides.

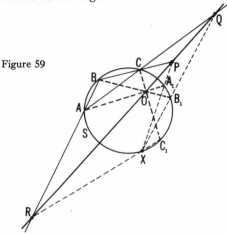

Figure 59

45. Let AA_1, BB_1, CC_1 be three chords of a circle S which intersect in a point O, and let X be an arbitrary point of S. Show that the points P, Q, R of intersection of the lines XA_1, XB_1, XC_1 with the sides BC, CA, AB of $\triangle ABC$ lie on a line through O (Fig. 59).

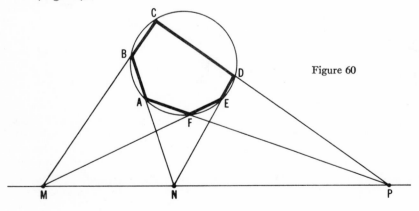

Figure 60

46. *Pascal's Theorem*. Show that the three points of intersection of opposite sides of a hexagon inscribed in a circle are collinear (Fig. 60).

Pascal's Theorem is stated once more (in somewhat more general form) in §5 (cf. Problem 80, p. 93).

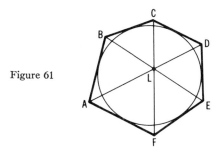

Figure 61

47. *Brianchon's Theorem.* Prove that the three diagonals joining the opposite vertices of a hexagon circumscribed about a circle are concurrent (Fig. 61).

Brianchon's Theorem appears in another connection in §5, Ch. 2, Problem 282.[T] A rather surprising proof of Brianchon's theorem is found in the Supplement (cf. Problem 98 on p. 118). For the connection between the theorems of Brianchon and Pascal see Problem 63 in §4, p. 81.

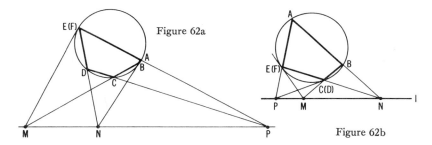

Figure 62a

Figure 62b

Certain results pertaining to inscribed and circumscribed pentagons, quadrilaterals and triangles are limiting cases of the theorems of Brianchon and Pascal. Thus, for example, assume that the vertex F of a hexagon $ABCDEF$ moves on a circle and approaches the point E. Then side EF tends to the tangent to the circle at E, and in the limit we obtain the following result: *The point of intersection of side BC of a pentagon $ABCDE$ inscribed in a circle with the tangent to the circle at E is collinear with the points of intersection of sides AB and DE, CD and AE* (Fig. 62a). Similarly, assuming that in the hexagon $ABCDEF$ the vertex F coincides with E and the vertex D with C, we obtain the result: *The point of intersection of sides AB and CE of a quadrilateral $ABCE$ inscribed in a circle is collinear with the point where BC meets the tangent to the circle at E, and the point where AE meets the tangent to the circle at C* (Fig. 62b). If, in the hexagon, we assume coincidence of the vertices

T Reference to untranslated Russian material.

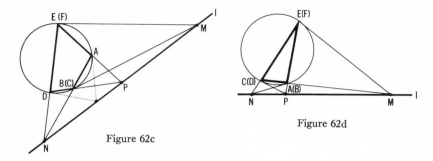

Figure 62c

Figure 62d

F and E, and C and B, then we see readily that *the point of inter-section of the tangents to a circle at the vertices E and B of an inscribed quadrilateral $ABDE$ lies on one line with the points of intersection of the opposite sides;* it is clear that the point of intersection of the tangents to the circle at the points A and D also lies on that line (Fig. 62c). Finally the assumption that the vertices A and B, C and D, E and F of the hexagon coincide implies that *the points of intersection of the sides of a triangle ACE with the lines tangent to its circumscribed circle at the opposite vertices are collinear* (Fig. 62d). We could agree to regard all of these propositions as special cases of Pascal's theorem, where one or more sides have length zero, and prove all of them in the manner of Pascal's Theorem (and in some cases the proof is considerably simplified).

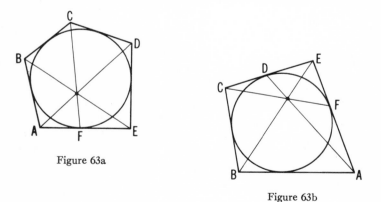

Figure 63a

Figure 63b

In much the same way it is possible to deduce a number of new proposi-tions from Brianchon's theorem. To this end we need only assume the circumscribed hexagon has one or more angles equal to $180°$. The several assertions are suggested by Figs. 63a–d and left to the reader to state. (Note that the theorems represented in Figs. 63c, 63d are identical with those in Problems 40(a) and 39(a).)

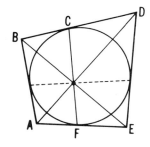

Figure 63c

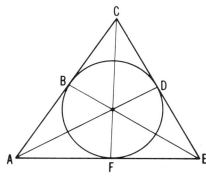

Figure 63d

48. Let A be a point on a circle. Draw a tangent to the circle at A using ruler alone.

Compare Problem 48 with Problem 54 in the next section, p. 71.

49. Let MN be an arc of a circle S, and let l be a line intersecting this arc in one point (Fig. 64). Find the other point of intersection of l with S using straightedge alone.

Compare Problem 49 with Problem 55 of the next section, p. 71.

Figure 64

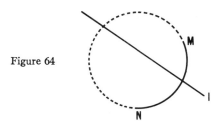

50. Let triangle ABC and a point Q be given. Let M, N, P be the points where lines AQ, BQ, CQ meet sides BC, CA, and AB (Fig. 65). Let S be the circle inscribed in $\triangle ABC$, tangent to its sides at points D', E', F'. Show that the three lines joining the vertices of $\triangle DEF$, formed by the second tangents to S from M, N, P,[T] with D', E', F' intersect at Q.

[T] where EF lies on the tangent from M, FD on the tangent from N, and DE on the tangent from P.

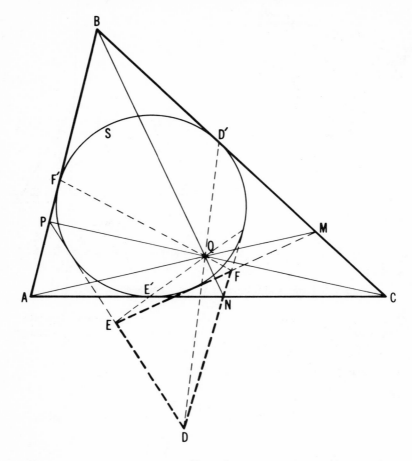

Figure 65

4. Reciprocation (polarity) in the plane.
Principle of duality.

The following theorem will play an important role in what follows.

THEOREM 1. *If we pass through a point* P *not on a circle* S *all possible pairs of secants intersecting* S *in points denoted typically by* A *and* A_1, B *and* B_1, *then the points of intersection of the lines* AB *and* A_1B_1, *as well as the points of intersection of the lines* AB_1 *and* A_1B, *all lie on a line* p *(Fig. 66).*

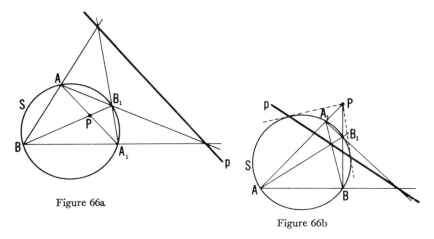

Figure 66a

Figure 66b

The line p is called the *polar* of the point P with respect to the circle S, and P is called the *pole* of p.†

At first sight Theorem 1 might appear to be of no particular interest. However, its remarkable implications amply justify the attention we shall give it.

Theorems 1 and $1'$ of the preceding section enable us to give an easy proof of Theorem 1. Indeed, if the point P lies in the interior of the circle S (Fig. 66a), then S can be carried into a circle S' and P into its center by means of a suitable central projection (cf. Theorem 1, §3). In the case when P is the center of S, Theorem 1 is obvious; in fact, the quadrilateral ABA_1B_1 is in that case a rectangle (all of its angles subtend diameters), $AB \parallel B_1A_1$, $AB_1 \parallel BA_1$, and, consequently, the required locus is the line at infinity of the plane (Fig. 67a). It follows that our theorem must hold for any point P in the interior of S. If P is outside S (Fig. 66b), then a suitable central projection will carry a line through P not intersecting S into the line at infinity (cf. Theorem $1'$, §3), and so P will be carried into a point at infinity. However, if P is a point at infinity, then Theorem 1 is obvious; in fact, quadrilateral AA_1B_1B is in that case a trapezoid inscribed in a circle (i.e., an isosceles trapezoid) with fixed direction of the bases (Fig. 67b), and the points of intersection of its sides AB and A_1B_1 and of its diagonals A_1B and AB_1 lie on its axis of symmetry, that is, on the diameter of S perpendicular to the direction of the bases of the trapezoid. This implies that Theorem 1 holds for a point P outside S.

---

† The polar of a point P relative to a circle S can also be defined as the locus of points lying on the secants through P and which, together with P, divide *harmonically* the segments determined on the secants by S (cf. the two paragraphs in fine print on p. 37).

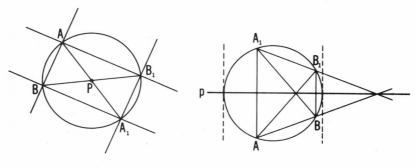

Figure 67a   Figure 67b

If P lies on S, then the locus of Theorem 1 loses meaning since, in that case, points A and B coincide with P, quadrilateral ABB_1A_1 reduces to triangle A_1B_1P, lines A_1B and B_1A intersect at P, and line AB is undefined (Fig. 68). However, it is easy to see that if a point P' not on S approaches P in any manner, then the polar p' of P' approaches the tangent to S at P (cf. Fig. 68). It is therefore natural to define the polar (relative to S) of a point P on S to be the *tangent* p to S at P.

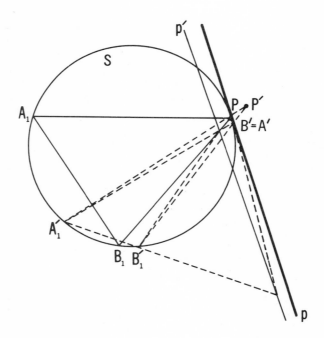

Figure 68

If P lies in the interior of S, then its polar p relative to S lies entirely outside S, and if P lies outside S, then its polar p intersects S (cf. Fig. 66). It is not difficult to prove that *if the point P lies outside the circle S, then its polar p is the line joining the points of contact of the tangents from P to S* (Fig. 66b). For proof note that this assertion is true when P is a point at infinity (cf. Fig. 67b). Now the required conclusion follows because a central projection which takes P into a point P' and S into a circle S' also takes the polar of P with respect to S into the polar of P' with respect to S' and tangents to S into tangents to S'.

We observe that *the polar p of a point P with respect to a circle S is perpendicular to the line through P and the center O of S. Conversely, the pole P of a line p lies on the perpendicular from the center O of S to p.* This follows, for example, from considerations of symmetry (Fig. 69).

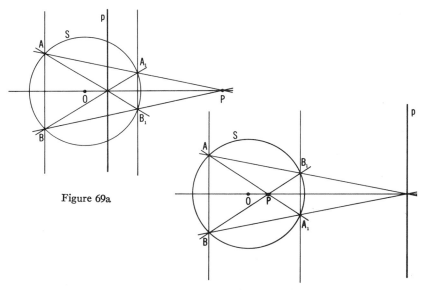

Figure 69a

Figure 69b

The construction of the polar of a point P with respect to a given circle S as well as the construction of the pole of an arbitrary line are implicit in the definitions of these concepts (cf. Figs. 66a, b). Both can be carried out with straightedge alone, a circumstance we shall use later.

The most important result concerning polars is:

THEOREM 2. *If a point A lies on the polar b of a point B, then B lies on the polar a of A* (Fig. 70).

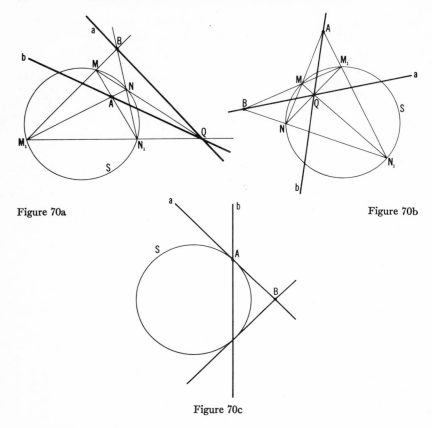

Figure 70a   Figure 70b

Figure 70c

This property is a direct consequence of the definition. For, if A is a point in the interior of the circle S, then B is necessarily outside S (Fig. 70a); otherwise its polar b would lie entirely outside S, contrary to the fact that the interior point A lies on b. Since A lies on the polar of B, there are two secants through B intersecting S in points M, M_1 and N, N_1 such that A is the point of intersection of the diagonals of quadrilateral MM_1N_1N. But then the polar of A is the line BQ, where Q is the point of intersection of MN and M_1N_1, and this means that the polar of A passes through B. A similar argument proves Theorem 2 if A lies outside S (in that case B can lie inside S—as in Fig. 70a, where we need only interchange A and B—or outside S as in Fig. 70b). If A is a point of S, the proof of Theorem 2 can be read off from Fig. 70c.

51. Prove that if the distance from the center O of a circle S of radius 1 to a point A is d, then the distance from O to the polar a of A relative to S is equal to $1/d$.

52. Let A and B be two points, a and b their polars with respect to a circle S with center O, AP and BQ the distances from A to b and from B to a. Show that

$$\frac{OA}{AP} = \frac{OB}{BQ}.$$

53. (a) Let $ABCD$ be a quadrilateral inscribed in a circle S. Show that the perpendicular from the center of S to the line joining the points of intersection of the opposite sides of the quadrilateral passes through the intersection point of its diagonals.
    (b) Prove the above proposition under the assumption that quadrilateral $ABCD$ is circumscribed about the circle S.

54. Let A be a point outside a circle S. Using only a straightedge draw the tangents from A to S.

    Compare this problem with Problem 48 of §3, p. 65.

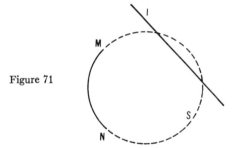

Figure 71

55. Let MN be a given arc of a circle S, and let l be a given line not intersecting this arc (Fig. 71). Using a straightedge alone, determine the points of intersection of l and S.

    Compare this problem with Problem 49, §3, p. 65.

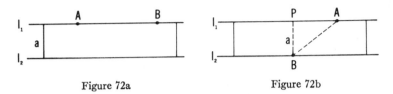

Figure 72a   Figure 72b

56. By a *parallel ruler* we mean a ruler with two parallel edges. Such a ruler can be used to draw two parallel lines l_1 and l_2 whose distance apart is the width a of the ruler and such that l_1 passes through two given points A and B (Fig. 72a), or such that l_1 passes

through A, and l_2 passes through B (Fig. 72b).† Show that using only a parallel ruler of width a, it is possible to find the points of intersection of a given line l with a circle of given center A and radius a, even though the circle has not been drawn.

A parallel ruler is a very popular drawing tool, and it is of interest to determine what constructions can be carried out by means of such a ruler alone. It is obvious that all constructions which can be carried out with a straightedge alone can be carried out with a parallel ruler, but the converse is false. For example, as we shall see in §5, it is impossible to draw a line through a given point M parallel to a given line l using straightedge alone (cf. p. 100); at the same time it is obviously possible to carry out some constructions of this type using a parallel ruler only (cf. Problem 3(b), §1, p. 13).

It is easy to see that all constructions which can be carried out with a parallel ruler can be carried out with straightedge and compasses (for, using these instruments, we can carry out both constructions represented in Fig. 72a, b; construction of the lines l_1 and l_2 in Fig. 72b reduces to the determination of the vertex P of the right triangle ABP, given its hypotenuse AB and side $BP = a$). In §5 we shall show that, conversely, *all constructions which can be performed with straightedge and compasses can be performed with parallel ruler alone;* in this connection the construction in Problem 56 will play a fundamental role.

57. Show that the lines joining the vertices of a triangle ABC with the poles A', B', C' of the opposite sides of the triangle relative to some circle S are concurrent.

The theorem of Problem 57 can be restated as follows. Define two triangles ABC and $A'B'C'$ to be *polar with respect to a given circle* if the sides of $\triangle A'B'C'$ are the polars of the corresponding vertices of $\triangle ABC$. Theorem 2 implies that the sides of $\triangle ABC$ are the polars of the vertices of $\triangle A'B'C'$. Thus the theorem in Problem 57 asserts that *polar triangles are always perspective* (cf. Problem 22, §2, and the comments which follow it, p. 30). It follows that the points of intersection of the corresponding sides of triangles ABC and $A'B'C'$ are collinear (cf. Problem 22). [The assertions in Problems 39(a) and (b) of §3 (p. 59) are special cases of the theorem in Problem 57.]

58. Let two triangles ABC and $A_1B_1C_1$ be given together with a circle S. Prove that if the lines joining the corresponding vertices of these triangles are concurrent, then the lines joining the poles of the sides of $\triangle ABC$ (relative to S) with the poles of the corresponding sides of $\triangle A_1B_1C_1$ are also concurrent. (In other words, if two triangles are perspective, then the triangles polar to them are also perspective; cf. the comments following the preceding problem.)

† Obviously, the latter can hold only if $AB \geq a$.

59. A triangle is said to be *self polar* with respect to a given circle if each of its sides is the polar of the opposite vertex. Prove that for an *obtuse* triangle ABC there exists a unique circle relative to which this triangle is self polar; also, the center of that circle is the point of intersection of the altitudes of $\triangle ABC$. A right triangle or an acute triangle is not self polar relative to any circle.

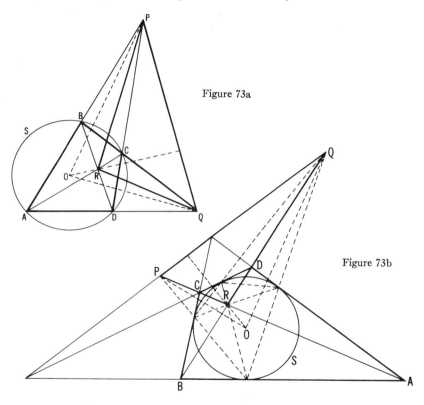

Figure 73a

Figure 73b

We note that Theorem 1 implies that, *if we inscribe a quadrilateral in a circle* S, *then the triangle whose vertices are the points where the diagonals of the quadrilateral meet and where pairs of opposite sides meet is self polar relative to* S (Fig. 73a). Similarly, *if we circumscribe a quadrilateral about a circle* S, *then the triangle whose sides are determined by the diagonals of the quadrilateral and the line joining the points of intersection of the opposite sides is self polar relative to* S (Fig. 73b).

[If the sides of the circumscribed quadrilateral in Fig. 73b are tangent to S at the vertices of the inscribed quadrilateral depicted in Fig. 73a, then $\triangle PQR$ in Fig. 73b coincides with $\triangle PQR$ in Fig. 73a; the proof of this assertion is left to the reader.] The result in Problem 59 implies that *both triangles under consideration are obtuse, and the points of intersection of their altitudes coincide with the center of* S.

The concept of the polar of a point with respect to a circle permits us to define a kind of transformation of the plane helpful in proving many theorems. Let F be a plane figure consisting of points and lines, and let S be a fixed circle. Associate with the figure F the figure F' obtained by replacing each point of F with its polar and each line of F with its pole relative to S. The transformation associating with the figure F the figure F' obtained in the manner just described is called a *reciprocation* or *polarity*.[T] At times we also use the term *polar transformation*.

Of course, a polarity is not a transformation in the sense we have used the term thus far, namely, in the sense of a mapping that carries points into points (a point transformation); it is, by definition, a mapping which interchanges points and lines. As such, a polarity is different from all transformations we have encountered thus far (motions, similarities, projections). In the sequel (cf. §5, Ch. II)[TT] we shall come across other instances of transformations which are not point transformations.

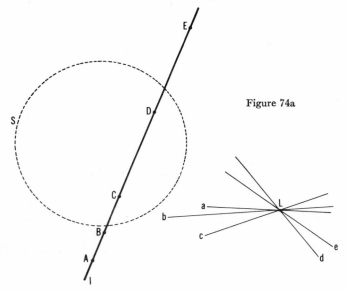

Figure 74a

Our definition of polarity is entirely satisfactory insofar as the problems stated below are concerned; it is, moreover, possible to consider a polarity as a *transformation of the plane to itself*, more correctly, as a transformation of the set of points and lines of the plane which carries every point into a certain line and every line into a certain point. Further, in view of Theorem 2, points lying on a line l go over into lines passing through the image point L of the line l (Fig. 74a). A polarity carries a curve γ,

---

[T] Although "polarity" often denotes a more general transformation (see p. 75) in which the points lying on their polars form a conic instead of a circle, or in which there are no such points at all, "polarity" in this book is used synonymously with "reciprocation".

[TT] Reference to untranslated Russian material.

viewed as the set of its points, into a new curve Γ, which is to be thought of as the
envelope of its tangents (Fig. 74b).†

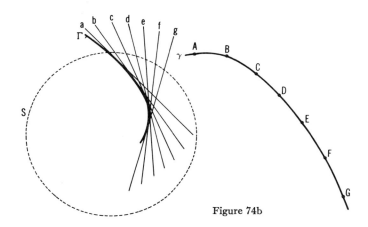

Figure 74b

We note that it is possible to define a polarity of a plane to itself without recourse
to Theorem 1 using the following stereometric construction. Let π and π' be parallel
planes, and let M be a point equidistant from both planes (Fig. 75). With each point
A in π (except O, the foot of the perpendicular from M), associate a line a obtained
as follows: Draw line l through A and M; pass a plane λ through M, perpendicular to l, and denote by a' the line where λ meets π'. Now "drop" π' on the

† Here is a relevant and interesting illustration. Clearly a polarity relative to a
circle S with center O and radius 1 carries a circle s with center O and radius r
into a circle s' with radius $1/r$, where s is thought of as the set of its points and s'
as the appropriate set of tangents, or conversely. (A point A at a distance r from O
goes over into a line a at a distance $1/r$ from O; cf. Problem 51 above.) Now assume
that the center B of the circle s (which at this point it is convenient to identify with
its set of tangents a) does *not* coincide with O (as before, the radius of s is r).
If b and A are the images of B and a under the polarity relative to S, then, by
the result of Problem 52, $OA/AP = OB/BQ \ (= OB/r)$, where AP and $BQ = r$
are the distances from A to b and from B to a. Hence the set of lines a (i.e., the
circle s) goes over into the set ("locus") s' of points A such that

$$OA/AP = \text{constant} \ (= OB/r),$$

that is, into the *locus of points A for which the ratio of the distances to O and b is
constant* (and equal to OB/r). But, as is well known, this locus represents an *ellipse*
(if $OB/r < 1$, i.e., if O is interior to s), *parabola* (if $OB/r = 1$, i.e., if O belongs
to s), or *hyperbola* (if $OB/r > 1$, i.e., if O is exterior to s). It follows that *a polarity
carries a circle s either into a circle* (this is the case when the center of s coincides
with the center O of the circle S of the polarity), *or an ellipse, parabola, or hyperbola.*
[See NML 19, pp. 136–143.] This fact implies many interesting properties of conic
sections.

plane π (that is, project π' orthogonally to π), thus letting a' go into the line a in π. It is not difficult to show that the transformation which associates with the point A the line a is the polarity with respect to the circle with center O and radius OM. We shall have no occasion to use this result and leave its proof to the reader. It is easy to deduce all properties of a polarity from the definition just given; we suggest that the reader try this on his own.

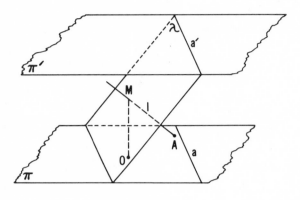

Figure 75

A polarity can sometimes be used to reduce a given problem to a simpler one (see, for example, Problems 67 and 68 below). A more important fact is that polarities serve as the means for obtaining new results from old ones. To elucidate this point, note that when we used central or parallel projections to solve problems in the preceding sections we aimed at reducing a given problem to a simple special case of *that same problem* (for example, in §1 we replaced an arbitrary triangle with an equilateral triangle, and in §§2 and 3 we replaced an arbitrary pair of lines with a pair of parallel lines). When we use a polarity we are not, in general, led to a special case of the given problem; in fact, a polarity transforms a diagram to a completely different diagram with point replaced by line and line by point. It follows that if we apply a polarity to a diagram accompanying a certain proposition, we obtain a diagram which corresponds to a new proposition. This new proposition may be simpler than the original one; and, by proving it, we shall have proved the original proposition as well. If the new proposition is not simpler than the original, we still profit, since a proof of either one yields the validity of both.

Theorems obtained from one another by polar transformations are called *dual theorems*, and the existence of pairs of theorems each of which is the dual of the other is known as the *principle of duality* which we shall illustrate with many examples in the sequel.

The duality principle, based on the notion of a polarity of the plane, enables us to obtain a new theorem from a given one by interchanging the words "point" and "line". In defining a polarity we made use of Theorem 1 in the beginning of this section. Its significance lies not so much in that it enables us to associate with every point a definite line and with every line a definite point—such correspondences are quite common (for example, we could associate with a point P the axis of symmetry p determined by P and some fixed point O, with O the line at infinity, say, and with a point at infinity the line through O perpendicular to the direction determined by that point at infinity)—but in that it allows us to associate with a point on a line a line through the corresponding point (cf. Theorem 2, p. 69). It turns out that every correspondence of the latter kind, that is, *every correspondence which associates with a point (line) a unique line (point), and with a point and a line through it a line and a point on it,* can be realized by means of a polarity with respect to some circle S and, possibly, a central projection of the plane to itself, or a half turn and a central projection (in this connection see Ch. 8 of H. S. M. Coxeter's *Projective Geometry*, Blaisdell Publishing Co., New York, 1964).

One more comment. We may have given the reader the impression that polarities are basically a means for obtaining new theorems out of old ones, whereas central and parallel projections serve exclusively as techniques for proving geometric propositions. This distinction is not quite correct for, as we mentioned above, polarities can sometimes be used for proving given geometric propositions and, as we are about to explain, central and parallel projections are occasionally used to obtain new theorems out of old ones: by applying a central or parallel projection to the diagram of a theorem we are sometimes led to a new one. Consider a theorem involving solely concepts preserved under parallel projections (that is, a theorem of affine geometry; cf. the Introduction to this book). Clearly, applying a parallel projection to such a theorem cannot yield a new theorem (just as a motion applied to the diagram of any theorem never leads to a new theorem; for a more detailed discussion of this point consult the Introduction to NML 8) but rather, hopefully, it may lead to a simple special case of the same theorem; many relevant examples of this type are given in §1. On the other hand, application of a parallel projection to the diagram of a theorem involving other than affine concepts may yield a new theorem; for example, by projecting a right triangle to an equilateral triangle we can obtain from any theorem about a right triangle a new theorem. Similarly, applying central projections to affine theorems may lead to new theorems; relevant examples were given above (cf. Problems 29 and 31, 32(a) and 33 in §1). All in all, it is safe to say that central and parallel projections are used *most frequently* for proving theorems, and polarities for obtaining new theorems out of old ones.

It is important to note that the duality principle holds only in the *projective plane*, that is, in the plane supplemented with "elements at infinity" (a polarity with respect to a circle S carries the center of S into the line at infinity and its diameters into points at infinity). This is because the duality principle permits us to interchange points and lines in geometric propositions, and thus signifies, in a sense, equivalence of points and lines. Prior to the introduction of elements at infinity points and lines were in no sense equivalent, for, if they were, then the existence of parallel lines (lines without a common point) would imply the existence of "parallel" points (points without a "common line", that is, points without a line passing through them) and no such points exist. Introduction of elements at infinity does away with the special status of parallel lines; in the projective plane two lines have invariably a unique point in common (a finite point or a point at infinity), and two points invariably determine a unique line passing through both of them (cf. p. 37 ff.).

It is possible to show that the symmetry of basic properties of points and lines in the projective plane noted above *implies* the principle of duality, that is, the possibility of obtaining from a given theorem a new theorem (its dual) by interchanging the terms "point" and "line" and the terms "lies on" and "passes through". Indeed, in proving any geometric theorem we reduce it to a simpler theorem which, in turn, is reduced to a still simpler theorem, and so on, until we reach the very simplest geometric propositions, the axioms, which are assumed without proof. Now in the projective plane the basic properties of points and lines are entirely equivalent, that is, if we interchange in any given axiom the terms "point" and "line" and the terms "lies on" and "passes through" we obtain a valid proposition. It is convenient to include these propositions in the list of axioms. While the resulting list of axioms is redundant, it is also self dual. But then the dual of any (valid) theorem is a new valid theorem provable in much the same way as the original one, with the sole exception that now the process of proof leads back to axioms dual to those we are led to in the proof of the original theorem. (For details consult Ch. 3 of H. S. M. Coxeter's *Projective Geometry*, Blaisdell Publishing Co., New York 1964.)

One other comment. We can obtain many more dual theorems by using polarities than by using the equivalence of the basic properties of points and lines, because the use of this equivalence (embodied in the existence of pairs of dual axioms) for the purpose of obtaining dual theorems is restricted to theorems not involving angles or distances (since we have no duals of these concepts).† On the other hand, properties B and C of a polarity given on p. 82 below enable us to apply the duality principle to a much larger class of theorems.

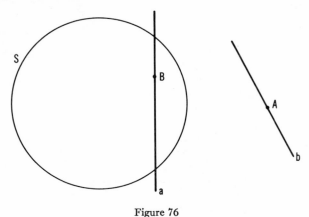

Figure 76

† In other words, the equivalence of the basic properties of points and lines in the projective plane permits us to apply the duality principle only to theorems of projective geometry (cf. the Introduction to this book).

We shall now consider some of the properties of polarities. The most important of these is:

A. *A polarity carries a point A and a line b passing through A into a line a and a point B lying on a* (Fig. 76).

This property of a polarity is an immediate consequence of Theorem 2.

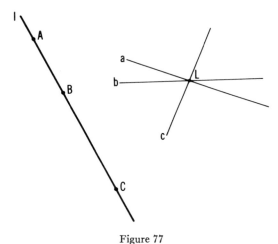

Figure 77

Property A implies that a polarity carries three points A, B, C lying on a line l into three lines a, b, c passing through a point L (Fig. 77; cf. also Fig. 74a) and that, conversely, it carries three concurrent lines (passing through the same finite point or point at infinity) into three collinear points. This fact alone permits us to obtain new theorems from given ones. Consider, for example, the theorem of Problem 38(a), p. 51: *If A_1, B_1, C_1 are points on the sides of a triangle ABC* (to be called $\triangle T$, for brevity) *such that the lines AA_1, BB_1, CC_1 intersect in a point O, and if A_2, B_2, C_2 are points on the sides of triangle $A_1B_1C_1$ ($\triangle T_1$) such that lines A_1A_2, B_1B_2, C_1C_2 intersect in a point O_1, then lines AA_2, BB_2, CC_2 also intersect in a point* (Fig. 78a). We apply to this theorem a polarity. Then the triangle T goes into a triangle t whose sides are the polars a, b, c of the vertices of T; the point O goes into a line o, and the triangle T_1, into the triangle t_1 whose sides are the lines a_1, b_1, c_1 joining the vertices of t to the points of intersection of o with the opposite sides; the point O_1 goes into a line o_1, and the points A_2, B_2, C_2 into the lines a_2, b_2, c_2 joining the vertices of t_1 to the points of intersection of o_1 with the opposite sides (Fig. 78b).

Since the theorem of Problem 38(a) tells us that the lines AA_2, BB_2 and CC_2 are concurrent, it follows that the points of intersection of the pairs of lines a and a_2, b and b_2, c and c_2 are collinear. We are thus

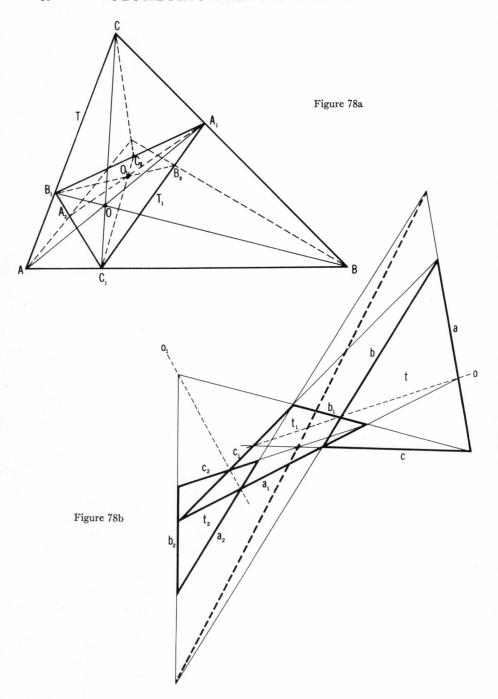

Figure 78a

Figure 78b

led to the following theorem: *If t_1 is a triangle whose sides are on the lines joining the vertices of a triangle t to the points of intersection of the opposite sides with a line o, and t_2 is a triangle whose sides are on lines joining the vertices of t_1 to the points of intersection of the opposite sides with some line o_1, then the points of intersection of the corresponding sides of triangles t and t_2 are collinear.* This is an entirely new theorem depicted by a new diagram, yet we need not supply an independent proof; its validity follows from the theorem of Problem 38(a) and property A of a polarity.†

60. What theorems are obtained by applying polarities to the theorems in Problems 17(a), (b); 21(a), (b); 22; 25; 26; 27; 28?

61. Let n concurrent lines l_1, l_2, $\cdots$, l_n and n points M_1, M_2, $\cdots$, M_n be given in a plane. Construct an n-gon $A_1 A_2 \cdots A_n$ whose vertices lie on the lines l_1, l_2, $\cdots$, l_n and whose sides pass through the points M_1, M_2, $\cdots$, M_n.

Problem 90 in §5, p. 99 represents a considerable generalization of Problem 61.

62. What theorems are obtained by applying polarities to the theorems in Problems 36(a)–(d); 37(a)–(c); 38(b)?

63. What theorems are obtained from Problems 39(a), (b); 40(a), (b); 41; 43(a), (b); 45; 46; 47; 50 by means of polarities with respect to the circles specified in the statements of these problems?

64. What theorem is obtained from Problem 42 if we apply to it the polarity with respect to the circle S?

65. Let a circle S and three lines l, l_1, l_2 be given. Circumscribe about S a quadrilateral $ABCD$ such that A and C lie on l, B lies on l_1, and D on l_2.

This problem is generalized in Problem 84(b), §5, p. 97.

66. Use polarities to obtain the theorem of Ceva (cf. Problem 34(b), §2, p. 43) from the theorem of Menelaus (Problem 34(a)) and, conversely, the theorem of Menelaus from the theorem of Ceva.

† We note that, strictly speaking, deduction of new theorems by means of polarities requires *two* applications of a polarity. This becomes clear if we give additional thought to the example just presented. Application of a polar transformation to a given theorem (in our case the theorem of Problem 38(a)) yields the *statement* of a new theorem. We cannot be absolutely certain that the new theorem is true in all cases (we cannot claim that Fig. 78b, with t, o, and o_1 entirely arbitrary, can be obtained by applying a polarity to Fig. 78a); to *prove* the obtained theorem we must reduce it by means of a second polarity to the original theorem.

We shall now consider further properties of polarities.

B. *A polarity with respect to a circle S carries parallel lines into points collinear with the center O of S and, conversely, points collinear with the center O of S into parallel lines* (Fig. 79).

This property is an immediate consequence of the fact that the pole of a line *a* lies on the line through the center of *S* perpendicular to *a* (cf. p. 69).

C. *Let A and B be two points, and a and b their images under a polarity with respect to some circle S with center O. Then the angle between the lines a and b is equal to the angle subtended by the segment AB at O (or to its supplement).*

This property also follows from the perpendicularity of the polar *a* of a point *A* and the line *OA* which, in turn, implies that the sides of the angle between the lines *a* and *b* and the sides of the angle between *OA* and *OB* are perpendicular in pairs (Fig. 80).

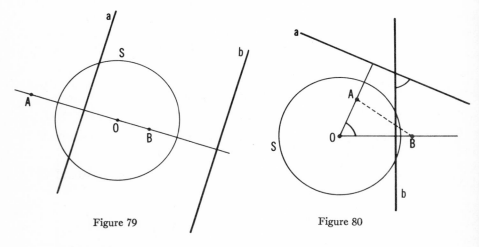

Figure 79   Figure 80

Properties B and C of a polarity enable us to obtain new theorems from many of the theorems of elementary geometry. For example, consider the proposition: *An angle inscribed in a semicircle is a right angle* (Fig. 81a). The polarity relative to the circle *S* in question carries the points *A*, *B*, *C* into the tangents *a*, *b*, *c* to *S*; in particular, if *A* and *B* are diametrically opposite points of *S*, then the tangents *a* and *b* are parallel (cf. property B of a polarity).

Bearing in mind property C of a polarity we can now assert that *if S is a circle with center O and two parallel tangents to S meet a third tangent to S in points K and L, then the angle KOL is a right angle* (Fig. 81b).

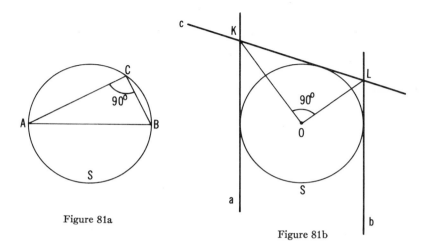

Figure 81a

Figure 81b

Here is another, more complicated example. It is almost obvious that *a quadrilateral whose vertices are the midpoints of the sides of a parallelogram is itself a parallelogram* (Fig. 82a; see Problem 16(a) in NML 8). Let us see what proposition we obtain by applying a polarity to this theorem.

First we must define the midpoints of the sides of the parallelogram in terms of entities with known images under a polarity (for we do not know the image of the midpoint of a segment under a polarity). One such definition is: *The midpoints of the sides of a parallelogram are the points of intersection of its sides and its midlines—lines passing through the point of intersection of the diagonals and parallel to the sides.* It is this definition that we adopt.

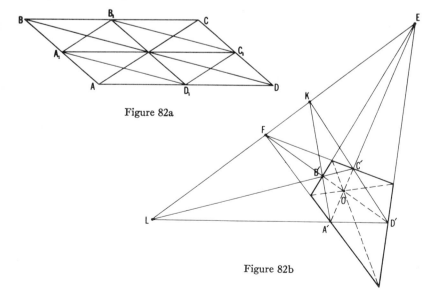

Figure 82a

Figure 82b

In view of property B of a polarity, $\square ABCD$ is carried into a quadrilateral $A'B'C'D'$ such that the point of intersection of its diagonals coincides with the center O of S (see Fig. 82b; S is not shown in the figure). Opposite vertices of the parallelogram go over into opposite sides of quadrilateral $A'B'C'D'$, the diagonals of the parallelogram go over into the points K and L of intersection of pairs of opposite sides of the quadrilateral, and the point of intersection of the diagonals goes over into the line KL. In view of properties B and C of a polarity, the midlines of the parallelogram go over into the points E and F of intersection of line KL with the diagonals $A'C'$ and $B'D'$ of quadrilateral $A'B'C'D'$. This implies that the midpoints of the sides of the parallelogram go over into the lines EB' and ED', FA' and FC', and the original proposition gives rise to the following dual proposition: *The point of intersection of the diagonals of the quadrilateral whose sides are on the lines FA', EB', FC', and ED' coincides with the point of intersection of the diagonals of the quadrilateral $A'B'C'D'$* (Fig. 82b).

The new proposition is neither obvious nor simple. Its direct proof is fairly complicated.

67. Use Property B of a polarity to prove Desargues's Theorem (Problem 22, §2, p. 30).

68. Let l be a line tangent to the circle S inscribed in the triangle ABC, and let M, N, P be the points of intersection of l with the sides of that triangle (Fig. 83). At the center O of S erect perpendiculars to the lines OM, ON, OP, and denote their points of intersection with the corresponding sides of the triangle by M_1, N_1, P_1. Prove that the points M_1, N_1, P_1 lie on a line tangent to S.

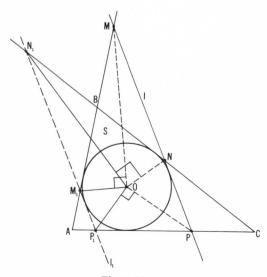

Figure 83

69. State the theorem resulting from the application of a polarity to the following theorem: In a circle, inscribed angles intercepting the same arc are equal.

70. State the theorem resulting from the application of a polarity to the theorem concerning Simson's line (Problem 61 of Ch. 2, §1, NML 21).

71. State the theorem resulting from the application of a polarity to the theorem that the medians of a triangle are concurrent, when S is the circumscribed circle of the triangle.

72. State the theorem resulting from the application of a polarity to the theorem that if the diagonals of a parallelogram are perpendicular, then they bisect its angles.

73. State the theorems resulting from the application of polarities to the following theorems:
    (a) The altitudes of a triangle are concurrent.
    (b) The angle bisectors of a triangle are concurrent.

74. Give examples of pairs of dual theorems.

In addition to properties A–C polarities have other properties such as those encountered in Problems 51 and 52 (p. 70), which are useful in obtaining new theorems from old ones.† Thus, for example, if we make use of property C and the theorem of Problem 51, then it is easy to show that, by means of a polarity, we obtain from the theorem of Problem 81 (a) in Ch. 2, §2, NML 21 the following theorem: *If p_1, p_2, p_3 are the distances of the sides of a triangle ABC from a point O such that the angles subtended by the sides at O are equal (or supplementary),‡ then the largest of the numbers*

---

† Problem 51 implies that a polarity relative to a circle S with center O and radius 1 carries a point A at a distance d from O into a line a at a distance $1/d$ from O, and two points A and B at a distance d from each other into two lines a and b such that $A'B'/(OA' \cdot OB') = d$; here A' and B' denote the projections of O to a and b. Problem 52 implies that the same polarity carries a point A and a line b at a distance d from A into a line a and a point B at a distance $d \cdot OB/OA$ from a. For applications of these assertions see, for example, the footnote on p. 75.

‡ If all angles of the triangle ABC are less than $120°$, then O is an interior point of the triangle, and the angles in question are all equal to $120°$. If the triangle is obtuse with the obtuse angle greater than $120°$, then there exists no point such that the angles in question are all equal; O is then exterior to the triangle, two of the angles in question are equal to $60°$, and the third angle, associated with the largest side of the triangle, is equal to $120°$. Finally, if one of the angles of the triangle is equal to $120°$, then the point O coincides with the vertex of that angle and the theorem is meaningless.

The point O has a number of remarkable properties (some of which are considered in Ch. 2, §2, NML 21); it is sometimes referred to in the literature as the *Toricelli point* of the triangle.

$1/p_1$, $1/p_2$, $1/p_3$ *does not exceed the sum of the remaining two numbers.* Similarly, with the aid of Problem 52, it is possible to obtain from Problems 254(a), (b) in §4, Ch. 2,[T] the following results:

Let S be a circle inscribed in a 2n-gon $A_1A_2\cdots A_{2n}$, and let l be any tangent to S. Then the product of the distances from the even-numbered vertices of the 2n-gon to l is equal to the product of the distances from the odd-numbered vertices to l.

Let S be a circle inscribed in an n-gon $A_1A_2\cdots A_n$, and let l be any tangent to S. The product of the distances from the vertices of the n-gon to l is equal to the product of the distances from the points of tangency of the n-gon and the circle to l.

Let S be a circle inscribed in a regular n-gon $A_1A_2\cdots A_n$, and let l be any tangent to S. If d_0 is the least of the distances d_0, d_1, $d_2 \cdots$, d_{n-1} from the vertices of the n-gon to l, then

$$\frac{1}{d_0} = \frac{1}{d_1} + \frac{1}{d_2} + \cdots + \frac{1}{d_{n-1}}.$$

We leave it to the reader to obtain these results using reciprocations.

— • —

Figure 84

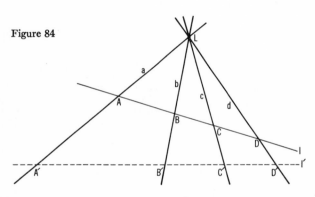

We note one more property of a polarity which plays a basic role in more advanced work involving this transformation. To formulate this property we must first introduce the analogue of the cross-ratio of four collinear points (cf. p. 34) known as the *cross-ratio of four concurrent lines a, b; c, d* and defined as the cross-ratio A, B; C, D of the points of intersection of the four given lines with any fifth line l (not passing through the point common to the four given lines; cf. Fig. 84). It is clear that the cross-ratio of four lines a, b; c, d is independent of the choice of the line l; for, if a line l' intersects a, b, c, d in points A', B', C', D', then the cross-ratio of the points A', B'; C', D' is equal to the cross-ratio of the points A, B; C, D (in view of property C of a central projection; cf. Fig. 84 and Fig. 34).[†]

[T] Reference to untranslated Russian material.

[†] One can show that the cross-ratio of four lines a, b; c, d is equal to

$$\frac{\sin \sphericalangle (a, c)}{\sin \sphericalangle (b, c)} \bigg/ \frac{\sin \sphericalangle (a, d)}{\sin \sphericalangle (b, d)};$$

here $\sphericalangle (x, y)$ stands for the angle formed by the lines x and y.

We can now state the additional property of a polarity:

D. *If a polarity carries four points* A, B, C, D *on a line* l *into four lines* a, b, c, d (which, by property A of polar transformations, intersect in a point L), *then the cross-ratio of the four lines* a, b; c, d *is equal to the cross-ratio of the four points* A, B; C, D.

The proof of property D is straightforward. Consider four points A, B, C, D lying on a line l and their polars a, b, c, d with respect to a circle S (Fig. 85). The definition of the cross-ratio of four lines implies that the cross-ratio of the points A, B; C, D is equal to the cross-ratio of the lines OA, OB; OC, OD, where O is the center of S. Since the polar of a point relative to a circle S is perpendicular to the line joining that point to the center of S (cf. p. 69), it follows that lines OA, OB, OC, OD are perpendicular to lines a, b, c, d, respectively. From this we conclude that the two tetrads of lines a, b, c, d, and OA, OB, OC, OD can be brought into coincidence by a suitable motion; in fact, this can be achieved by first translating the lines OA, OB, OC, OD so that O coincides with L, and then rotating these lines through $90°$ about L. It follows that the cross-ratio of the four lines OA, OB; OC, OD is equal to the cross-ratio of the four lines a, b; c, d; but then the cross-ratio of the four points A, B; C, D is also equal to the cross-ratio of the four lines a, b; c, d, and that is what we set out to prove.

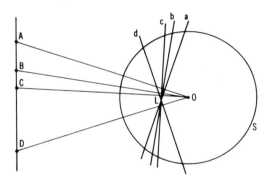

Figure 85

5. Projective transformation of a line and a circle. Straightedge constructions.

Let l and l' be two different lines in a plane, and let O be a point in that plane not on either of these lines. *Project* l *to* l' *from* O, that is, associate with each point P on l the point P' in which l' is intersected by the line OP (Fig. 86). Note that if l is not parallel to l', then the point X in which l intersects the line through O parallel to l' is not projected to any point of l'. To put X on an equal footing with other points we say that it is projected to the *point at infinity* of l'.

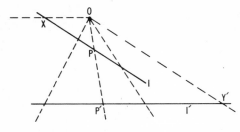

Figure 86

Similarly, we say that the point Y' where l' meets the line through O parallel to l is the image, under our projection, of the *point at infinity* of l. If lines l and l' are parallel (Fig. 87a), then we say that our projection carries the point at infinity of l into the point at infinity of l'. The same terminology is used if the projection from l to l' is a parallel projection (Fig. 87b).

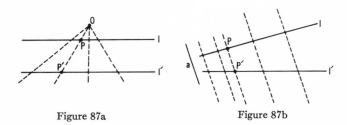

Figure 87a   Figure 87b

A central (or parallel) projection is not a transformation of a line onto itself, but rather a mapping of one line onto another. Now project a line l from a point O onto a line l_1, then project l_1 from a point O_1 onto a line l_2, then project l_2 from a point O_2 onto a line l_3, and so on, and, finally project the line l_n from a point O_n back onto l (Fig. 88). This chain of projections takes a point A on l into a point A_1 on l_1, then into a point A_2 on l_2, then into a point A_3 on l_3, and so on, and, finally, into a point A' of the initial line l. Thus this sequence of central projections defines a transformation of l onto itself which carries the point A into A'. We shall call such a transformation of a line a *projective transformation* or *projectivity*. We shall also speak of projective transformations in case one or more of the projections in our sequence are parallel rather than central projections.†

† As soon as we introduce the notion of points at infinity of a plane (cf. p. 38) we can regard a parallel projection of a line onto a line as a central projection whose center is a point at infinity.

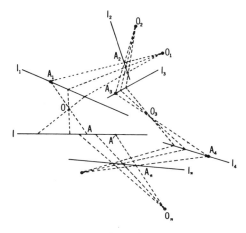

Figure 88

The following is a fundamental property of projectivities: *A projectivity of a line preserves the cross-ratio of four points.* Indeed, a central projection of one line onto another preserves the cross-ratio of four points (cf. property C of a central projection, p. 35). Similarly, a parallel projection of a line onto a line preserves the cross-ratio of four points (it preserves even the simple ratio AC/BC of three points A, B, C). It follows that a projectivity of a line (realized by means of a sequence of projections) carries four points into four points with the same cross-ratio.

This fundamental property implies that *a projectivity of a line is completely determined by the images of three points.* Indeed, if the images of three points A, B, and C under a projective transformation are three known points A', B', and C', then the image of any point M of the line is the point M' such that

$$(*) \qquad \frac{AC}{BC} \Big/ \frac{AM}{BM} = \frac{A'C'}{B'C'} \Big/ \frac{A'M'}{B'M'}.$$

This relation uniquely determines the position of M'.

On the other hand, there exists a projectivity of the line which carries three given points A, B, C into three preassigned points A', B', C'. In order to realize such a transformation we first project our line l onto an arbitrary line l_1 so that the points A, B, C go over into the points A_1, B_1, C_1 on l_1; then we project the line l_1 onto any line l_2 which intersects l in the point A' so that A_1 goes into A', and B_1, C_1 go into points B_2, C_2 on l_2; finally, we project l_2 onto the line l using as center of projection the point O of intersection of lines $B'B_2$ and $C'C_2$ (Fig. 89). As usual, O may be a finite point or a point at infinity.

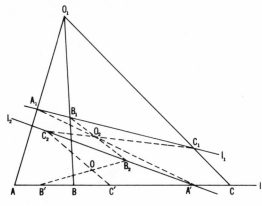

Figure 89

It is now easy to show that *every transformation of a line which preserves the cross-ratio of four points on that line is a projectivity* (that is, it can be realized by means of a sequence of projections). Indeed, consider a transformation of a line which preserves the cross-ratio of any four points and suppose that three points A, B, C are carried into points A', B', C'. We know that there exists a projectivity which carries A, B, C into A', B', C'. However, if two transformations of a line, both preserving the cross-ratio of four points, agree on the same set of three points of the line, then both take any fourth point M into the same point M' (whose position is determined by the formula (*) on the preceding page), i.e., they are identical.

75. Use properties of a projectivity of a line to prove Pappus's theorem (cf. Problem 28, §2).

76. Use properties of a projectivity of a line to prove the theorem of Problem 37(a), §2.

77. A point M_1 on the side A_1A_2 of a regular n-gon $A_1A_2\cdots A_n$ is projected from A_n to a point M_2 on the side A_2A_3; M_2 is then projected from A_1 to a point M_3 on the side A_3A_4; next M_3 is projected from A_2 to a point M_4 on the side A_4A_5, and so on. Prove that:
(a) If $n = 4$ then the point M_{13}, obtained after three circuits of the n-gon, coincides with the initial point M_1 (and, therefore, M_{14} coincides with M_2, M_{15} with M_3, etc.).
(b) If $n = 6$ then the point M_{13}, obtained after two circuits of the n-gon, coincides with the initial point M_1 (and, therefore, M_{14} coincides with M_2, M_{15} with M_3, etc.).
(c) If $n = 10$ then the point M_{11}, obtained after one circuit of the n-gon, coincides with the initial point M_1 (and, therefore, M_{12} coincides with M_2, M_{13} with M_3, etc.).

We shall now consider a sequence of projections involving *lines and circles*. For example, project a circle S from a point O_1 on S onto a line l_1; then project l_1 from a point O_2 onto a line l_2; then project l_2 from a point O_3 on a circle S_3 onto that circle; then project S_3 from another point O_4 of S_3 onto a line l_4; and finally, project l_4 from a point O_5 of S onto the circle S (Fig. 90).† The first projection takes a point A on S into a point A_1 on l_1, the second projection takes A_1 into a point A_2 on l_2, the third projection takes A_2 into a point A_3 on S_3, the fourth projection takes A_3 into a point A_4 on l_4 and, finally, the last projection takes the point A_4 into a point A' on S.

Thus our sequence of projections determines a transformation of the circle S onto itself which takes A into A'. We shall call a transformation of a circle which can be realized by a sequence of projections of the kind illustrated above a *projectivity* (on the circle in question).

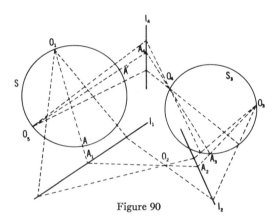

Figure 90

By the *cross-ratio of four points A, B; C, D of a circle S* we shall mean the cross-ratio of the four images A_1, B_1; C_1, D_1 of A, B, C, D under a projection from a point P of S onto any line l (Fig. 91). It is not difficult to show that the cross-ratio of four points on a circle S is independent of the choice of the point P on S and the line l; that is, its value is entirely determined by the four points A, B, C, D. Indeed, let A_1, B_1, C_1, D_1 be the images of the points A, B, C, D under a projection of S from the point P onto the line l, and let A_2, B_2, C_2, D_2 be the images of the same points under a projection of S from a point Q of S to some line m (Fig. 91). In view of a well known property of

† A circle must be projected from a point O *on the circle;* indeed, if O were interior to the circle, then two points of the circle would be projected to the same point on the line, and if O were exterior to the circle, then some points on the line would have two preimages and others none.

inscribed angles, lines PA, PB, PC, PD form the same angles (or their supplements) as lines QA, QB, QC, QD. Now we lay off on the lines QA, QB, QC, QD segments $QA^* = PA_1$, $QB^* = PB_1$, $QC^* = PC_1$, $QD^* = PD_1$. The figures $QA^*B^*C^*D^*$ and $PA_1B_1C_1D_1$ are congruent (they can be made to coincide by a motion: move Q into P and align rays QA^* and QB^* with rays PA_1 and PB_1). This implies that the points A^*, B^*, C^*, D^* lie on a line m^*, and the cross-ratio of the four points A^*, B^*; C^*, D^* is equal to the cross-ratio of the four points A_1, B_1; C_1, D_1. On the other hand, A^*, B^*, C^*, D^* are the images of A_2, B_2, C_2, D_2 under the projection of line m onto line m^* from the center Q; hence the cross-ratios A^*, B^*; C^*, D^* and A_2, B_2; C_2, D_2 are equal. The asserted equality of the cross-ratios A_2, B_2; C_2, D_2 and A_1, B_1; C_1, D_1 follows.

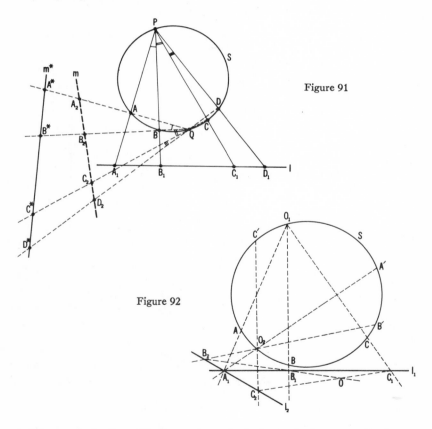

Figure 91

Figure 92

Since a projection of a line onto a circle (or a circle onto a line) preserves the cross-ratio of four points, we see that *a projectivity on a circle preserves the cross-ratio of four points.* Just as in the case of a projectivity of a line, we can now assert that *a projectivity on a circle is completely determined by the images of three points.* Finally, it is easy to show that every transformation of a circle which preserves the cross ratio of four points is a projectivity (that is, it can be realized by means of a sequence of projections). To this end it suffices to show that there exists a projectivity taking three given points A, B, C of the circle S into three preassigned points A', B', C' of that circle (cf. page 90). To realize such a transformation, we project S from a point O_1 onto a line l_1 and denote the images of the points A, B, C by A_1, B_1, C_1; from the point O_2, where the line through A' and A_1 meets S again, we project S onto a line l_2 passing through A_1 and denote the images of A', B', C' by A_1, B_2, C_2; finally, we project l_1 onto l_2 so that A_1, B_1, C_1 go into A_1, B_2, C_2 (Fig. 92); we denote the center of this projection by O. It is clear that the sequence of projections: S onto l_1 from O_1; l_1 onto l_2 from O; and l_2 onto S from O_2 carries the points A, B, C into the points A', B', C', as required.

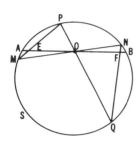

Figure 93

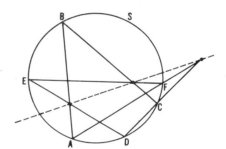

Figure 94

78. (a) Let O be the midpoint of a chord AB of a circle S, and let MN and PQ be two other chords passing through O. Let E, F be the points where MP and NQ intersect AB. Show that O is the center of the segment EF (Fig. 93).

(b) Let O be the foot of the perpendicular from the center of circle S to a line l, and let MN and PQ be chords of S which intersect l in points C and D such that $OC = OD$. Denote by E and F the points where MP and NQ intersect l. Show that O is the midpoint of EF.

79. Prove the theorems in Problems 41(a)–(c) of §3, using properties of a projectivity on a circle.

80. Use properties of a projectivity on a circle to prove *Pascal's Theorem:* If A, B, C, D, E, F are six points on a circle, then the points of intersection of AB and DE, BC and EF, CD and FA, are collinear (Fig. 94; cf. Problem 46 of §3).

We note that the result stated in Problem 80 is stronger than that of Problem 46, where we assumed that the hexagon *ABCDEF* inscribed in a circle is *convex*, while in Problem 80 the hexagon *ABCDEF* may be self intersecting. For every hexagon considered in Problem 46 there are 60 hexagons with the same vertices in Problem 80 corresponding to the 60 possible permutations of the names of the vertices† and consequently, there are 60 "Pascal lines" associated with six points of a circle.‡

We observe that since Brianchon's Theorem (cf. Problem 47, §3, p. 63) can be deduced from Pascal's Theorem (cf. the solution of Problem 63, §4), the theorem of Problem 80 implies that Brianchon's Theorem holds for self intersecting hexagons (Fig. 95).

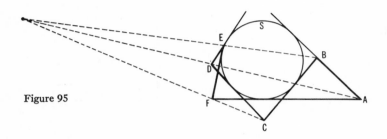

Figure 95

81. (a) Deduce from Pascal's Theorem the assertion of Problem 45 of §3 (p. 62).

(b) From a point *T* in the plane of a triangle *ABC* drop perpendiculars *TP* and *TQ* to its sides *AB* and *AC*; next join *T* to the vertices *B* and *C*, and drop perpendiculars *AR* and *AS* to the lines *TC* and *TB* (Fig. 96). Show that the point of intersection of lines *PR* and *QS* lies on line *BC*.

(c) Let *MP*, *MQ*, *MR* be perpendiculars from a point *M* to the sides of a triangle *ABC*, and let *P'*, *Q'*, *R'* be the second points of intersection of the sides of the triangle with the circle *S* passing

† There are 60 hexagons whose vertices are six given points. Indeed, beginning with any of the vertices we can choose the second vertex in five ways, the third vertex in four ways, the fourth vertex in three ways, the fifth vertex in two ways, and the last vertex is then uniquely determined. The resulting number is $5 \cdot 4 \cdot 3 \cdot 2 \cdot 1 = 120$, which must be halved to account for the fact that each hexagon is considered twice (in accordance with the two possible ways of traversing it).

‡ The set of 60 lines obtained in the indicated manner has many remarkable properties studied by the geometers of the last century. Thus, for example, these 60 lines intersect in groups of four in 45 points (each Pascal line has three of these points) and in groups of three in 80 points (each Pascal line has four such points); the latter 80 points lie, in addition to the Pascal lines, on 20 new lines, which, in turn, intersect in groups of four in 15 new points, and so on. All of these results can be rather easily deduced from the theorems of Desargues (Problem 22, §2), Pascal and Brianchon; however, the proofs would carry us too far afield.

through P, Q, R (Fig. 97). Show that the points of intersection of PQ' and $P'Q$, PR' and $P'R$, QR' and $Q'R$ lie on the line OM, where O is the center of S.

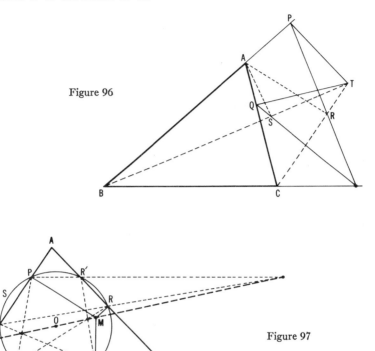

Figure 96

Figure 97

It is frequently necessary to determine the *fixed points* of a projectivity on a circle, that is, the points carried into themselves by the given projective transformation. Suppose the projectivity is determined by the condition that it takes three given points A, B, C on S into three known points A', B', C' on S. We may assume that points A, B, C do not coincide with A', B', C'; for otherwise our projectivity would be the identity, and all points of the circle would be fixed points.† Thus, for example, let A' be different from A; further, let M be a point of the circle S, and let M' be its image under our projectivity (Fig. 98). We propose to show that *the lines AM' and $A'M$ intersect on the line UV through the point of intersection U of AB' and $A'B$ and the point of intersection V of AC' and $A'C$.*

† Since a projectivity on a circle is uniquely determined by the images of three points, the transformation which leaves three points fixed must necessarily be the identity.

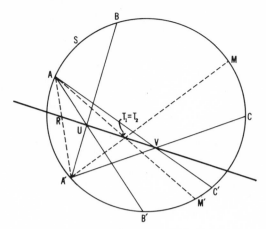

Figure 98

Assume that this is not the case, and denote by T_1 and T_2 the points of intersection of the lines $A'M$ and AM' with UV; further, let R denote the point of intersection of line AA' with UV. By projecting S onto UV first from A' and then from A, we see that the cross-ratio of the four points A, B; C, M on S is equal to that of the points R, U; V, T_1 on UV, and the cross-ratio of the points A', B'; C', M' on S is equal to that of the points R, U; V, T_2 on UV. Now, in view of the existence of a projectivity which takes A, B, C, M into A', B', C', M', the cross-ratios of these two tetrads of points must be equal. This implies the equality of the cross-ratios R, U; V, T_1 and R, U; V, T_2, and so the asserted identity of T_1 and T_2.

We now see that in order to construct the image M' of a given point M under our projectivity, we must join A to the point T of intersection of $A'M$ and UV (here U is the point of intersection of AB' and BA', V that of AC' and $A'C$); then M' is the point of intersection of the line AT with S. This construction implies that *the fixed points of a projectivity on a circle are the points of intersection of the line UV with S.* It follows that the transformation has two fixed points, one fixed point, or no fixed points according as UV intersects S in two points (this is the case depicted in Fig. 98), is tangent to S or lies entirely in the exterior of S.

Observe that the construction of the fixed points of a projectivity on a circle S which takes three points A, B, C into three points A', B', C' can be carried out by means of a *straightedge alone.*

82. Let S be a circle, AB and CD two of its chords. Find a point X on S such that the lines AX and BX determine on CD
    (a) a segment of given length a;
    (b) a segment whose midpoint is a preassigned point E on CD.

Problems 82(a) and (b) appear in a different connection in NML 8 (cf. Problem 6, §1, and Problem 11, §2).

83. (a) Let l be a line, P a point not on l. Find a segment XY on l which subtends a given angle α at P.

(b) Let l_1 and l_2 be two lines, P and Q two points not on these lines. Find a point X on l_1 and a point Y on l_2 such that the segment XY subtends a given angle α at P and a given angle β at Q.

84. (a) In a given circle inscribe an n-gon such that its sides pass through n given points M_1, M_2, $\cdots$, M_n (Fig. 99a), or such that some sides pass through given points and others are parallel to given lines.

(b) Circumscribe an n-gon about a given circle so that its vertices lie on n given lines l_1, l_2, $\cdots$, l_n (Fig. 99b).

[Problems 84(a) and (b) admit of the following formulation:

(a) Construct an n-gon inscribed in a given circle S and circumscribed about a given n-gon $M_1M_2\cdots M_n$ (cf. footnote on p. 31).

(b) Construct an n-gon inscribed in a given n-gon $N_1N_2\cdots N_n$ and circumscribed about a given circle S.]

Special cases of Problem 84 are Problems 41(a), (b) in NML 8 (p. 57) and Problem 44(b), §3 of the present book. Problem 84(a) appears in a different context in §§2 and 4 of Ch. 2 (cf. Problems 231 and 259) and Problem 84(b) in §5 (Problem 283) of the same chapter.[T]

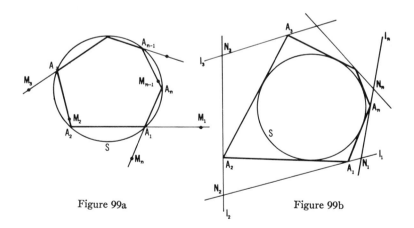

Figure 99a   Figure 99b

85. (a) In a given circle S inscribe a triangle ABC, given the length of side AB, the direction of side BC, and a point through which side AC is required to pass.

(b) In a given circle S inscribe a quadrilateral $ABCD$, given two points on two opposite sides of the quadrilateral and the lengths of its remaining two sides.

[T] The last sentence of this paragraph refers to untranslated Russian material.

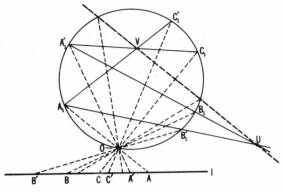

Figure 100

We shall now consider a projective transformation of a *line* l which carries three given points A, B, C (on l) into three given points A', B', C' (on l) with a view to determining its *fixed points*. To solve this problem we introduce an auxiliary circle S and project l onto S from a point O on S (Fig. 100). With every transformation of the line which carries a point M into a point M' there is associated, via the projection from l onto S, a transformation of the circle which carries the image M_1 of M under the projection into the image M_1' of M' under this projection. If the transformation of l is projective, that is, preserves cross-ratios, then the same is true of the associated transformation of S (since the cross-ratio of four points on S is equal to the cross-ratio of the corresponding four points on l). Now let A, B, C; A', B', C' be points on l and A_1, B_1, C_1; A_1', B_1', C_1', their projections on S (Fig. 100). The counterpart of the projective transformation of l which carries A, B, C into A', B', C' is the projective transformation of S which carries A_1, B_1, C_1 into A_1', B_1', C_1'. The fixed points of the two projective transformations correspond under the projection from l to S. Since we know how to find the fixed points of a projective transformation of a circle (cf. Fig. 98 above) we see that *the fixed points of the projective transformation of the line l are the points of intersection of l with the lines joining O to the points of intersection of circle S with the line UV, U being the point of intersection of lines A_1B_1' and $A_1'B_1$, and V being the point of intersection of lines A_1C_1' and $A_1'C_1$* (here we assume that A and A' are distinct, which implies that A_1 and A_1' are distinct; if A', B', C' coincide with A, B, C then *all* the points of l are fixed points). A projectivity (other than the identity) of a line can have two, one, or no fixed points. Note that a fixed point may be a point at infinity; this happens when the line joining O to a fixed point of the projectivity on the circle is parallel to l.

Observe that, given circle S, we can find the fixed points of a projective transformation of a line which carries points A, B, C into points A', B', C' by means of straightedge alone.

86. Let two lines l_1 and l_2 and two points A and B not on these lines be given. Find a point X on l_1 such that the segment determined on l_2 by the lines AX and BX has
    (a) given length a;
    (b) a given point E on l_2 as its center.

    Compare this problem with Problem 82 (p. 96).

87. Let two lines l_1 and l_2 be given together with a point A on l_1, a point B on l_2, and a point P on neither l_1 nor l_2. Pass a line through P which intersects l_1 and l_2 in points X and Y such that
    (a) $AX/BY = m/n$, where m/n is given;
    (b) $AX \cdot BY = k^2$, where k is given.

    Problem 87(a) appears in another connection in NML 8, Problem 45b, p. 68; also, see the comment referring to that problem in NML 21, p. 56.

88. Let three lines l_1, l_2 and l_3 be given in a plane together with a point P. Pass a line through P so that the two segments determined on it by the three given lines are equal.

89. Let two lines l_1 and l_2 and a point P not on these lines be given. Pass two lines through P such that the segments X_1Y_1 and X_2Y_2 which they determine on l_1 and l_2 have given lengths: $X_1Y_1 = a_1$, $X_2Y_2 = a_2$.

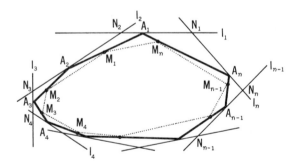

Figure 101

90. Let n lines l_1, l_2, $\cdots$, l_n be given in a plane together with n points M_1, M_2, $\cdots$, M_n (Fig. 101). Construct an n-gon whose vertices lie on the given lines and whose sides pass through the given points (or some of the sides pass through given points and others have preassigned directions).

    [This problem can also be stated as follows: Inscribe in a given n-gon an n-gon whose sides pass through n given points (or some of the sides pass through given points and others have preassigned directions); or, in yet another form, as follows: Construct an n-gon inscribed in a given n-gon $N_1 N_2 \cdots N_n$ and circumscribed about another given n-gon $M_1 M_2 \cdots M_n$.]

The following problems are special cases of Problem 90: Problems 9(b) and 10(c) of NML 21; 24(a)–(c) of §2 of the present book (p. 31); and finally, Problem 61 in §4 of the present book (p. 81).

— • —

There is a close connection between the material in this section and the problem of *construction by straightedge alone*. The usual geometric constructions are straightedge and compasses constructions. It turns out, however, that the scope of possible constructions is not very much diminished if we restrict ourselves to only one of these two instruments; in fact, we shall show in §2 of the next chapter[T] that all construction problems which can be solved by straightedge and compasses can be solved by means of compasses alone. Here we consider constructions by straightedge alone.

It is easy to see that not all straightedge and compasses constructions can be carried out with straightedge alone. Thus we shall show that, with straightedge alone, it is not possible to pass a line through a given point P parallel to a given line l. Indeed, assume it were possible to determine such a line m by a construction involving only the drawing of lines. Project our hypothetical diagram in the plane π (consisting of lines only) onto another plane π' so that the parallel lines l, m go into *intersecting* lines l', m'. This shows that our hypothetical construction for the determination of the line m, carried out in π', where the role of l is played by l', yields a line m' not parallel to l'. Thus the construction in question does not always yield a line parallel to the given line.

It is possible to show that in all constructions of elementary geometry we need use compasses *only once*. Having used them to draw an *arbitrary* circle we need not use them again in any further construction. In other words, *given a circle S in the plane with known center O, we can use it to carry out any straightedge and compasses construction by means of straightedge alone.* The remaining problems in the present section aim at establishing this proposition.

All straightedge and compasses constructions reduce to the drawing of a number of lines and circles. Each line is determined by two points in the diagram, and each circle is determined by a known point, its center, and a known segment, its radius. The points appearing in these constructions are given to begin with, or are points of intersection of auxiliary lines and circles. Thus each straightedge and compasses construction reduces to a combination of the following basic constructions:

[T] Reference to untranslated Russian material.

A. Pass a line through two given points.

B. Draw a circle with known center and radius.

C. Determine the point of intersection of two given lines.

D. Determine a point of intersection of a given line with a given circle.

E. Determine a point of intersection of two given circles.

Constructions A and C can be carried out with straightedge alone. As for construction B, it obviously cannot be carried out with straightedge alone; however, given an auxiliary circle it is possible to determine arbitrarily many points of a circle of given center and radius with straightedge alone (cf. Problem 92 below; this is the precise meaning of the rather sweeping assertion that, given an auxiliary circle, it is possible to carry out all straightedge and compasses constructions using straightedge alone). Also, with the aid of an auxiliary circle it is possible to realize constructions D and E (cf. Problems 93 and 94). All in all, an auxiliary circle and a straightedge enable us to perform all straightedge and compasses constructions, provided that we interpret the assignment of drawing a circle with given center and radius as that of determining arbitrarily many of its points.

In Problems 91–94 it is supposed that we are given a fixed circle S with known center O. All constructions must be carried out by straightedge alone. In solving these problems we are aided by the fact that the pole of a point and the polar of a line with respect to a known circle can be constructed without the use of compasses (cf. §4, p. 69).

91. (a) Pass a line through a given point P parallel to a given line l.

(b) At a given point M lay off a segment MN equal and parallel to a given segment AB.

(c) From a given point P drop a perpendicular to a given line l.

92. How does one construct arbitrarily many points of a circle given its center A and its radius?

93. Find the points of intersection of a given line l and a circle S, given its center A and radius BC.

94. Find the points of intersection of two circles S_1 and S_2, given their centers A_1 and A_2 and their radii B_1C_1 and B_2C_2.

We note that if, instead of the auxiliary circle S, we are given an arbitrarily small *arc MN* of S (and its center O), we are still able to carry out all straightedge and compasses constructions with straightedge alone. This is because the points of intersection of a line l with a circle S can be determined by straightedge alone provided we are given an arc MN of S (cf. Problem 49, §3, and Problem 55, §4).

It is indispensable that we be given the center O of the auxiliary circle S (or of the auxiliary arc MN). We can show rather easily that if we are not given the center of S, then we cannot determine it without compasses. To prove this assertion we use much the same approach as that used to prove that there is no straightedge construction for drawing a line parallel to a given line. Suppose there were a straightedge construction to determine the center O of a circle S. The diagram of this hypothetical construction is a system of lines connected in some way with the circle S, and two of these lines intersect at the center O of S. We project the plane π of our diagram onto a new plane π' so that S goes over into a circle S' and the center O of S goes over into a point O', not the center of S'; that this is possible is made clear by the results in §3 (cf., in particular, Theorem 1, p. 54). The diagram in π' is entirely analogous to that in π, except that the point O' is *not* the center of S'. This shows that there is no straightedge construction for determining the center of an arbitrary circle. To sum up: If we are not given the center of the auxiliary circle S, we are not in a position to carry out all straightedge and compasses constructions by straightedge alone (in particular it is possible to determine the center of S with straightedge and compasses, but *not* with straightedge alone).

Further, even if we are given two non-intersecting circles in the plane with unknown centers, then these centers cannot be determined by means of straightedge alone[†] (except when the circles are known to be concentric; cf. Problem 95(c) below). What can be shown is that there exist straightedge constructions to determine the centers of two intersecting or tangent circles (cf. Problems 95(a), (b)), or of three arbitrary circles which do not belong to the same pencil.[‡]

95. Let two circles S_1 and S_2 be given in a plane. Find a straightedge construction for the determination of their centers if the two circles (a) intersect in two points;   (b) are tangent;   (c) are concentric.

We can now prove the theorem on constructions by means of *parallel ruler* stated in §4 (p. 72). Indeed, since it is possible by means of parallel ruler alone to find the points of intersection of a line l with a circle S of known center A and radius a (cf. Problem 56, §4, p. 71), it is surely possible to solve by means of a parallel ruler all those problems that can be solved by straightedge alone when we are given in the plane an auxiliary circle with known center, that is, all problems solvable by means of straightedge and compasses.

† Cf., for example, Rademacher and Toeplitz, *The Enjoyment of Mathematics*, (Princeton Un. Press, 1957) pp. 177–187.

‡ Cf. §3, Ch. 2, p. 215 ff. (Reference to untranslated Russian material.)

Non-Euclidean Geometry of Lobachevsky-Bolyai (Hyperbolic Geometry)

In the Introduction we noted that with every group of transformations there is associated a geometry concerned with those properties of geometric figures which remain unaltered by the transformations of the group in question. Thus classical Euclidean geometry studied in high school is not the only possible geometry; by choosing a group of transformations other than the group of motions (or the group of similarities leading to a geometry very closely related to Euclidean) we are led to a new, "non-Euclidean", geometry. An instance of such a "non-Euclidean" geometry is *projective geometry*, concerned with those properties of figures which do not change under projective transformations. Projective geometry is not merely not Euclidean geometry; it is "very much non-Euclidean". For example, distance between points is not a projective property, for it is possible to carry any segment into any other segment by means of a projective transformation; in other words, in projective geometry all segments are "congruent". Likewise, all angles are "congruent", so that the usual notion of angle between lines is without meaning in projective geometry. Also, any two quadrilaterals in the plane are "congruent" in the sense of projective geometry (in this connection see Theorem 1, §2, p. 45) so that it makes no sense to speak of various classes of quadrilaterals (such as parallelograms, trapezoids, and so on). Again, any two triangles are "congruent"; in fact, it is possible to map a triangle T_1 onto another triangle T_2 by means of a projective transformation in such a way that a given point in the interior of T_1 is carried into a given point in the interior of T_2. This fact does away with "remarkable points in a triangle" (all points in a triangle are projectively equivalent).

To sum up, let us say that the study of triangles and quadrilaterals, of such importance in high school geometry, is absent from projective geometry, and the study of polygons begins with pentagons, for which we can have meaningful classification and "congruence" criteria.

All these singular features of projective geometry are due to the fact that the class of projective transformations is far *larger* than the class of motions (motions are very special projective transformations). As a result there are far *fewer* geometric properties in projective than in Euclidean geometry; most properties invariant under motions are not invariant under projective transformations (e.g. length of a segment, magnitude of an angle, the property of being a parallelogram, etc.). In order to obtain a geometry with more invariant properties than projective geometry, we must choose a subset of the class of projective transformations; the subset must, of course, form a group. Choosing the subset of motions leads to Euclidean geometry. However, other choices of subgroups (i.e., subsets forming a group) of the group of projective transformations are possible and lead to new and interesting geometries.

The following is a very simple way of choosing a group of projective transformations small enough to lead to a geometry rich in geometric properties. Consider the totality of projective transformations which carry a given disk **K** in a plane onto itself. Clearly, these transformations form a group: if two transformations carry the disk **K** onto itself, the same is true of their product; the remaining group requirements can be verified with equal ease. We call the transformations of this group *hyperbolic motions* and the study of invariant properties of figures under hyperbolic motions, *hyperbolic geometry*.

At first one might think that the group of hyperbolic motions was not a very fortunate choice. We saw that the largeness of the group of projective transformations was to blame for the meaninglessness of the notion of length of a segment in projective geometry. Now the smallness of the group of hyperbolic motions seems to present a difficulty. Specifically, since there is no hyperbolic motion which carries a point of the disk **K** into a point exterior to **K**, one might think that in this geometry, too, we have no notion of length of a segment (for not all segments are comparable). To obviate this difficulty we designate as the *points of hyperbolic geometry* the points of the interior of disk **K** and, as the *lines of hyperbolic geometry*, the segments of lines lying inside **K**. Now all points in our geometry are equivalent; it is easy to see that there is always a hyperbolic motion which carries an interior point A of **K** into any other interior point A' of **K** (cf. Theorem 1, §3, p. 54). Further, it can be shown that *if AP and $A'P'$ are two rays* (by a ray with origin A we mean a line segment bounded by the point A and the boundary Σ of **K**; cf. Fig. 102) *then there exists a hyperbolic motion which carries A into A' and the ray AP into the ray $A'P'$.* For proof note that in view of Theorem 1 of §3, there exists a hyperbolic motion M_1 that takes A into the center O of the disk **K** and a hyperbolic motion M_2 that takes A' into O. Denote the images of the rays AP and $A'P'$ under M_1 and M_2 respectively by OQ and OQ', and denote by M_2^{-1} the hyperbolic motion which is the inverse of M_2 (M_2^{-1} carries the ray OQ' into the ray $A'P'$, and its existence follows from the group properties of hyperbolic motions). Now consider the sequence of hyperbolic motions consisting of M_1, the rotation $\mathfrak{R}$ of $\mathbf{K}$ through the angle QOQ', and M_2^{-1}. The first carries AP into OQ, the second OQ into OQ', and the third OQ' into $A'P'$. Thus the product of our three non-Euclidean motions carries AP into $A'P'$, and this proves our assertion.

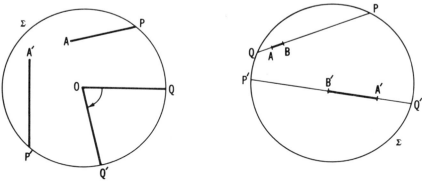

Figure 102   Figure 103

As we have just seen, in hyperbolic geometry every point can be carried into every other point, and every ray into every other ray. It is natural to ask whether one can carry any segment AB into any other segment $A'B'$. This turns out to be impossible. Indeed, if a hyperbolic motion carried the segment AB into the segment $A'B'$ (Fig. 103), it would take the entire hyperbolic line AB through A and B into the hyperbolic line $A'B'$; and, since every hyperbolic motion carries the circle Σ bounding the disk $\mathbf{K}$ into itself, the points P and Q where AB meets Σ would go into the points P' and Q' where $A'B'$ meets Σ. Thus our hyperbolic motion would carry the four points A, B, P, Q into the four points A', B', P', Q'. Like all projective transformations, hyperbolic motions preserve the cross-ratio of four points (cf. p. 35), and this implies the equality

$$\frac{AP/BP}{AQ/BQ} = \frac{A'P'/B'P'}{A'Q'/B'Q'} \, ;$$

if this equality does not hold, then there exists no hyperbolic motion taking the segment AB into the segment $A'B'$.†

† One consequence of our equality is that, if the order of the points on the (Euclidean) lines is Q, A, B, P and Q', A', B', P', then the hyperbolic motion which carries segment AB into segment $A'B'$ must carry P into P' and Q into Q' (not P into Q' and Q into P'). Indeed, the cross ratios $(AP/BP)/(AQ/BQ)$ and $(A'P'/B'P')/(A'Q'/B'Q')$ are both greater than 1 $(AP/BP > 1, \ AQ/BQ < 1)$ whereas the cross-ratio $(A'Q'/B'Q')/(A'P'/B'P')$ is less than 1 $(A'Q'/B'Q' < 1, \ A'P'/B'P' > 1)$; this rules out the equality

$$(AP/BP)/(AQ/BQ) = (A'Q'/B'Q')/(A'P'/B'P').$$

We have thus shown that *if it is possible to carry the segment AB into the segment $A'B'$ by means of a hyperbolic motion, then*

(*)
$$\frac{AP/BP}{AQ/BQ} = \frac{A'P'/B'P'}{A'Q'/B'Q'}.$$

We shall now show that, conversely, *if equality* (*) *holds, then there exists a hyperbolic motion which carries the segment AB into the segment $A'B'$.* Let us take A into A' so that the ray AP goes over into the ray $A'P'$ (we showed earlier that this can always be done); this motion will take Q into Q'. Let B_1 denote the image of B. Since a projective transformation preserves the cross-ratio of four points we must have

$$\frac{AP/BP}{AQ/BQ} = \frac{A'P'/B_1P'}{A'Q'/B_1Q'}.$$

From this and from the assumed equality (*), we obtain

$$\frac{A'P'/B_1P'}{A'Q'/B_1Q'} = \frac{A'P'/B'P'}{A'Q'/B'Q'}.$$

This allows us to conclude that B_1 coincides with B', that is, that our hyperbolic motion carries the segment AB into the segment $A'B'$, as asserted.

We see that the cross-ratio $(AP/BP)/(AQ/BQ)$ characterizes the "hyperbolic length" of the segment AB in the sense that *two segments AB and $A'B'$ are congruent from the point of view of hyperbolic geometry if and only if the cross-ratios $(AP/BP)/(AQ/BQ)$ and $(A'P'/B'P')/(A'Q'/B'Q')$ are equal.* This fact alone, however, does not quite justify calling the cross-ratio $(AP/BP)/(AQ/BQ)$ the "hyperbolic length" of the segment AB; after all, in Euclidean geometry any invertible function of length (e.g., the square of the length, or the cube root of the length) also characterizes congruent segments. What we are used to in addition is that, *if a point C divides a segment AB into two smaller segments AC and CB* (Fig. 104a), *then the length of AB is the sum of the lengths of the segments AC and CB.* In this respect the cross-ratio, as a potential measure of hyperbolic length, is unsatisfactory; for, if the point C divides the segment AB into two smaller segments AC and CB (Fig. 104b) then, clearly,

$$\frac{AP/BP}{AQ/BQ} = \left(\frac{AP/CP}{AQ/CQ}\right)\cdot\left(\frac{CP/BP}{CQ/BQ}\right),$$

that is, the cross-ratio $(AP/BP)/(AQ/BQ)$ is the *product* rather than the sum of the cross-ratios $(AP/CP)/(AQ/CQ)$ and $(CP/BP)/(CQ/BQ)$.

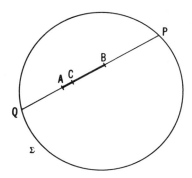

Figure 104b

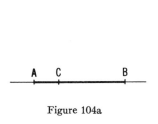

Figure 104a

Observe, however, that[†]

$$\log\left(\frac{AP/BP}{AQ/BQ}\right) = \log\left(\frac{AP/CP}{AQ/CQ}\right) + \log\left(\frac{CP/BP}{CQ/BQ}\right),$$

since the logarithm of a product is the sum of the logarithm of the factors. This suggests that we define

(**) $$\log\frac{AP/BP}{AQ/BQ} = d_{AB}$$

to be the hyperbolic length d_{AB} of the segment AB where, as always, P and Q are the points of intersection of the line AB and the circle Σ; for then

$$d_{AB} = d_{AC} + d_{CB}.$$

This additive property, and the result that $d_{AB} = d_{A'B'}$ if and only if the segments AB and $A'B'$ are congruent in the sense of our present geometry, justify calling the number d_{AB} defined by (**) *the hyperbolic length* of the segment AB.[‡]

[†] We note that our requirement concerning the order of the relevant points on the line AB (cf. footnote on p. 105) guarantees that the cross-ratio $(AP/BP)/(AQ/BQ)$ is greater than 1, and hence that it has a positive logarithm. A similar comment holds for the two other cross-ratios.

[‡] We could equally well have defined the hyperbolic length of the segment AB by means of the number $k \log\left[(AP/BP)/(AQ/BQ)\right]$, where k is an arbitrary positive constant. The choice of a particular k amounts to the choice of a particular unit of length in hyperbolic geometry. This comment shows that the choice of a particular logarithm base in the formula (**) is of little significance since a change of the logarithm base is equivalent to multiplication of all "lengths" d_{AB} by the same constant.

We observe that if the point B moves along line AP towards the point P, then the cross-ratio $(AP/BP)/(AQ/BQ)$ increases beyond all bounds $(BP \to 0)$; consequently, the hyperbolic length d_{AB} of segment AB increases beyond all bounds. This implies that the *hyperbolic length of the ray AP* (as well as that of the whole line PQ) *is infinite,* in spite of the fact that the whole hyperbolic line is represented by a segment of finite Euclidean length.

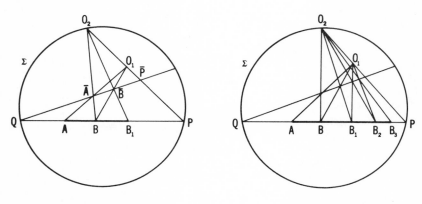

Figure 105a   Figure 105b

That a hyperbolic line is unbounded can be demonstrated without reference to cross ratios. The relevant constructions are shown in Fig. 105; Fig. 105a shows how to double segment AB of the hyperbolic line PQ, and Fig. 105b shows that the process of laying off on ray AP (beginning at A) a succession of segments equal to the segment AB can be continued indefinitely without reaching the point P. We now clarify the details of the "doubling construction" shown in Fig. 105a; the cross-ratios $(AP/BP)/(AQ/BQ)$ and $(\bar{A}\bar{P}/\bar{B}\bar{P})/(\bar{A}Q/\bar{B}Q)$ are equal because the tetrads A, B, P, Q and $\bar{A}, \bar{B}, \bar{P}, Q$ are perspective from O_1, and the cross-ratios $(\bar{A}\bar{P}/\bar{B}\bar{P})/(\bar{A}Q/\bar{B}Q)$ and $(BP/B_1P)/(BQ/B_1Q)$ are equal because the tetrads $\bar{A}, \bar{B}, P, Q$ and B, B_1, P, Q are perspective from O_2. Hence

$$\frac{AP/BP}{AQ/BQ} = \frac{BP/B_1P}{BQ/B_1Q},$$

or equivalently,

$$d_{AB} = d_{BB_1}.$$

This implies the congruence (in the sense of hyperbolic geometry) of segments AB and BB_1. Figure 105b simply applies the construction described in Fig. 105a first to AB (yielding BB_1), then to BB_1 (yielding B_1B_2), and so on.

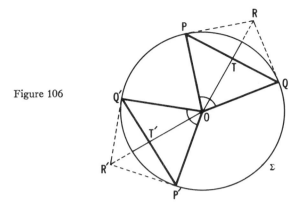

Figure 106

Next we investigate the problem of *angles between lines* in hyperbolic geometry. First we consider the case of two pairs of rays OP and OQ, OP' and OQ' issuing from the center O of the disk $\mathbf{K}$. It is clear that *if the ordinary (Euclidean) angles POQ and P'OQ' are equal* (Fig. 106), *then there exists a hyperbolic motion which carries the angle POQ into the angle P'OQ':* the required motion is a rotation about the center O (a rotation about O is a hyperbolic motion since it is a projective transformation which carries the disk $\mathbf{K}$ onto itself†). We shall show that, conversely, *if there exists a hyperbolic motion which carries angle POQ into angle P'OQ', then the (ordinary i.e., Euclidean) angles POQ and P'OQ' are congruent.* Indeed, such a projective transformation of the plane which takes $\mathbf{K}$ onto itself carries points P and Q into points P' and Q' and thus the line PQ into the line $P'Q'$; it carries the tangents PR and QR to the circle Σ at points P and Q into the tangents $P'R'$ and $Q'R'$ at points P' and Q' (for every hyperbolic motion carries Σ into itself and tangents to Σ into tangents to Σ; cf. p. 59). Moreover, it carries the line OR into the line OR' and the point T of intersection of PQ and OR into the point T' of intersection of $P'Q'$ and OR' (Fig. 106). Thus our hyperbolic motion carries segment OT into segment OT', and this means that these two segments are congruent in the sense of hyperbolic geometry. But this implies their congruence in the sense of Euclidean geometry; for, if segment OT, say, were smaller than segment OT' then we could carry segment OT into a part of the segment OT' by a rotation about O (which is a hyperbolic motion), and this would show that the hyperbolic lengths of the two segments are different, contrary to the demonstrated hyperbolic congruence of these segments.

† The angles POQ and $P'OQ'$ (supposed equal in the Euclidean sense) can be made to coincide by a hyperbolic motion in such a way that OP coincides with OP' and OQ with OQ' (rather than OP with OQ' and OQ with OP'). To this end we need only rotate the disk $\mathbf{K}$ through the angle POP' about the center O and then, possibly, reflect $\mathbf{K}$ in the diameter OP (a reflection in a diameter of $\mathbf{K}$ is a hyperbolic motion).

In turn, the equality $OT = OT'$ implies that $\sphericalangle POQ = \sphericalangle P'OQ'$, since $OT = r \cos \frac{1}{2} \sphericalangle POQ$, $OT' = r \cos \frac{1}{2} \sphericalangle P'OQ'$, where r is the radius of the disk **K**.

As we see, the magnitude of the angle POQ characterizes the "hyperbolic angle" between OP and OQ in much the same way as the cross-ratio $(AP/BP)/(AQ/BQ)$ characterizes the hyperbolic length of a segment AB. Also, if a ray OU divides the angle POQ (internally) into angles POU and UOQ, then $\sphericalangle POQ = \sphericalangle POU + \sphericalangle UOQ$ (*the magnitude of the sum of two angles is equal to the sum of their magnitudes*). We are thus justified in defining the *magnitude* δ_{POQ} *of the hyperbolic angle* between two rays OP and OQ issuing from the center O of the disk **K** to be the Euclidean magnitude of the angle POQ.

Next we consider an angle PAQ with vertex at an arbitrary point A of the disk **K** (Fig. 107). We carry out a hyperbolic motion that takes A into the center O of **K**, and denote the image of the angle PAQ by $P'OQ'$. There are, of course, many ways of choosing such a motion (cf. p. 104); however, if M_1 and M_2 are two motions taking the angle PAQ into two different central angles $P'OQ'$ and P_1OQ_1, then the inverse M_1^{-1} of M_1 carries $\sphericalangle P'OQ'$ into $\sphericalangle PAQ$, and thus the product of the hyperbolic motions M_1^{-1} and M_2 carries $\sphericalangle P'OQ'$ into $\sphericalangle P_1OQ_1$. This shows that angles $P'OQ'$ and P_1OQ_1 are congruent in the sense of hyperbolic geometry, and therefore also in the usual (Euclidean) sense. *We can therefore define the magnitude* δ_{PAQ} *of the hyperbolic angle between two rays* AP *and* AQ *as the Euclidean magnitude of any central angle* $P'OQ'$ *of the disk* **K** *into which it is possible to carry angle* PAQ *by means of a hyperbolic motion.* Clearly, this non-Euclidean measure of angles possesses the basic properties of the usual Euclidean measure of angles; namely, it is the same for two angles if and only if there exists a hyperbolic motion which carries one into the other; and if a ray AR divides an angle PAQ internally into angles PAR and RAQ, then $\delta_{PAQ} = \delta_{PAR} + \delta_{RAQ}$.

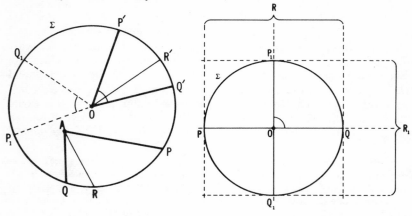

Figure 107   Figure 108a

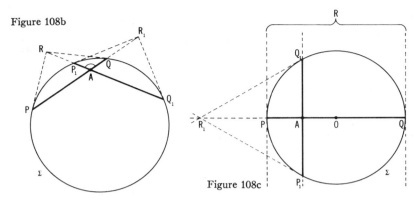

Figure 108b

Figure 108c

Since hyperbolic motions carry lines into lines, it follows that the magnitude of a straight angle at any point A coincides with the magnitude of a straight angle at the point O, that is, with the Euclidean magnitude of a straight angle; in other words, in hyperbolic as well as in Euclidean geometry, a straight angle is equal to 180°. Also, in hyperbolic as well as in Euclidean geometry, a full angle is always equal to two straight angles, or 360°. A right angle, that is, an angle congruent to its supplement, is equal to half of a straight angle, or 90°. However, two perpendicular lines (forming a right angle) in hyperbolic geometry will not, in general, be perpendicular in the ordinary (Euclidean) sense. The question of when two hyperbolic lines PQ and P_1Q_1 *are perpendicular in the sense of hyperbolic geometry* will be investigated next.

If the two lines PQ and P_1Q_1 intersect at the center O of $\mathbf{K}$, then, to be perpendicular in the sense of hyperbolic geometry, they must be perpendicular in the ordinary (Euclidean) sense. Hence, in this case, the tangents to the circle Σ at P and Q must be parallel to the line P_1Q_1 (Fig. 108a); in projective terminology, the two tangents and the line P_1Q_1 must all pass through the same point at infinity in the projective plane. Under a hyperbolic motion which carries the point O into a point A, the diagram in Fig. 108a will go into the diagram in Fig. 108b, and under the inverse transformation which carries A into O, the diagram in Fig. 108b will go into the diagram in Fig. 108a. It follows that *two hyperbolic lines PQ and P_1Q_1 are perpendicular if and only if the extension of line P_1Q_1 beyond the disk $\mathbf{K}$ passes through the point of intersection of the tangents to Σ at P and Q* (Fig. 108b).† In particular, if the line PQ

---

† In other words, *the line P_1Q_1 is perpendicular to the line PQ if its extension beyond the disk $\mathbf{K}$ passes through the pole of the line PQ with respect to the circle Σ* (cf. §4, p. 69); if this condition holds then, in view of Theorem 2, §4, p. 69, the extension of the line PQ will likewise pass through the pole of the line P_1Q_1 with respect to Σ, that is, through the point of intersection of the tangents to Σ at P_1 and Q_1. This implies that in hyperbolic geometry (just as in Euclidean geometry) the relation of perpendicularity of lines is *symmetric:* If $P_1Q_1 \perp PQ$, then $PQ \perp P_1Q_1$ (cf. also Fig. 108a).

is a diameter of the disk (Fig. 108c) then the tangents to Σ at P and Q are parallel to each other and perpendicular (in the Euclidean sense) to that diameter. It follows that a line P_1Q_1 perpendicular to a diameter PQ in the non-Euclidean sense will be perpendicular to it in the Euclidean sense as well (regardless of whether line P_1Q_1 passes through the center of the disk or not). It is clear that *in hyperbolic geometry there is a unique perpendicular from a point B to a line PQ;* to construct it we need only join the point B to the point of intersection of the tangents to Σ at the points P and Q. It is natural to call the foot of this perpendicular the *projection* of the point B on the line PQ. If B happens to be on PQ, then our construction shows how to erect a perpendicular to a given line at a given point of that line.

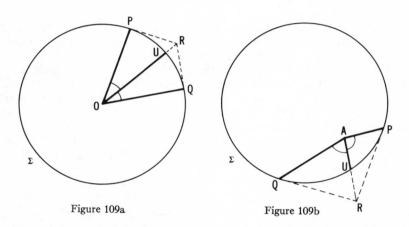

Figure 109a   Figure 109b

Now we show how to *bisect an angle* in hyperbolic geometry. If the angle is a central angle, then a line OU bisects it in the non-Euclidean sense if it bisects it in the ordinary (Euclidean) sense (Fig. 109a), that is, if its extension beyond the disk $\mathbf{K}$ passes through the point R of intersection of the tangents to Σ at P and Q. This implies that *a line AU bisects the non-Euclidean angle PAQ* (with vertex at any point A of the hyperbolic plane) *if its extension beyond the disk* $\mathbf{K}$ *passes through the point R of intersection of the tangents to* Σ *at P and Q* (Fig. 109b).†

There is a simple procedure for constructing a central angle $P'OQ'$ of the disk $\mathbf{K}$ congruent to a given angle PAQ (Fig. 110a; throughout this discussion, congruence of segments and angles means congruence in the sense of hyperbolic geometry). Consider two angles $\bar{P}\bar{A}\bar{Q}$ and $\bar{P}_1\bar{A}_1\bar{Q}_1$ symmetric (in the ordinary sense) with respect

† That is, *if the extension of AU passes through the pole of the line PQ with respect to the circle* Σ (cf. the footnote on p. 111). In particular, if PAQ is a straight angle, then the construction of the angle bisector is seen to be identical with the erection of a perpendicular to the line PQ at a given point A of that line.

to a diameter MN of the disk $\mathbf{K}$ (Fig. 110b), and such that the angles $\bar{A}_1\bar{A}\bar{P}$ and $\bar{A}_1\bar{A}\bar{Q}$ are congruent to the angles OAP and OAQ (which implies the congruence of angles $\bar{P}\bar{A}\bar{Q}$ and PAQ), and such that the distance $d_{\bar{A}\bar{A}_1}$ is equal to the distance d_{AO}. The angles $\bar{P}\bar{A}\bar{Q}$ and $\bar{P}_1\bar{A}_1\bar{Q}_1$ are certainly congruent, for they can be carried into each other by a hyperbolic motion, namely, the reflection in the diameter MN. The hyperbolic motion which carries the segment $\bar{A}\bar{A}_1$ into the segment AO carries $\sphericalangle\bar{P}\bar{A}\bar{Q}$ into $\sphericalangle PAQ$ (this is why we needed the congruence of angles $\bar{A}_1\bar{A}\bar{P}$ and OAP, $\bar{A}_1\bar{A}\bar{Q}$ and OAQ), and angle $\bar{P}_1\bar{A}_1\bar{Q}_1$ into the central angle $P'OQ'$ congruent to $\sphericalangle PAQ$ (a hyperbolic motion carries congruent angles into congruent angles). Our problem is to show how *to construct* the angle $P'OQ'$, given the angle PAQ.

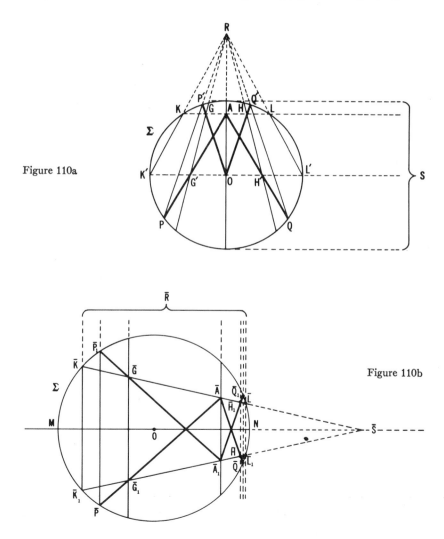

Figure 110a

Figure 110b

Assume for definiteness that angles PAO and QAO are acute. Erect at the points A and O hyperbolic perpendiculars KL and $K'L'$ to AO (since AO is a diameter, KL and $K'L'$ are also Euclidean perpendiculars to AO; cf. Fig. 108c) and denote the points of intersection of the sides of angles $P'OQ'$ and PAQ with lines KL and $K'L'$ by G, H, and G', H' as shown in Fig. 110a. Similarly, erect at the points $\bar{A}$ and $\bar{A}_1$ hyperbolic perpendiculars $\bar{K}\bar{L}$ and $\bar{K}_1\bar{L}_1$ to $\bar{A}\bar{A}_1$, and denote the points of intersection of the sides of the angles $\bar{P}_1\bar{A}_1\bar{Q}_1$ and $\bar{P}\bar{A}\bar{Q}$ with the lines $\bar{K}\bar{L}$ and $\bar{K}_1\bar{L}_1$ by $\bar{G}$, $\bar{H}$, and $\bar{G}_1$, $\bar{H}_1$, as shown in Fig. 110b. It is clear from Fig. 110b that the Euclidean lines $\bar{K}\bar{K}_1$, $\bar{G}\bar{G}_1$, $\bar{H}\bar{H}_1$ (and $\bar{A}\bar{A}_1$) meet at the same point at infinity $\bar{R}$. Since the diagram in Fig. 110a is obtained from that in Fig. 110b by a hyperbolic motion, the lines KK', LL', GG', HH' (and AO) all meet in a point R.

This shows how to construct the angle $P'OQ'$; namely, *in order to take the vertex A of $\angle PAQ$ to the center O of the disk* $\mathbf{K}$ *by means of a hyperbolic motion, erect at the points A and O (ordinary) perpendiculars KL and $K'L'$ to the diameter AO* (K, L and K', L' are the points of intersection of these perpendiculars with the circle Σ; K and K' lie on the same side of OA) *and join the points G' and H' of intersection of AP and AQ with $K'L'$ to the point R of intersection* (outside $\mathbf{K}$) *of the lines KK' and LL'. Let G and H denote the points of intersection of the lines RG' and RH' with the line KL;* then $\delta_{G'AH'} = \delta_{GOH}$.† Now since $\delta_{GOH} = \angle GOH$ (here δ_{GOH} denotes the hyperbolic measure of the angle between OG and OH, and $\angle GOH$ the Euclidean measure of that angle) we finally obtain

$$\delta_{PAQ} = \angle GOH.$$

We also note the fact, implied by Fig. 110a, that if $A \neq 0$, then

$$\delta_{PAQ} = \angle GOH < \angle PAQ$$

(for $AG < OG'$, $AH < OH'$ and so $\angle GOA < \angle G'AO$, $\angle HOA < \angle H'AO$).

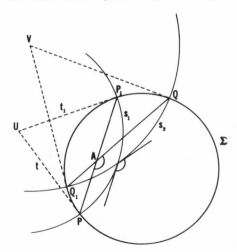

Figure 110c

Here is yet another (simpler) construction of the hyperbolic angle between lines PP_1 and QQ_1 intersecting at A in the hyperbolic plane (Fig. 110c): Let t and t_1 be tangents to the circle Σ at the endpoints P, P_1 of the chord PP_1, and let t and t_1 intersect at U. Let s_1 be the arc in $\mathbf{K}$ of the circle with center U and radius $UP = UP_1$. (If $t \parallel t_1$, then the role of the arc s_1 is played by the chord PP_1 of $\mathbf{K}$.) Similarly, let s_2 be the arc in $\mathbf{K}$ of the circle whose center is the point of intersection V of the tangents QV and Q_1V to Σ, and whose radius is $VQ = VQ_1$. *Then the ordinary (Euclidean) angle between the arcs s_1 and s_2* (i.e., the angle between the tangents to these arcs at their point of intersection, Fig. 110c) *is equal to the hyperbolic angle PAQ*. The proof of this fact is most easily established in the setting of the so-called "Poincaré model" of hyperbolic geometry and is given in Chapter 2.[T]

We shall now compare the non-Euclidean geometry of Lobachevski–Bolyai with the geometry of Euclid studied in high school. One is immediately struck by how much the two geometries have in common. In both geometries two points determine a unique line, and two lines can have at most one point in common (this follows from the fact that lines of hyperbolic geometry are segments of lines in the plane). Further, in both geometries it is possible to carry a point and a ray issuing from it, by a motion, into any other point and a preassigned ray issuing from the latter point. The hyperbolic length of a segment and magnitude of an angle share many properties with their Euclidean counterparts; for example, in both geometries the length of the sum of two segments is the sum of their lengths, and the measure of the sum of two angles is equal to the sum of their measures.

In hyperbolic geometry, just as in the usual geometry of Euclid, it is possible to lay off at a given point of a line and in either one of two directions a segment of arbitrary length (here the important fact is that the hyperbolic line is infinite; cf. p. 108); similarly, at a given point of a line and on either side of that line it is possible to lay off a given angle. This implies that all familiar theorems of high school geometry whose proofs are based on the simple propositions (axioms) of Euclidean geometry just listed hold without any modifications in hyperbolic geometry. For example, in hyperbolic geometry there remain in force the theorems on supplementary and vertical angles (and the theorems that the bisectors of vertical angles form a line and that the bisectors of supplementary angles are perpendicular); all tests for congruence of triangles (including tests for congruence of right triangles); theorems on properties of isosceles triangles; on the property of a perpendicular bisector of a segment and on that of an angle bisector; the theorem on the concurrence of the angle bisectors in a triangle, and so on. From the congruence tests for triangles one can deduce, in the usual manner, the theorem about an exterior angle of a triangle (that it is greater than each of the opposite interior angles) and this theorem, in turn, implies the relations between the sides and angles in a triangle and the theorem to the effect that the length of any side of a triangle is less than the sum of the lengths of the other two.

[T] Reference to untranslated Russian material.

From these results we can deduce theorems on the relative lengths of perpendicular and inclined segments from a point to a line (which justify the definition of *distance from a point to a line* as the length of the perpendicular from the point to the line in question) and the theorem that a segment is shorter than any other polygonal path joining its endpoints. If one now defines the length of a curve as the limit of lengths of polygonal paths inscribed in it, then one can conclude in hyperbolic geometry as well as in Euclidean geometry that the curve of smallest length joining two points is the line segment determined by them. This permits us to define the *distance between two points* as the length of the line segment joining them. All of these propositions emphasize the similarity of the two geometries.

By way of example we prove two of the theorems just mentioned.

Proof of the first test for congruence of triangles in hyperbolic geometry. Let ABC and $A_1B_1C_1$ be two triangles such that $d_{AC} = d_{A_1C_1}$, $d_{AB} = d_{A_1B_1}$ and $\delta_{BAC} = \delta_{B_1A_1C_1}$. To prove that these triangles are congruent (Fig. 111), we carry the point A into the point A_1 by means of a hyperbolic motion such that the image of side AC is aligned with A_1C_1. Since $d_{AC} = d_{A_1C_1}$, the point C coincides with C_1, and since the angles A and A_1 are congruent, the image of side AB is aligned with A_1B_1; in view of the equality $d_{AB} = d_{A_1B_1}$, point B coincides with B_1. Therefore side CB coincides with side C_1B_1 (two points determine a unique line); thus the two triangles coincide, and so are congruent.[†] This argument repeats literally the proof of the first test for congruence of triangles found in Kiselyov's textbook;[T] although, of course, in the present case the picture is quite different.

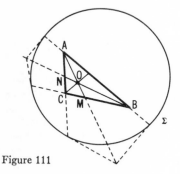

Figure 111

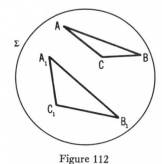

Figure 112

[†] The non-Euclidean motion carrying A into A_1 and the ray AC into the ray A_1C_1 can be realized as explained on p. 104 or in the following manner: First apply a motion M_1 which takes A into O, then a rotation $\mathfrak{R}$ about O, then (possibly) the reflection $\mathfrak{s}$ of the disk $\mathbf{K}$ in the diameter OQ' into which the ray AC is carried by the first two motions, and then a motion M_2^{-1} which takes O into A_1. If $\delta_{BAC} = \delta_{B_1A_1C_1}$, then one of these two hyperbolic motions which carry the ray AC into the ray A_1C_1 is bound to carry the ray AB into the ray A_1B_1.

[T] See footnote on p. 3.

Proof of the theorem: The angle bisectors in a triangle are concurrent.
As already mentioned, the theorem stating that a point on an angle
bisector is equidistant from the sides of the angle and the converse of this
theorem hold in hyperbolic geometry (prove it!). Now consider the angle
bisectors AM and BN of angles A and B in $\triangle ABC$ (Fig. 112).
Clearly, these two angle bisectors must intersect in an interior point Q
of our triangle. Since Q is a common point of the angle bisectors BN
and AM, it is equidistant from the sides BA and BC as well as from
the sides AB and AC and therefore also from the sides AC and BC;
but then Q is a point of the bisector of the angle C. This proves that
the angle bisectors in a triangle are concurrent, as asserted. Again the
present proof is virtually a repetition of the proof found in Kiselyov's
textbook.[T] We suggest that the reader try to supply proofs of the various
theorems stated above.

We note that every theorem of hyperbolic geometry can be stated as
a theorem of Euclidean geometry pertaining to chords and points of the
disk **K**. For example, the theorem of hyperbolic geometry which asserts
that *the bisector of an angle is the locus of points equidistant from the
sides of the angle* has the following "Euclidean" meaning. Let PR, QS
and MN be three chords of a circle Σ through a point A, and suppose
that the extension of MN passes through the point of intersection of the
tangents to Σ at the points P and Q (MN is the "hyperbolic angle
bisector" of the angle PAQ; cf. Fig. 113). Let K be a point of the chord
MN. Join K to the points T_1 and T_2 of intersection of the tangents
to Σ at the points P and R, Q and S (i.e. drop "hyperbolic perpendiculars" from K to lines PR and QS). Let U_1V_1 be the chord on
line T_1K, and C its point of intersection with PR. Similarly, let U_2V_2
be the chord on line T_2K and D its point of intersection with QS.
Then *the cross-ratio of the four points K, C; U_1, V_1 is equal to the cross-
ratio of the four points K, D; V_2, U_2.*

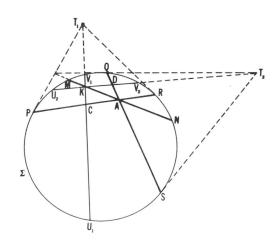

Figure 113

The connection between theorems of hyperbolic geometry and Euclidean geometry enables us to reduce the proof of any theorem of hyperbolic geometry to the proof of a certain theorem involving points and chords of the disk **K**, that is, it gives us a general method for a detailed study of hyperbolic geometry in Euclidean terms (cf. Problem 99 below as well as Problems 100–112). Another aspect of this connection is that the proof of a theorem of hyperbolic geometry automatically yields a proof of the associated theorem of Euclidean geometry. A good illustration is the example just considered, where the validity of the theorem on the angle bisectors in hyperbolic geometry implied the equality

$$\frac{KU_1/CU_1}{KV_1/CV_1} = \frac{KV_2/DV_2}{KU_2/DU_2}$$

(cf. Fig. 113) whose direct proof is rather complicated. Such use of hyperbolic geometry for proving theorems of Euclidean geometry can sometimes lead to interesting results.

96. Prove that the theorem of hyperbolic geometry asserting that the bisectors of vertical angles form a single line is equivalent to the theorem of Euclidean geometry of Problem 40(a), §3, p. 60.

97. What is the Euclidean equivalent of the theorem of hyperbolic geometry asserting that the bisectors of supplementary angles are perpendicular?

98. Show that the theorem of hyperbolic geometry stating that the angle bisectors in a triangle are concurrent is equivalent to *Brianchon's Theorem* in Euclidean geometry (cf. Problem 47 of §3, p. 63).

99. Use the expression for the hyperbolic length of a segment to prove directly that in hyperbolic geometry the length of any side of a triangle is less than the sum of the lengths of the remaining sides.

So far we have emphasized the similarities between ordinary (Euclidean) and hyperbolic geometry; now we shall point out their sharp differences. We consider first the status, in hyperbolic geometry, of the so-called *axiom of parallels:*

If a is a line and A a point not on a, then there is exactly one line through A and not intersecting a.

This axiom contains two assertions: the *existence* of the line through A (and this remains valid in hyperbolic geometry), and its *uniqueness*. What fails in hyperbolic geometry is the uniqueness part of the parallel axiom. In fact, in hyperbolic geometry two lines PQ and RS are said to intersect if and only if they intersect in a point inside the disk **K** (Fig. 114), since points in the exterior of **K** and on its boundary (the points of the circle Σ) are not regarded as points of the hyperbolic plane. This implies that it is possible to pass through a point A not on a line PQ infinitely many lines which do not intersect PQ (one such line is the line MN in Fig. 114). Thus *the axiom of parallels fails in hyperbolic geometry.* This means that all those theorems of high school geometry whose proofs make use of the axiom of parallels (and this means the majority of theorems of high school geometry) regarded as theorems of hyperbolic geometry may be true (cf. Problems 102, 103, 104) or false (cf. for example, Problems 100(a), (b), 108–112).†

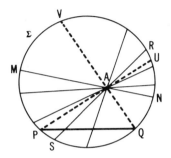

Figure 114

Lines QP and UP that intersect in a point P of the circle Σ (Fig. 114) will be called *parallel lines* of hyperbolic geometry. Parallel lines do not intersect, since the points of Σ are not regarded as points of the hyperbolic plane. On the other hand, there are, of course, non-intersecting lines which are not parallel. Thus the usual definition of parallel lines as lines which do not intersect is not equivalent to the above definition of parallel lines in hyperbolic geometry.

As can be seen in Fig. 114, the lines AU and AV parallel to PQ separate the lines through A which intersect PQ from those which do not. We may therefore define the lines through A parallel to PQ as *lines AU and AV not intersecting PQ, but such that all lines through A in the interior of the angle UAV do intersect PQ.* It is of interest to note that this "non-Euclidean" definition of parallels holds in Euclidean geometry except that there the lines AU and AV coincide and the angle UAV is a straight angle. This fact is the reason for defining the lines AU and AV as parallels to PQ and it hints at many similarities between Euclidean and hyperbolic parallels.

Lines in hyperbolic geometry which are neither parallel nor intersecting are called *ultraparallel,* sometimes also "diverging" since, as one moves along such lines in either direction, the distance between them increases beyond all bounds (see Problem 100(c) below).

---

† The fact that the parallel axiom is used in a proof of a particular theorem does not imply that there exists no proof of that theorem which avoids use of the axiom of parallels. Thus the failure of a certain proof of a theorem to carry over to hyperbolic geometry does not imply that the theorem in question is false in that geometry.

100. (a) Let PQ and RS be two lines of the hyperbolic plane intersecting in a point B. Prove that the distances from the points of
RS to the line PQ increase beyond all bounds on either side of B.
Also, the feet of the perpendiculars from the points of RS to PQ,
i.e., the projections of the points of RS to PQ, take up only a
finite segment P_1Q_1 on the line PQ; in other words, the projection
of RS onto PQ is a finite segment P_1Q_1 on PQ. The perpendiculars to PQ at the points P_1 and Q_1 are parallel to RS.

All these features of the disposition of intersecting lines PQ and
RS are shown in schematic form in Fig. 115a, where the curve
RBS represents the "hyperbolic line" RS. The lines P_1R and
Q_1S parallel to RS are shown to approach RS; this feature of the
diagram is based on part (b) of the present problem.

(b) Let PQ and UP be two parallel lines in the hyperbolic plane.
Show that the distances from the points of UP to PQ decrease
beyond all bounds in the direction of the ray AP (A is an arbitrary
point on UP) and increase beyond all bounds in the direction of
the ray AU. The projection of UP to PQ is a ray Q_1P; also,
the perpendicular to PQ at Q_1 is parallel to UP.

All these features of the disposition of parallel lines PQ and UP
are shown in Fig. 115b.

(c) Prove that ultraparallel lines PQ and MN in the hyperbolic
plane have a (unique) common perpendicular KL, and that, conversely, two lines with a common perpendicular are ultraparallel.
The distances from the points of line MN to line PQ increase
beyond all bounds on either side of the foot K of the common
perpendicular. The projection of MN to PQ is a finite segment
P_1Q_1; the perpendiculars to PQ at points P_1 and Q_1 are parallel
to MN.

The features of the disposition of ultraparallel lines PQ and MN
are shown in schematic form in Fig. 115c.

Figure 115a

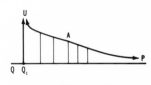

Figure 115b

Figure 115c

Since of all distances from a point A on a line MN to a line PQ the shortest distance is that measured along the perpendicular from A to PQ (the relevant Euclidean theorem holds in hyperbolic geometry; see comments on p. 116), and since the distances from the points of a line MN to a line PQ ultraparallel to MN increase on both sides of the foot K of the common perpendicular KL to these lines (cf. Problem $100(c)$), it follows that the length of KL is the shortest distance between them; this justifies calling the length of the segment KL *the distance between the ultraparallel lines PQ and MN.* In distinction to Euclidean geometry there is no sensible notion of distance between parallel lines in hyperbolic geometry (it can be shown that any pair of parallel lines in the hyperbolic plane can be carried into any other pair of parallel lines by a hyperbolic motion).

Since two intersecting or parallel lines in the hyperbolic plane have no common perpendicular, and since two ultraparallel lines have exactly one common perpendicular (cf. Problem $100(c)$), it follows that in hyperbolic geometry two lines cannot have two common perpendiculars; in other words, there are no rectangles (quadrilaterals with four right angles) in hyperbolic geometry. (Cf. also Problem $108(b)$ below.)

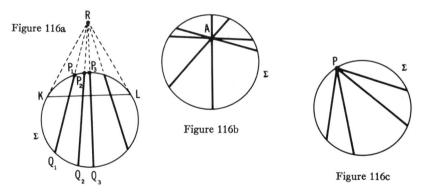

Figure 116a

Figure 116b

Figure 116c

Problem $100(c)$ points to another difference: In Euclidean geometry two lines perpendicular to a third are parallel; conversely, two (or more) parallel lines can always be regarded as perpendicular to one and the same line. In hyperbolic geometry, on the other hand, two lines perpendicular to the same line cannot be parallel; Problem $100(c)$ implies that such lines are ultraparallel. The nature of a set of three or more ultraparallel lines (i.e., of three or more lines perpendicular to the same line) becomes clear if we note that, if lines P_1Q_1, P_2Q_2, P_3Q_3, $\cdots$ in the hyperbolic plane are perpendicular to the same line KL, then the extensions of chords P_1Q_1, P_2Q_2, P_3Q_3, $\cdots$ beyond the disk $\mathbf{K}$ must pass through the same point R, namely, the point of intersection of the tangents to the circle Σ at points K and L (Fig. 116a). Thus chords of the disk $\mathbf{K}$ intersecting in an interior point A of $\mathbf{K}$ form a *pencil of intersecting lines* of the hyperbolic plane (Fig. 116b); chords intersecting in a point P of the circle Σ form a *pencil of parallel lines* (Fig. 116c); and the chords whose extensions intersect in a point R outside $\mathbf{K}$ form a *pencil of ultraparallel lines* (Fig. 116a).

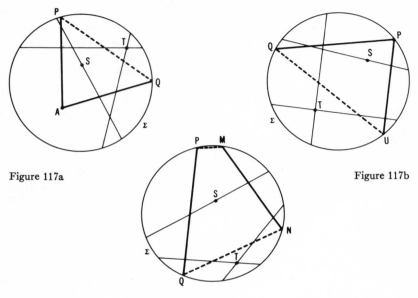

Figure 117a

Figure 117b

Figure 117c

We continue our description of singular features of the disposition of points and lines in hyperbolic geometry. Let PAQ be a hyperbolic angle formed by rays AP and AQ. Then the line PQ in the interior of the angle PAQ is parallel to AP, and AQ and separates points through which it is possible to pass lines intersecting both sides of the angle from points through which no such lines can be passed (Fig. 117a; we recall that in Euclidean geometry it is always possible to pass through an arbitrary interior point of an angle a line intersecting both sides of the angle). Similarly, if QP and UP are two parallel lines in the hyperbolic plane, then the line UQ in the interior of the strip bounded by the two given lines is parallel to these lines, and separates points through which it is possible to pass lines intersecting QP and UP from points through which no such lines can be passed (Fig. 117b). Finally, in the case of two ultraparallel lines PQ and MN there are two lines MP and NQ which separate points through which it is possible to pass lines intersecting both PQ and MN from points through which no such lines can be passed; also each of the lines MP and NQ is parallel to the lines PQ and MN (Fig. 117c). All these singular features of hyperbolic geometry are represented schematically in Figs. 118a–c.

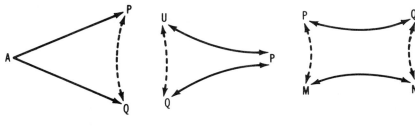

Figure 118a   Figure 118b   Figure 118c

101. (a) Prove that two lines l_1 and l_2 of the hyperbolic plane always have an axis of symmetry l (symmetry with respect to a line is defined in hyperbolic geometry just as in Euclidean geometry; cf. the beginning of Ch. 2, §1 in NML 8). Also, l_1, l_2 and l belong to a pencil (i.e., they are concurrent, parallel, or perpendicular to the same line; cf. p. 121).

(b) Show that if lines l_1, l_2 and l of the hyperbolic plane belong to the same pencil, and if l is the axis of symmetry of points A_1 and A_2 on l_1 and l_2, then l is the axis of symmetry of the lines l_1 and l_2.

102. By a *hyperbolic parallelogram* we mean a quadrilateral in the hyperbolic plane whose diagonals are bisected by their point of intersection. Prove that:
(a) The opposite sides of a hyperbolic parallelogram are congruent.
(b) Opposite angles of a hyperbolic parallelogram are congruent.
(c) If the diagonals of a hyperbolic parallelogram are perpendicular, then all of its sides are congruent, and the diagonals bisect the angles at the vertices; such a parallelogram is called a *hyperbolic rhombus*.
(d) If the diagonals of a hyperbolic parallelogram are congruent, then all of its angles are congruent; such a parallelogram could be called a *hyperbolic rectangle*, although, of course, its angles are not right angles (cf. p. 121).
(e) If the diagonals of a hyperbolic parallelogram are both congruent and perpendicular, then all of its sides are congruent and all of its angles are congruent; such a parallelogram could be called a *hyperbolic square*.

103. Are the opposite sides of a hyperbolic parallelogram (cf. the preceding problem) parallel?

104. Prove that in hyperbolic geometry the altitudes of an acute triangle are concurrent. Does this theorem hold for obtuse triangles?

105. Prove that in hyperbolic geometry the medians of a triangle are concurrent.

106. Does the following Euclidean proposition hold in hyperbolic geometry: The point of intersection of the medians of a triangle divides them (beginning with the vertices) in the ratio 2 to 1.

107. Show that in hyperbolic geometry the perpendicular bisectors of the sides of a triangle belong to the same pencil (i.e., they are concurrent, parallel, or perpendicular to the same line; cf. p. 121).

108. (a) Show that the sum of the angles of a triangle in the hyperbolic plane is always less than 180°.†
     (b) Show that the sum of the angles of an n-gon in the hyperbolic plane is always less than $180°(n-2)$.

109. Show that the area of an n-gon in the hyperbolic plane is proportional to the difference between $180°(n-2)$ and the sum of the angles of the n-gon; in particular, the area of a triangle with angles A, B and C is $k(180° - \measuredangle A - \measuredangle B - \measuredangle C)$, where the coefficient k depends on the choice of the unit of area.

The difference between $180°(n-2)$ (the sum of the angles of an n-gon in Euclidean geometry) and the sum of the angles of an n-gon in the hyperbolic plane is called the *angular defect* of that n-gon. Thus the theorem of Problem 109 can be stated as follows: *The area of an n-gon in the hyperbolic plane is proportional to its angular defect.* It follows, in particular, that the sum of the angles of an n-gon of small area is close to $180°(n-2)$.

110. Prove the *fourth test for congruence of triangles* in hyperbolic geometry: Two triangles are congruent if the three angles of one triangle are congruent to the three angles of the other triangle.

One consequence of Problem 110 is a fact of fundamental importance: There are no similar incongruent figures in hyperbolic geometry. As pointed out in the Introduction to NML 21, the theorems of Euclidean geometry are actually theorems of the geometry of similarities, i.e., they deal with properties of geometric figures preserved by similarities. This is connected with the fact that no theorem of Euclidean geometry can depend on the choice of a unit of length; hence, no theorem can refer to the length of a segment, but must instead refer to ratios of lengths. In hyperbolic geometry, however, there are no similar and at the same time

---

† One can show that for every choice of angles A, B, and C whose sum is less than 180°, there exists a hyperbolic triangle whose angles are A, B, and C. The surprising results of Problems 109 and 110 are connected with this fact. In Euclidean geometry, prescribing three angles of a triangle amounts to prescribing two of its elements (since there the third angle is determined by the first two) and so does not determine a unique triangle. On the other hand, in hyperbolic geometry the three angles are three independent elements of a triangle, and they determine the triangle.

incongruent figures and, consequently, no transformations (other than hyperbolic motions) which could be called "hyperbolic similarities". In view of our long experience with Euclidean geometry this difference may strike us as particularly strange; that is why we propose to discuss the matter in some detail.

We note that theorems of Euclidean geometry may depend on the choice of a unit of measurement of angles; for example, the statement: "The sum of the angles in a triangle is 180°" will clearly change if we define a degree as $\frac{1}{100}$ part of a right angle, rather than $\frac{1}{90}$ part of a right angle.† This difference between distances and angle measures is due to the possibility, in Euclidean geometry, of giving a purely geometric definition of a unit of angle measurement (one such unit is a right angle defined as congruent to its supplement, or a definite part of a right angle; another is one radian, a central angle subtending an arc of the same length as the radius), whereas there are no geometric considerations which favor a particular unit of length. In distinction to this, in hyperbolic geometry one can give a purely geometric definition of a unit of length; for example, one could take as a unit of length a side of an equilateral triangle with a 45° angle (in view of Problem 110 this is a well defined segment). This means that the statement of a theorem in hyperbolic geometry may depend on the choice of the unit of length.

We note that Problems 109 and 110 imply that in hyperbolic geometry it is possible to give a geometric definition of a unit of area by stipulating, say, that the area of an n-gon is equal to its angular defect, or that the unit of area is the area of a triangle with prescribed angles.

— • —

The final issue we propose to discuss is the *classification of motions* of the hyperbolic plane. In NML 8 we saw that two directly congruent figures of Euclidean geometry can be brought into coincidence by means of two reflections in a line (see Ch. 2, §2, NML 8, especially the material in fine print on p. 66). We prove in much the same way that in hyperbolic geometry *two directly congruent figures can be brought into coincidence by means of two reflections in a line*. The definitions of reflection in a line, directly congruent, and oppositely congruent in hyperbolic geometry are the same as in Euclidean geometry; cf. the beginning of §§1 and 2 of

---

† In other words, in Euclidean geometry a theorem may refer to magnitudes of angles and to ratios of magnitudes of segments rather than to magnitudes of segments (cf., for example, the references to lengths and angles in the following theorem: In a right triangle with a 30° angle, the side opposite that angle is equal to half the hypotenuse). That is why, for example, the adoption of the metric system by Russia in 1918 did not require any change in the Kiselyov textbook of that time; had there been a change in the unit of measurement of angles, it would have been necessary to change the statements of many theorems.

Ch. 2 in NML 8).† However, while in Euclidean geometry two lines can be related in *two* essentially different ways, namely, they can be parallel or intersecting, in hyperbolic geometry they can be related in *three* essentially different ways: intersecting, parallel and ultraparallel. This explains why the number of types of direct motions (displacements) in Euclidean geometry is two (rotation and translation, i.e., product of the reflections in two intersecting lines and product of the reflections in two parallel lines), while the number of types of direct motions in hyperbolic geometry is three. A discussion of these three types of direct motions follows.

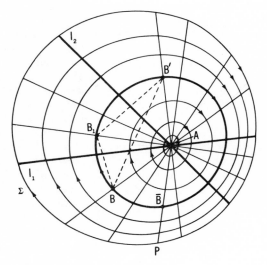

Figure 119a

(1) *The product of reflections in lines l_1 and l_2 intersecting in a point* A (Fig. 119a). In this motion the point A remains fixed, and thus the pencil Π_1 of lines through A goes over into itself; that is, every line of the pencil is carried into some line of the same pencil. Now let B be a point in the hyperbolic plane, let B_1 be the image of B under the reflection in l_1, and let B' be the image of B under the product of the reflections in l_1 and l_2. Then B_1 is symmetric to B with respect to l_1, and to B' with respect to l_2. It is easy to see that B' is symmetric to B with respect to the axis of symmetry of the lines BA and $B'A$.

---

† We suggest that the reader verify that these definitions, as well as the arguments in fine print on p. 66 of NML 8, carry over without modifications to hyperbolic geometry.

By an argument analogous to that used in Euclidean geometry it can be shown that two oppositely congruent figures can be brought into coincidence by means of three reflections in a line.

Indeed, in view of the theorem in Problem 107 (applied to the triangle BB_1B') the axis of symmetry of the points B and B' belongs to the pencil Π_1 which includes l_1 and l_2. But then, in view of the result in Problem 101(b), the axis of symmetry of the points B and B' coincides with the axis of symmetry of the lines BA and $B'A$, as asserted.

On each line AP of the pencil Π_1, we single out the point $\bar{B}$ symmetric to B with respect to the axis of symmetry of lines AP and AB, and call the locus of points $\bar{B}$ a hyperbolic *circle* with center A. We can now say briefly that under the motion (1) a point and its image belong to the same circle with center A (cf. Fig. 119a).

A circle with center A can be defined more simply as *a locus of points equidistant†from* A, because a motion which leaves A fixed also leaves the distance from a moving point to A fixed. A hyperbolic motion of the type (1) with a fixed point A may be called a hyperbolic *rotation* about A.

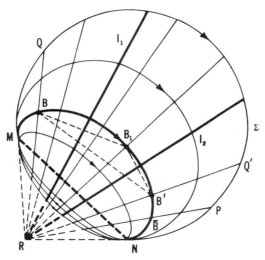

Figure 119b

(2) *The product of reflections in two ultraparallel lines l_1 and l_2 perpendicular to a line MN* (Fig. 119b). Under this motion the line MN remains fixed, and this means that the pencil Π_2 of ultraparallel lines perpendicular to MN goes into itself (each line of Π_2 goes into a line of Π_2). Now let B be a point in the hyperbolic plane, let B_1 be the image of B under the reflection in l_1, and let B' be the image of B under the product of the reflections in l_1 and l_2. Then B_1 is symmetric

† Equidistant in the hyperbolic sense. From the point of view of Euclidean geometry the locus in question is, of course, not a circle. One can prove that the curves in question (as well as the curves representing equidistant curves and horocycles of the hyperbolic plane discussed in the sequel) are represented by Euclidean ellipses.

to B with respect to l_1 and to B' with respect to l_2. It is easy to see that B' is symmetric to B with respect to the axis of symmetry of the lines BQ and $B'Q'$ of the pencil Π_2. Indeed, in view of the theorem in Problem 107 (applied to the triangle BB_1B'), the axis of symmetry of points B and B' belongs to the pencil Π_2, which includes lines l_1 and l_2. But then, by the result in Problem 101b, the axis of symmetry of B and B' coincides with the axis of symmetry of lines BQ and $B'Q'$, as asserted.

On each line of the pencil Π_2 we single out the point $\bar{B}$ symmetric to B with respect to the axis of symmetry of that line and the line BQ. We call the locus of points $\bar{B}$ *an equidistant curve* and the line MN its *axis*. Thus under the motion (2) a point and its image lie on the same equidistant curve with axis MN (Fig. 119b).

An equidistant curve with axis MN can be defined more simply as *a locus of points equidistant from the line MN* and on one side of MN. This is so because a motion which leaves a line fixed also leaves the distance from a moving point to that line fixed.† A motion of the type (2), characterized by the presence of a fixed line MN (this line "slides along itself"), may be called a hyperbolic *translation* along the line MN.

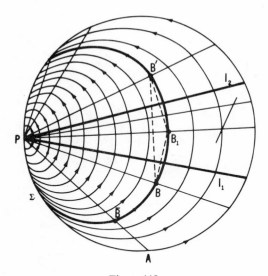

Figure 119c

---

† Hence the name "an equidistant curve". Note that, by results in Problems 100(a)–(c), a locus of points equidistant from a given line MN (and on one side of MN) cannot be a line.

We note that in the literature on hyperbolic geometry an equidistant curve is sometimes defined as a locus of points whose distance from a line MN is a constant; thus this definition dispenses with our restriction that the points of the locus be on one side of the line MN.

(3) *The product of reflections in two parallel lines* l_1 *and* l_2 (Fig. 119c). This motion carries the pencil Π_3 of lines parallel to l_1 and l_2 into itself; reflection of a line of Π_3 in either one of the lines l_1 and l_2 carries it into a line of Π_3, and so the same is true of the product of these reflections. Now let B be a point in the hyperbolic plane, let B_1 be the image of B under the reflection in l_1, and let B' be the image of B under the product of the reflections in l_1 and l_2. Then B_1 is symmetric to B with respect to l_1 and to B' with respect to l_2. It is easy to see that B' is symmetric to B with respect to the axis of symmetry of lines BP and $B'P$. Indeed, by the theorem in Problem 107, the axis of symmetry of the points B and B' belongs to the pencil Π_3, which includes the lines l_1 and l_2. But then, by the result in Problem 101(b), the axis of symmetry of points B and B' is the same as the axis of symmetry of lines BP and $B'P$, as asserted.

On each line AP of the pencil Π_3 we single out the point $\bar{B}$ symmetric to B with respect to the axis of symmetry of the lines AP and BP. We call the locus of points $\bar{B}$ a *horocycle*. Thus under a motion of the type (3), a point moves along a horocycle (Fig. 119c).

In Euclidean geometry a sequence of circles passing through a point A and tangent at that point to a given line l tends to the line l as the radii of these circles tend to infinity; this is why one sometimes says that "a line is a circle of infinite radius" (Fig. 120a).† In hyperbolic geometry the situation is different. Here, as is readily seen, a sequence of circles passing through a point A and tangent at A to a given line l tends to the horocycle through A tangent to l as the radii of the circles tend to infinity, i.e., here a "circle of infinite radius" is a horocycle rather than a line (for this reason horocycles are sometimes called "limit circles"). On the other hand, a sequence of equidistant curves through A tangent at A to l tends to the above horocycle at A or to the line l according as the widths of the equidistant curves tend to infinity or to zero (the width of an equidistant curve is the distance from its points to its axis, Fig. 120b).

Each of the three curves: a circle, a horocycle and an equidistant curve can be defined as a *curve perpendicular to the lines of a pencil*;‡ in the case of a circle the pencil is a pencil of intersecting lines, in the case of a horocycle it is a pencil of parallel lines, and in the case of an equidistant curve it is a pencil of ultraparallel lines.

† By the distance from a point B to a curve Γ we mean the minimum of the distances from B to the points of Γ. Thus if Γ is a line l, then the distance from B to l is equal to the length of the perpendicular from B to l, and if Γ is a circle S with center O, then the distance from B to S is the length of the smaller of the two segments BM, BN, where M and N are the points of intersection of the line BO with the circle S. What is asserted is that *if the radii of the circles* S_1, S_2, S_3, $\cdots$ *tangent to the line* l *at* A *tend to infinity, then the distances* BM_1, BM_2, BM_3, $\cdots$ *from an arbitrary point* B *of* l *to the circles* S_1, S_2, S_3, $\cdots$ *tend to zero* (Fig. 120a). The subsequent assertions of hyperbolic geometry should be interpreted in an analogous manner.

‡ By the angle between two curves at a point of intersection we mean the angle between the tangents to these curves at the point in question.

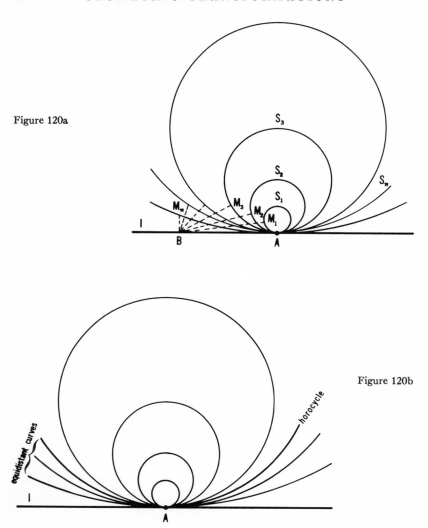

Figure 120a

Figure 120b

111. Show that it is possible to circumscribe about a given triangle in the hyperbolic plane a circle, a horocycle, or an equidistant curve.

We note that, since the point of intersection of the angle bisectors of a triangle is equidistant from its sides, it is always possible to inscribe a circle in a triangle.

112. Show that in hyperbolic geometry the ratio of the circumference of a circle to its radius is not constant.

Problem 112 shows that in hyperbolic geometry noncongruent circles are not similar (cf. p. 124).†

We have come to the end of our study of hyperbolic geometry. Our development was based on the definition on p. 104. All theorems of hyperbolic geometry reduced to ordinary theorems concerning points (and chords) of a disk **K**, and the study of hyperbolic geometry consisted in singling out those properties of the disk **K** (and of the figures in its interior) which are preserved under projective transformations that map **K** onto itself. There is, however, another approach to the study of hyperbolic geometry (as well as any other geometry). That approach, already hinted at on pp. 115–118 (cf. the proof of the first test of congruence of triangles and the proof of the theorem on the concurrence of the angle bisectors in a triangle), consists in basing the theorems of non-Euclidean geometry on a finite number of axioms, and is entirely analogous to the development of Euclidean geometry as presented in high school. When we deduce hyperbolic geometry from axioms, we need modify only one of the axioms of Euclidean geometry, namely, the axiom of parallels. It is replaced by the assertion that, if A is a point not on a line l, then there are *many* lines through A which do not intersect l. In this development of hyperbolic geometry its connection with the points and chords of the disk **K** is irrelevant; instead of the diagrams featuring that disk we illustrate various situations by means of schematic diagrams analogous to Figs. 115, 118 or 120b.

Historically, hyperbolic geometry was first developed on an axiomatic basis. It arose as a result of efforts to prove the axiom of parallels from the other axioms. Doubt persisted for a long time as to whether this axiom could be deduced from the remaining axioms of Euclidean geometry. In their attempts to prove this axiom, mathematicians used the method of "proof by contradiction" i.e., they assumed that the axiom of parallels was false and tried, on the basis of this assumption, to obtain a contradiction. All of these attempts were fruitless. True, the theorems obtained by negating the axiom of parallels appeared strange, but they did not contradict one another. The issue was resolved when C. F. Gauss, N. I. Lobachevski and J. Bolyai first stated explicitly that by negating

---

† Another consequence is that the usual definition of the radian measure of an angle α (as the ratio of the length of the circular arc corresponding to the central angle α to the radius of the circle) does not carry over to hyperbolic geometry, for here this ratio depends not only on α but also on the magnitude of the radius. Radian measure of an angle can be introduced into hyperbolic geometry in a purely formal manner by designating the number $\pi = 3.14159\ldots$ as the measure of a straight angle, or by means of the following rather complicated geometric construction: The radian measure of an angle α is defined as the limit of the ratios of the length of the circular arc corresponding to the central angle α to the radius of the circle as the latter tends to zero.

the axiom of parallels one arrives at a new geometry, just as consistent
as the usual (Euclidean) geometry.[T] Lobachevski and Bolyai developed
the new geometry to such a point that it became the equal of Euclidean
geometry in content and logical cohesion. The rise of hyperbolic geometry
(circa 1829, when Lobachevski first published his discovery) proved that
the axiom of parallels could not be deduced from the remaining axioms
of Euclidean geometry.

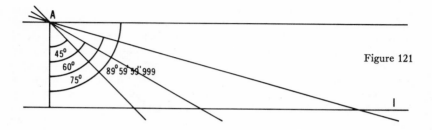

Figure 121

We said above that hyperbolic geometry is just as consistent as
Euclidean geometry. It would seem, however, that when it comes to
physical space, only one of these geometries is applicable; in fact, it seems
obvious that from the point of view of physical space the only "true"
geometry is Euclidean geometry.[†] However, the question of the connection of either geometry with physical reality is actually far more complicated. No direct test can decide the truth or falsity of the axiom of
parallels for, obviously, it is not possible to show by means of an experiment that there is only one line through a given point A which does
not intersect a fixed line l. Appeals to geometric intuition are likewise
inconclusive. It is clear that if A is close to l, then a line through A
which forms a "sufficiently small" angle (say, 45°, 60° or 75°; cf. Fig. 121)
with the perpendicular from A to l will definitely intersect l, but it is
hardly obvious that this is true for a line which forms with the perpendicular "practically a right angle", say, the angle 89°59′59.999″. There

---

[T] A good account of the very interesting history of the discovery of hyperbolic
geometry by N. I. Lobachevski and J. Bolyai, and of the contribution of C. F. Gauss,
who independently arrived at the ideas of hyperbolic geometry, is found in R. Bonola,
Non-Euclidean Geometry, Dover Publications, New York, 1955.

[†] It would be more accurate to say that of the two geometries, Euclidean seems to
reflect more accurately the properties of physical space. In fact, it makes no sense to
ask which geometry holds in physical space, for the basic entities of geometry—points,
lines, etc.—are not physically realizable objects, but merely idealizations of properties
of objects in our environment. That is why geometry cannot be included among the
natural sciences such as physics, chemistry or biology, whose assertions are subject
to experimental verification. All we can debate is which geometry yields a more accurate
description of the properties of very small portions of space that we take as points,
and of the trajectories of light rays that we take as lines.

is even less sense in appeals to geometric intuition when the distance from A to l is very large, larger, say, than the distance from the earth to the sun. One could, of course, try to settle experimentally the issue of the sum of the angles in a triangle (cf. Problem 108); this approach to the solution of the problem of the geometric nature of space was suggested by Gauss and also by Lobachevski. Using geodesic measurements, Gauss tried to determine the sum of the angles of a large triangle whose vertices were three mountain tops separated by large distances. Lobachevski tried to determine, on the basis of astronomical data, the sum of the angles of a very large triangle formed by three stars.† The difficulty here is that all our measurements are of limited accuracy determined by the properties of the measuring instruments, and all we can claim on the basis of an experiment is that the sum of the angles in a triangle is approximately equal to such and such a magnitude, and give an estimate of the error. Hence an experiment of this kind could not prove conclusively that the sum of the angles in a triangle is equal to 180°. It is conceivable, however, that an experiment could show that the sum of the angles of a triangle is not equal to 180° and that, consequently, Euclidean geometry is no accurate reflection of the properties of space. What can be said in this connection is that in all measurements the observed deviation from 180° of the sum of the angles in a triangle did not exceed the bounds of experimental error.

Thus we see that, until the issue of the true geometry of space is decided by some particularly refined experiment, both our geometries are equally useful in studying the laws of the physical universe.‡ Attempts to explain which possible geometric system (such include many geometries other than Euclidean and hyperbolic geometry; cf. the discussion which follows) is best suited for the description of the properties of physical space have considerably advanced the development of physics. The most remarkable achievement in this area is the so-called theory of relativity[T] ("Special Theory of Relativity"—A. Einstein, 1905; "General Theory of Relativity"—A. Einstein, 1916), which changed in a funda-

---

† We recall that, in view of the result of Problem 109, the larger the area of a hyperbolic triangle, the more the sum of its angles differs from 180°.

‡ The fact that in studying hyperbolic geometry we must use distorted diagrams like those in Fig. 115 and Fig. 118 has no bearing on whether or not hyperbolic geometry is the "true" geometry of space. The fact that in Euclidean geometry we can employ accurate diagrams is very closely connected with the existence of similarity transformations that enable us to produce a scaled down version of a large region of the plane (cf. the Introduction to NML 21). In hyperbolic geometry there are no similarities (cf. p. 124) so that when depicting large regions on a sheet of paper we must use distorted diagrams (represent lines by means of curves, etc.).

[T] An elementary introduction to some aspects of relativity is found in J. T. Schwartz, *Relativity in Illustrations*, N.Y.U. Press, N.Y. 1962. Another introduction, from a different point of view, is volume 16 in this NML series: *From Pythagoras to Einstein*, K. O. Friedrichs.

mental way our notions concerning the geometry of large regions in space and dismissed altogether the question of the truth or falsehood of hyperbolic geometry in the form in which that question was originally formulated. We regret that we cannot here go more deeply into this theory which is closely connected with the theme of this book.

The great merit of C. F. Gauss, N. I. Lobachevski and J. Bolyai is that they were the first to destroy the notion that Euclidean geometry was unique and irreplaceable. While it is true that Gauss, Lobachevski and Bolyai developed their geometry quite extensively without encountering contradictions, they nevertheless left unanswered the question whether it was, in principle, free of contradictions.[†]

In this connection the work of E. Beltrami was of major interest. In 1868 he showed that hyperbolic geometry could be realized on certain remarkable surfaces of ordinary (Euclidean) space (if one defines the distance between two points A and B on the surface to be the length of the shortest curve on that surface joining A and B; such "shortest" curves play the role of lines in the geometry of the surface). This discovery placed hyperbolic geometry on the same footing as Euclidean geometry in the sense that it showed that if Euclidean geometry is free of contradictions, then the same is true of hyperbolic geometry.

Two years after the appearance of the work of Beltrami, F. Klein published his first papers on non-Euclidean geometry. The existence of two different geometries led Klein to consider the question of what was meant by a geometry; his answer to this question is presented in the introduction to the present book. Klein put hyperbolic geometry from the beginning on the same footing as Euclidean geometry. He must also be credited with the definition of hyperbolic geometry given on p. 104. The implied possibility of realizing hyperbolic geometry in the interior of a disk $\mathbf{K}$ of the ordinary Euclidean plane (already hinted at by Beltrami) also shows that this geometry is free of contradictions, i.e., shows that the axiom of parallels cannot be deduced from the other axioms of Euclidean geometry. Klein went even further; namely, by singling out various sufficiently small groups of projective transformations he arrived at a number (specifically, nine) of plane geometries in each of which there is a natural notion of distance between points and of angle between lines.[‡] Nowadays all geometries other than Euclidean

---

† C. F. Gauss and N. I. Lobachevski were so deeply convinced of the consistency of the new geometry that the whole issue was of little concern to them. Bolyai, on the other hand, was greatly exercised by this question; his deep insight into the whole complex of problems connected with hyperbolic geometry is truly astounding. Bolyai tried very hard to prove rigorously that hyperbolic geometry is consistent, but he failed, because his mathematical training was far inferior to that of Gauss and Lobachevski.

‡ See, for example, the Appendix to I. M. Yaglom, *Complex Numbers in Geometry*, Academic Press, New York 1968.

geometry are referred to as *non-Euclidean,* and this makes hyperbolic geometry one of many non-Euclidean geometries.†

We note that the proofs of Beltrami and Klein of the consistency of hyperbolic geometry are not the only proofs possible. One can construct, in Euclidean space, models of hyperbolic geometry other than the Beltrami model (the points of a special curved surface with distance measured on the surface) or the Klein model (the points of a disk **K** with distance measured in a manner different from the ordinary.) ‡ Another interesting model is the Poincaré model discussed in the supplement to Chapter Two.ᵀ

† Hyperbolic geometry is exceptional among non-Euclidean geometries because it satisfies all the axioms of Euclidean geometry except for the axiom of parallels. Other non-Euclidean geometries differ more radically from Euclidean geometry; in some of them a line segment cannot be produced indefinitely in both directions, and in others, two points cannot always be joined by a line. [In connection with one such non-Euclidean geometry, namely Riemannian, see supplement to Ch. 2 (untranslated).] These remarks presuppose the "traditional" axiomatization of Euclidean geometry perfected by D. Hilbert in his *Foundations of Geometry* (1899). Adoption of a different approach to the concept of a Euclidean plane may influence the relative "proximity" of a given geometrical system to Euclidean geometry. For example, from the point of view of "vectorial" (i.e., based on the notion of a vector space) axiomatization of Euclidean geometry, apparently due to H. Weyl (1918), the "non-Euclidean geometry of Klein" closest to Euclidean geometry is the so-called (two dimensional) "Minkowski geometry" which is the basis of the (special) theory of relativity. In the same framework, a geometry very distant from Euclidean geometry is hyperbolic geometry which does not use the notion of vector at all.

‡ We cannot here explain what shortcomings of the Beltrami model justify the assertion that the Klein model constituted the first acceptable proof of the consistency of hyperbolic geometry. In this connection it should be pointed out that Beltrami was nevertheless the first to prove consistency, since his paper also contained, in essence, the model of hyperbolic geometry described in this Supplement and known today as the "Klein model" or the "Beltrami–Klein" model. (Klein discovered it independently. Beltrami's contemporaries were so impressed with his first, essentially incorrect, proof of the consistency of hyperbolic geometry that they simply ignored the second, correct proof contained in the same paper.)

ᵀ Reference to untranslated Russian material. For a discussion of the Poincaré model in English, see H. Meschkowski, *Noneuclidean Geometry*, Academic Press, New York 1964; or E. E. Moise, *Elementary Geometry from an Advanced Standpoint*, Addison Wesley 1963, Ch. 25 (pp. 348–366); or D. Pedoe, *A Course of Geometry for Colleges and Universities*, Cambridge Univ. Press 1970, Ch. 6 (pp. 206–241).

SOLUTIONS

Chapter One. Affine and projective transformations

§1

1. Let ABC be an arbitrary triangle in the plane π. Under a suitable parallel projection of π to a plane π', the image of $\triangle ABC$ will be an equilateral triangle $A'B'C'$. In view of property C of parallel projection, the maps of the midpoints of the sides of $\triangle ABC$ are midpoints of the sides of $\triangle A'B'C'$. Since $A'B'C'$ is equilateral, it follows that its medians are also bisectors of its angles and so intersect in a point, the center of the inscribed circle; but then the medians of the original triangle ABC are concurrent.†

2. Let $ABCD$ be at rapezoid, E the point of intersection of (the extensions of) its non-parallel sides, F the point of intersection of its diagonals. Under a suitable parallel projection of the plane π of the trapezoid onto a plane π', the image of the triangle ABE will be an isosceles triangle $A'B'E'$; at the same time, in view of property B of a parallel projection, trapezoid $ABCD$ will go over into a trapezoid $A'B'C'D'$ (Fig. 122). Clearly $E'F'$, the image of line EF, is an axis of symmetry of the isosceles triangle $A'B'E'$ and so bisects the bases $A'B'$ and $C'D'$ of trapezoid $A'B'C'D'$. In view of property C of a parallel projection, this implies that line EF bisects the bases AB and CD of the original trapezoid $ABCD$.

We note that in this way we can also prove the converse of the above theorem: If a point F on the median EM of a triangle ABE is joined by lines to the vertices A and B, and if these lines meet the sides of the triangle in points C and D, then the line CD is parallel to AB (Fig. 122b shows that this is the case if the triangle ABE is isosceles).

---

† The concurrence of the angle bisectors of a triangle follows directly from the fact that an angle bisector is the locus of points equidistant from the sides of the angle. The usual proof of the concurrence of the medians of a triangle requires auxiliary constructions which are superfluous in the present approach.

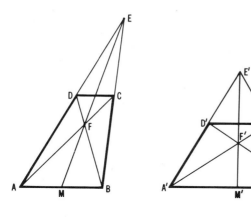

Figure 122a   Figure 122b

3. (a) We choose in the plane a point E not on the lines l or l_1 and join it to the points A and B on l. Let D and C be the points of intersection of lines EA and EB with line l_1, and let F be the point of intersection of lines AC and BD (Fig. 123a). Line EF bisects the segment AB (cf. Problem 2).

(b) Choose two points A and B on l and find the midpoint G of segment AB (cf. part (a)). Let E be a point on line AM, H the point of intersection of lines EG and BM, and N the point of intersection of lines AH and BE (Fig. 123b). Line MN is the required parallel to l (cf. the remark following the solution of Problem 2).

[In carrying out the above construction it is convenient to use the same triangle ABE for finding the midpoint of AB and for constructing the parallel to l.]

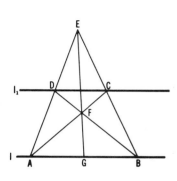

Figure 123a

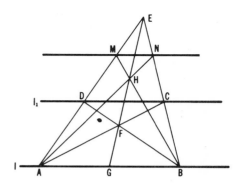

Figure 123b

4. (a) A suitable parallel projection will map the triangle ABC onto an equilateral triangle $A'B'C'$ in a plane π'; also, in view of property C of a parallel projection, the mapping will take the points M, N, P into points M', N', P' such that $A'M'/M'B' = B'N'/N'C' = C'P'/P'A'$ (Fig. 124). Rotation of $\triangle A'B'C'$ about its center through an angle of 120° takes sides $A'B'$, $B'C'$, $C'A'$ into sides $B'C'$, $C'A'$, $A'B'$, in this order, and points M', N', P' into points N', P', M', in this order. Hence a rotation of $\triangle A'B'C'$ about its center through 120° takes $\triangle M'N'P'$ into itself; but this means that the latter triangle is equilateral and its center coincides with the center of $\triangle A'B'C'$. In other words, the point of intersection of the medians of $\triangle M'N'P'$ coincides with the point of intersection of the medians of $\triangle A'B'C'$. Since a parallel projection maps medians of a triangle into medians of the image triangle, the point of intersection of the medians of $\triangle MNP$ coincides with the point of intersection of the medians of $\triangle ABC$.†

(b) Proof analogous to the solution of part (a).

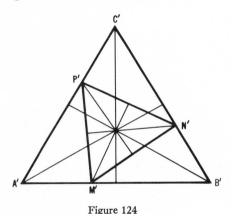

Figure 124

5. If the triangle ABC is *equilateral* then, clearly, the required point M must be equidistant from the sides of $\triangle ABC$; that is, M is the

---

† The center of an equilateral triangle is identical with the point of intersection of its angle bisectors (center of inscribed circle), the point of intersection of the perpendicular bisectors of its sides (center of circumscribed circle), the point of intersection of its altitudes (orthocenter) and, finally, the point of intersection of its medians (centroid). However, the coincidence of the point of intersection of the angle bisectors of $\triangle A'B'C'$ with the point of intersection of the angle bisectors of $\triangle M'N'P'$ does not, of course, imply that the analogous statement holds for triangles ABC and MNP (parallel projection does *not*, in general, carry angle bisectors into angle bisectors); nor can it be claimed that triangles ABC and MNP have the same point of intersection of altitudes, or that the centers of their circumscribed circles coincide. What can be claimed is that the points of intersection of the medians of these triangles coincide, since *a parallel projection takes the medians of a triangle into the medians of the image triangle.*

center of the circle inscribed in $\triangle ABC$, or, alternatively, the point of intersection of the medians of $\triangle ABC$. It follows that in an *arbitrary* triangle ABC the required point M must coincide with the point of intersection of its medians (cf. footnote accompanying the solution of Problem 4a).

6. If ABC is an *equilateral* triangle (Fig. 125) then the sides of triangles ABC and $A_2B_2C_2$ are parallel (why?), that is, these triangles are centrally similar (cf. NML 21). It follows that in the general case the triangles ABC and $A_2B_2C_2$ are centrally similar† and therefore similar.

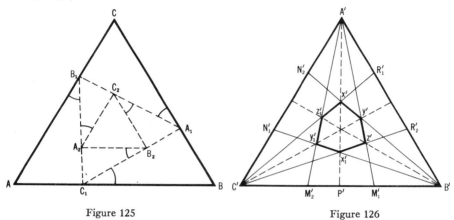

Figure 125   Figure 126

7. The theorem is obviously true for an *equilateral* triangle. It follows that it is likewise true for an *arbitrary* triangle (cf., for example, solution of Problem 1).

8. It suffices to prove our assertion for an *equilateral* triangle $A'B'C'$ (cf. the solutions of Problems 1 and 4). Since $A'N_2' = \frac{1}{3}A'C'$ and $A'R_1' = \frac{1}{3}A'B'$ (see Fig. 126), lines $C'R_1'$ and $B'N_2'$ are symmetric with respect to the axis of symmetry $A'P'$ of $\triangle A'B'C'$, and, therefore, the point of intersection X' of these lines lies on $A'P'$. Similarly, from $B'R_2' = \frac{1}{3}B'A'$, $C'N_1' = \frac{1}{3}C'A'$ we conclude that the point X_1' of intersection of lines $B'N_1'$ and $C'R_2'$ also lies on that axis. Hence, the diagonal $X'X_1'$ of our hexagon coincides with the axis of symmetry $A'P'$ of $A'B'C'$. In the same way we prove that the diagonals $Y'Y_1'$ and $Z'Z_1'$ of our hexagon coincide with the remaining two axes of symmetry of the equilateral triangle $A'B'C'$. But then the three diagonals in question must meet in a point, the center of the equilateral triangle. It follows that in $\triangle ABC$, diagonals XX_1, YY_1, ZZ_1 meet in a point.

† Note that a parallel projection preserves centrally similar figures without necessarily preserving similar figures. This is the reason for the "detour" in our argument.

Note. Our solution shows that the lines XX_1, YY_1, ZZ_1 are the medians of $\triangle ABC$, and their point of intersection is the point of intersection of the medians.

9. (a) In view of properties C and D of a parallel projection and Theorem 1 on p. 13, it suffices to prove our result for an *equilateral* triangle $A'B'C'$ (Fig. 127a; cf. the solutions of Problems 1 and 4). Let p denote the magnitude of the segments $B'M'$ and $A'M'_1$, r the magnitude of the segments $A'P'$ and $C'P'_1$, q the magnitude of the segments $C'N'$ and $B'N'_1$, and a the magnitude of a side of the equilateral triangle $A'B'C'$; denote the area of $\triangle XYZ$ by S_{XYZ}. Then

$$S_{A'B'C'} - S_{M'N'P'} = S_{A'P'M'} + S_{B'M'N'} + S_{C'N'P'}$$
$$= \tfrac{1}{2} \sin 60°[r(a-p) + p(a-q) + q(a-r)]$$
$$= \tfrac{1}{2} \sin 60°[a(p+q+r) - (pq+qr+rp)]$$

and

$$S_{A'B'C'} - S_{M_1'N_1'P_1'} = S_{A'P_1'M_1'} + S_{B'M_1'N_1'} + S_{C'N_1'P_1'}$$
$$= \tfrac{1}{2} \sin 60°[(a-r)p + (a-p)q + (a-q)r]$$
$$= \tfrac{1}{2} \sin 60°[a(p+q+r) - (pq+qr+rp)].$$

Hence

$$S_{M'N'P'} = S_{M_1'N_1'P_1'}.$$

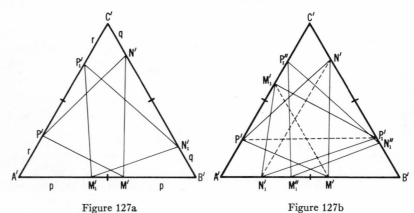

Figure 127a   Figure 127b

(b) Just as in part (a), it suffices to prove the assertion for an equilateral triangle $A'B'C'$ (Fig. 127b). Since $M'M'_1 \parallel B'C'$, $N'N'_1 \parallel C'A'$, $P'P'_1 \parallel A'B'$, it follows that

$$A'M' = A'M'_1, \qquad B'N' = B'N'_1, \qquad C'P' = C'P'_1.$$

Rotate $\triangle A'B'C'$ counterclockwise about its center through an angle of 120°. This rotation will take $\triangle A'B'C'$ into itself and, in view of the above equalities, it will take $\triangle M_1'N_1'P_1'$ into a triangle $M_1''N_1''P_1''$ whose vertices are symmetric to the vertices of $\triangle M'N'P'$ with respect to the midpoints of the appropriate sides of $\triangle A'B'C'$. This fact and the result established in part (a) above imply that

$$S_{M_1''N_1''P_1''} = S_{M'N'P'}, \quad \text{so that} \quad S_{M_1'N_1'P_1'} = S_{M'N'P'}.$$

It is not difficult to prove equality of the areas of the triangles $M'N'P'$ and $M_1'N_1'P_1'$ by direct computation as in the solution of part (a).

10. The solution is analogous to the solution of Problem 9(a) and is left to the reader.

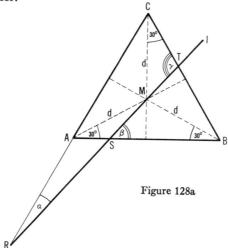

Figure 128a

11. (a) Let ABC be an *equilateral* triangle. Consider Fig. 128a. Applying the law of sines to the triangles AMR, BMS, CMT (and bearing in mind the fact that $d = \frac{2}{3}$ of the median of $\triangle ABC$) we see that

$$\frac{d}{MR} = \frac{\sin \alpha}{\sin 150°} = 2 \sin \alpha, \qquad \frac{d}{MS} = \frac{\sin \beta}{\sin 30°} = 2 \sin \beta,$$

$$\frac{d}{MT} = \frac{\sin \gamma}{\sin 30°} = 2 \sin \gamma,$$

so that

$$\frac{1}{MR} + \frac{1}{MS} = \frac{2}{d}(\sin \alpha + \sin \beta) \quad \text{and} \quad \frac{1}{MT} = \frac{2}{d} \sin \gamma.$$

Clearly,† $\alpha = 120° - \gamma$, $\beta = \gamma - 60°$. Therefore

$$\sin \alpha + \sin \beta = \sin (120° - \gamma) + \sin (\gamma - 60°)$$
$$= \sin (120° - \gamma) - \sin (120° + \gamma)$$
$$= -2 \cos 120° \sin \gamma = \sin \gamma;$$

that is, for an equilateral triangle ABC we have $1/MR + 1/MS = 1/MT$.

To see that this relation is valid for an arbitrary triangle ABC we note that it is equivalent to the relation $MT/MR + MT/MS = 1$, and that it is always possible to carry an equilateral triangle into *any* preassigned triangle ABC by means of an appropriate parallel projection and similarity.

Using similar reasoning it is possible to show that if we replaced M by, say, the midpoint N of the median AD, then the relation just established would go over into a similar relation with $1/MX$ (X denotes that point of the triple R, S, T which is associated with side BC of $\triangle ABC$) replaced by $2/NX$ (and $1/MY$ and $1/MZ$ replaced by $1/NY$ and $1/NZ$).

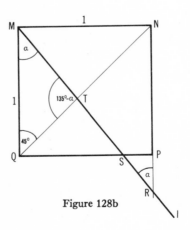

Figure 128b

(b) Let parallelogram $MNPQ$ be a *unit square* (Fig. 128b). Then in triangles MRN, MSQ, and MTQ we have

$$\frac{1}{MR} = \sin \alpha, \quad \frac{1}{MS} = \cos \alpha, \quad \frac{1}{MT} = \frac{\sin (135° - \alpha)}{\sin 45°} = \sqrt{2} \sin (135° - \alpha).†$$

† For the solution of the problem to be independent of a diagram it is necessary to introduce directed angles (cf. footnote on p. 50, NML 8).

Since

$$\sin (135° - \alpha) = \sin (45° + \alpha) = \sin 45° \cos \alpha + \cos 45° \sin \alpha$$

$$= \frac{1}{\sqrt{2}} (\sin \alpha + \cos \alpha),$$

we have

$$\frac{1}{MT} = \sqrt{2} \left[\frac{1}{\sqrt{2}} (\sin \alpha + \cos \alpha) \right] = \sin \alpha + \cos \alpha = \frac{1}{MR} + \frac{1}{MS} ;$$

that is, for a square $MNPQ$ we have

$$\frac{1}{MR} + \frac{1}{MS} = \frac{1}{MT} .$$

To see that this relation is valid for an arbitrary parallelogram, we note that it is equivalent to the relation $MT/MR + MT/MS = 1$, and that it is always possible to carry any parallelogram $ABCD$ into a square by a suitable parallel projection (for this it suffices to carry $\triangle ABC$ into an isosceles right triangle).

Figure 129a

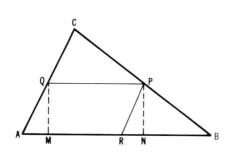

Figure 129b

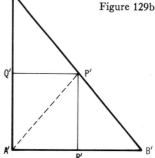

12. Our problem is equivalent to the following: Inscribe a parallelogram $ARPQ$ of given area σ in a given triangle ABC so that the two figures share the vertex A, and the remaining vertices of the parallelogram lie on the sides AC, BC and AB of the triangle. This follows readily from Fig. 129a, where parallelogram $ARPQ$ and rectangle $MNPQ$ are seen to have equal areas (since they share base PQ and height QM). In other words, if we can construct the parallelogram $ARPQ$, then we can also construct the rectangle $MNPQ$.

If a parallel projection maps $\triangle ABC$ in the plane π onto a triangle $A'B'C'$ in the plane π', then the parallelogram $ARPQ$ inscribed in ABC is mapped onto a parallelogram $A'R'P'Q'$ inscribed in $A'B'C'$.

[This is why we replaced the problem of constructing rectangle $MNPQ$ with that of constructing parallelogram $ARPQ$: a parallel projection does not, in general, map a rectangle onto a rectangle, and this makes it difficult to use a parallel projection to solve the original problem.] Assume that parallelogram $ARPQ$ is already inscribed. Map the $\triangle ABC$ by a suitable parallel projection onto a *right isosceles* triangle $A'B'C'$ (Fig. 129b). We may assume that triangles ABC and $A'B'C'$ have the same area (this can always be achieved by applying to the image of $\triangle ABC$ a suitable similarity); then parallelograms $ARPQ$ and $A'R'P'Q'$ (the latter is, of course, a rectangle) have the same area σ. If S is the area of $\triangle ABC$, then the combined area of the isosceles right triangles $B'R'P'$ and $C'P'Q'$ is $S - \sigma$. Since

$$S_{B'R'P'} = \tfrac{1}{2}R'P'^2, \qquad S_{C'P'Q'} = \tfrac{1}{2}Q'P'^2,$$

it follows that

$$R'P'^2 + Q'P'^2 = 2(S - \sigma),$$

or, since $R'P'^2 + Q'P'^2$ is the square of the diagonal $A'P'$ of the rectangle $A'R'P'Q'$, we have $A'P' = \sqrt{2(S - \sigma)}$.

This analysis suggests the following construction of rectangle $MNPQ$: Construct an isosceles right triangle $A'B'C'$ with area S equal to the area of the given triangle ABC (side $A'B'$ of this triangle is equal to the geometric mean of the base and height of $\triangle ABC$). Next, choose on the hypotenuse $B'C'$ a point P' so that $A'P' = \sqrt{2(S - \sigma)}$. Finally, divide side BC of the given $\triangle ABC$ in the ratio $BP/PC = B'P'/P'C'$ (property C of a parallel projection). Rectangle $MNPQ$ (with vertex Q on side AC and vertices M and N on side AB) is the required rectangle.

The problem can have two, one, or no solutions.

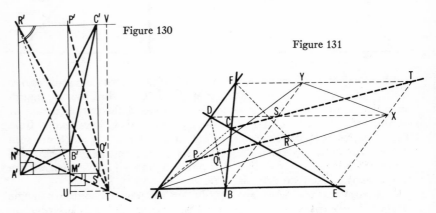

Figure 130

Figure 131

13. Let π be the plane of Fig. 13 in the text. We assert that π can be mapped by a parallel projection onto a plane π' so that angles AMN

and ARS in Fig. 13 go over into equal angles $A'M'N'$ and $A'R'S'$, and so that $R'A'M'$ is a right angle. Indeed, for the image triangles $A'M'N'$ and $A'R'S'$ (they share the angle A') to be similar (i.e., for $\sphericalangle A'M'N' = \sphericalangle A'R'S'$), it suffices that their sides be proportional:

$$(*) \qquad \frac{A'M'}{A'N'} = \frac{A'R'}{A'S'} .$$

Since the ratios

$$\frac{A'S'}{A'M'} = \frac{AS}{AM} = \alpha \quad \text{and} \quad \frac{A'N'}{A'R'} = \frac{AN}{AR} = \beta$$

are known, the sufficient condition (*) is equivalent to

$$\frac{A'M'}{\beta A'R'} = \frac{A'R'}{\alpha A'M'} , \quad \text{or} \quad \frac{A'M'}{A'R'} = \sqrt{\frac{\beta}{\alpha}} .$$

In view of Theorem 1 (p. 13) we can project $\triangle AMR$ into a triangle $A'M'R'$ so that $A'M'/A'R' = \sqrt{\beta/\alpha}$, and so that $R'A'M'$ is a right angle; this proves our assertion. This brings us to Fig. 130, where we must prove that the point T of intersection of $M'N'$ and $R'S'$ lies on line $P'Q'$. This we do next.

Similarity of triangles $M'S'T$ and $R'N'T$ (they have equal angles) implies $M'T/R'T = M'S'/R'N'$. Similarity of triangles TUM' and TVR', where U and V are the feet of the perpendiculars from T to $P'M'$ and $P'R'$ (in these right triangles $\sphericalangle TM'U = 90° - \sphericalangle TM'S' = 90° - \sphericalangle TR'N' = \sphericalangle TR'V$), implies $TU/TV = M'T/R'T$. Hence

$$\frac{TU}{TV} = \frac{M'T}{R'T} = \frac{M'S'}{R'N'} = \frac{Q'B'}{Q'C'} .$$

This implies that $TU/TV = Q'B'/Q'C'$ and proves that T lies on the line $P'Q'$.

14. Let P, Q, and R be the midpoints of AC, BD, and EF, respectively (Fig. 131). The central similarity with center A and coefficient 2 maps P, Q, R onto C, S, T ($ABSD$ and $AFTE$ are parallelograms). Hence in order to prove the collinearity of P, Q, R it suffices to prove the collinearity of C, S, T, or equivalently, that line TS passes through the point C of intersection of ED and BF. The latter conclusion is a direct consequence of Problem 13. Indeed, observe that in Fig. 131 $ADXE$, $XTYS$ and $YFAB$ are parallelograms whose sides have the same directions, and each side of $\triangle AXY$ is a diagonal of one of these parallelograms. But then their remaining diagonals, ED, TS and BF, are concurrent.

15. (a) It is clear that it suffices to consider the case when $ABCD$ is a *unit square* (cf. solution of Problem 11(b)). Quadrilateral $A_2B_2C_2D_2$ formed by the lines AA_1, BB_1, CC_1, DD_1 (see Fig. 132) is a square; to see this note that a 90° rotation about the center of square $ABCD$ carries the diagram into itself, and this implies that quadrilateral $A_2B_2C_2D_2$ is regular. (Incidentally, this implies that if $ABCD$ is a parallelogram, then so is $A_2B_2C_2D_2$.) The right triangles ABB_1 and ABA_2 are similar and their similarity coefficient k is equal to the ratio of their hypotenuses:

$$k = \frac{BB_1}{AB} = \frac{\sqrt{1 + (2/3)^2}}{1} = \frac{\sqrt{13}}{3}.$$

Since

$$S_{ABB_1} = \tfrac{1}{2} \cdot 1 \cdot \tfrac{2}{3} = \tfrac{1}{3},$$

we have

$$S_{ABA_2} = \frac{\tfrac{1}{3}}{k^2} = \frac{3}{13}.$$

Therefore

$$S_{A_2B_2C_2D_2} = S_{ABCD} - S_{ABA_2} - S_{BCB_2} - S_{CDC_2} - S_{DAD_2}$$
$$= S_{ABCD} - 4S_{ABA_2} = 1 - \tfrac{12}{13} = \tfrac{1}{13},$$

that is,

$$\frac{S_{A_2B_2C_2D_2}}{S_{ABCD}} = \frac{1}{13}.$$

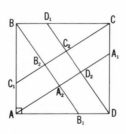

Figure 132

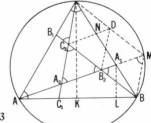

Figure 133

(b) *First solution.* It suffices to consider an *equilateral* triangle ABC with side 1. The triangle $A_2B_2C_2$ (formed by the lines AA_1, BB_1, CC_1) is equilateral, since a 120° rotation of $\triangle ABC$ about its center carries $\triangle A_2B_2C_2$ into itself. For an equilateral $\triangle ABC$, triangles CB_1C_2 and CAC_1 (see Fig. 133 supplemented in accordance with the second solution of the problem) are similar with similarity coefficient

$$k = \frac{CB_1}{CC_1} = \frac{\frac{1}{3}}{\sqrt{CK^2 + KC_1^2}} = \frac{\frac{1}{3}}{\sqrt{CA^2 - AK^2 + KC_1^2}}$$

$$= \frac{\frac{1}{3}}{\sqrt{1 - (1/2)^2 + (1/6)^2}} = \frac{1}{\sqrt{7}}.$$

Since $S_{CAC_1} = \frac{1}{3}S_{ABC}$, we have

$$S_{CB_1C_2} = \frac{1}{3}S_{ABC} \cdot k^2 = \frac{1}{21}S_{ABC}.$$

Therefore

$$S_{A_2B_2C_2} = S_{ABC} - S_{CAC_1} - S_{ABA_1} - S_{BCB_1}$$

$$+ S_{CB_1C_2} + S_{AC_1A_2} + S_{BA_1B_2}$$

$$= S_{ABC} - 3S_{CAC_1} + 3S_{CB_1C_2}$$

$$= S_{ABC} - 3 \cdot \frac{1}{3}S_{ABC} + 3 \cdot \frac{1}{21}S_{ABC} = \frac{1}{7}S_{ABC},$$

that is,

$$\frac{S_{A_2B_2C_2}}{S_{ABC}} = \frac{1}{7}.$$

Second solution. It suffices to consider an equilateral triangle ABC. As was shown in the first solution, triangle $A_2B_2C_2$ formed by lines AA_1, BB_1, CC_1 is equilateral. Let S be the circle circumscribed about $\triangle ABC$. Let M be the point of intersection of S and AA_1 (Fig. 133). The equality $\measuredangle BMA = \measuredangle BCA$ (these angles support the same circular arc) implies that $\triangle BMB_2$ is also equilateral ($\measuredangle BMB_2 = \measuredangle BB_2M = 60°$) and $BM \| C_1C$. Also $BM = BB_2$ and $BB_2 = CC_2$ ($\triangle BB_2A_1 \cong \triangle CC_2B_1$) imply that $BM = C_2C$, and therefore quadrilateral $BMCC_2$ is a parallelogram. Now we pass a line parallel to MA_1 through the point C_2 and denote by N its point of intersection with line BC. Since $\triangle CC_2N \cong \triangle BMA_1$, it follows that $BA_1 = NC$. This and the fact that $BA_1 = \frac{1}{3}BC$ allow us to conclude that $BA_1 = A_1N = NC$. The equality $BA_1 = A_1N$ implies $BB_2 = B_2C_2$ and, finally $\triangle BB_2M \cong \triangle A_2B_2C_2$.

Now it is easy to compute the area of $\triangle A_2B_2C_2$. Indeed, let B_2D be the midline of the parallelogram $BMCC_2$. Then

$$S_{B_2BM} = \frac{1}{2}S_{B_2BMD} = \frac{1}{4}S_{C_2BMC},$$

and since $S_{BC_2C} = \frac{1}{2}S_{BMCC_2}$, it follows that

$$S_{A_2B_2C_2} = S_{B_2BM} = \frac{1}{2}S_{BC_2C}.$$

However,

$$S_{ABC} = S_{BCC_2} + S_{CAA_2} + S_{ABB_2} + S_{A_2B_2C_2}$$
$$= 3S_{BCC_2} + S_{A_2B_2C_2} = 7S_{A_2B_2C_2}$$

and, consequently,

$$S_{A_2B_2C_2} = \tfrac{1}{7}S_{ABC},$$

as asserted.

Note. We observe that the relations $BB_2 = B_2C_2$, $CC_2 = C_2A_2$, $AA_2 = A_2B_2$, valid in the equilateral triangle, must have analogues in *any* triangle ABC.

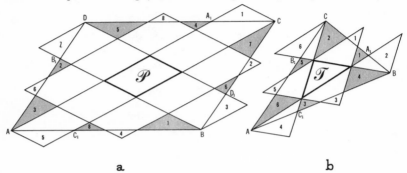

a   b

Editor's Remark: The following solutions to parts (a) and (b) of Problem 15 occurred to Professor B. Gordon when he read this manuscript:

In these figures, every "outer" piece is congruent to the shaded "inner" piece labelled with the same number. The unshaded area in the first figure is clearly 13 times that of the parallelogram $\mathcal{P}$, while the unshaded area in the second figure is 7 times that of the triangle $\mathcal{T}$.

16. In high school geometry courses one proves that in a triangle the medians, the altitudes and the angle bisectors form concurrent triples.

Our problem will be solved if we can map the plane of $\triangle ABC$ by a parallel projection onto another plane so that lines AN, BP and CM go over into three medians, three angle bisectors or three altitudes of the image $A'B'C'$ of $\triangle ABC$. It is clear that lines AN, BP and CM cannot be mapped by a parallel projection on the medians of a triangle unless they themselves are the medians of $\triangle ABC$. Again, it is not always possible to map lines AN, BP and CM onto the angle bisectors of a triangle.† It remains to try mapping lines AN, BP, CM, by a parallel projection onto the altitudes of a triangle.

† It can be shown (we urge the reader to attempt the proof!) that three lines AN, BP and CM passing through the vertices of a triangle ABC and intersecting in a point O in its interior can be mapped by a parallel projection onto the angle bisectors $A'N'$, $B'P'$ and $C'M'$ of a triangle $A'B'C'$ if and only if the point O lies in the interior of the small triangle whose sides are the midlines of $\triangle ABC$.

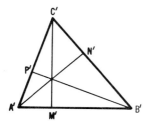

Figure 134a   Figure 134b

We prove that if $A'N'$, $B'P'$ and $C'M'$ are the altitudes of a triangle $A'B'C'$ (Fig. 134a), then

$$\frac{A'M'}{M'B'} \cdot \frac{B'N'}{N'C'} \cdot \frac{C'P'}{P'A'} = 1.$$

Indeed, the similarity of the right triangles $A'N'C'$ and $B'P'C'$ implies that $C'P'/N'C' = a/b$, where $a = B'C'$ and $b = A'C'$. In much the same way we can show that $B'N'/M'B' = c/a$, $A'M'/P'A' = b/c$, where $c = A'B'$. These three equalities imply that

$$\frac{A'M'}{M'B'} \cdot \frac{B'N'}{N'C'} \cdot \frac{C'P'}{P'A'} = \frac{A'M'}{P'A'} \cdot \frac{B'N'}{M'B'} \cdot \frac{C'P'}{N'C'} = \frac{b}{c} \cdot \frac{c}{a} \cdot \frac{a}{b} = 1.$$

Now we construct a triangle $A'B'C'$ such that the feet N', M' and P' of its altitudes divide the sides of the triangle in the given ratios

$$\frac{A'M'}{M'B'} = \frac{AM}{MB}, \qquad \frac{B'N'}{N'C'} = \frac{BN}{NC}, \qquad \frac{C'P'}{P'A'} = \frac{CP}{PA}.$$

We divide an arbitrary segment $B'C'$ in the ratio $B'N'/N'C' = BN/NC$. At N' we erect a perpendicular to $B'C'$. Then we divide segment $C'N'$ in the ratio $C'Q/QN' = CP/PA$ and erect at Q a perpendicular to $C'B'$ (Fig. 134b). Let P' be the point where this perpendicular meets the semicircle constructed on the segment $C'B'$ as diameter, and let A' be the point where the line $C'P'$ meets the perpendicular to $C'B'$ at N'. We claim that $A'B'C'$ is the required triangle. Indeed, $A'N'$ and $B'P'$ are two altitudes of this triangle; let $C'M'$ be its third altitude. Since $B'N'/N'C' = BN/NC$ and $C'P'/P'A' = C'Q/QN' = CP/PA$, and since

$$\frac{A'M'}{M'B'} \cdot \frac{B'N'}{N'C'} \cdot \frac{C'P'}{P'A'} = 1 = \frac{AM}{MB} \cdot \frac{BN}{NC} \cdot \frac{CP}{PA},$$

it follows that $A'M'/M'B' = AM/MB$.

We now map $\triangle ABC$ by a parallel projection onto a triangle similar to $\triangle A'B'C'$. In view of property C of a parallel projection, points N, P, M are mapped onto the feet of the altitudes of the image of $\triangle ABC$ and the lines AN, BP, and CM onto its altitudes. Since the altitudes of a triangle are concurrent, the same is true of the lines AN, BP and CM.

Note. We can now easily prove the converse proposition: If three lines passing through the vertices of a triangle are concurrent, then the points N, P and M where these lines meet the sides of $\triangle ABC$ divide the sides so that

$$\frac{AM}{MB} \cdot \frac{BN}{NC} \cdot \frac{CP}{PA} = 1.$$

Indeed, suppose P_1 is a point on the side AC such that

$$\frac{AM}{MB} \frac{BN}{NC} \frac{CP_1}{P_1A} = 1.$$

Then lines AN, BP_1, and CM are concurrent, i.e., BP_1 passes through the point of intersection of AN and CM. But this is possible only if BP_1 coincides with BP, i.e., if P_1 coincides with P.

We thus have the following theorem, sometimes referred to as Ceva's Theorem: *Let N, P, M be points on the sides of a triangle ABC (but not on their extensions!). For the lines AN, BP and CM to be concurrent it is necessary and sufficient that*

$$\frac{AM}{MB} \cdot \frac{BN}{NC} \cdot \frac{CP}{PA} = 1.$$

§2

17. (a) Let Q be the point of intersection of lines l_1 and l_2. We project the plane π of Fig. 24a to a plane π' so that PQ is the special line of the plane π. To do that it suffices to pass through QP an arbitrary plane π_1, different from π, and project π from a point O of π_1 to a plane π' parallel to π_1; cf. Fig. 135a. Then Fig. 24a (in the plane π) goes into Fig. 135b (in the plane π') and the locus of points M of intersection of lines AC and BD goes into a line p' parallel to and equidistant from l_1' and l_2'. It follows from property A of a central projection that the locus of points M is a line.

If $l_1 \parallel l_2$ then we arrive at Fig. 135b by projecting the plane π to a plane π' so that the line through P parallel to l_1 and l_2 is the special line of π.

It follows immediately from property B of a central projection that if l_1 and l_2 intersect in a point Q, then p passes through Q, and if $l_1 \parallel l_2$, then p is parallel to l_1 and l_2.

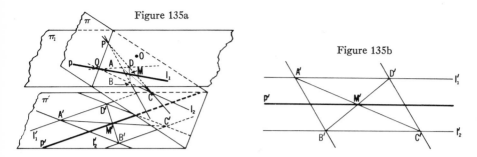

Figure 135a

Figure 135b

If P_1 is an arbitrary point of line PQ then, under our projection, the lines intersecting at P_1 will go into parallel lines, and the locus of points M_1 of intersection of the lines A_1C_1 and B_1D_1 will go into the line p'. It follows that the locus of points M_1 coincides with p. (Similarly, if $l_1 \parallel l_2$ and hence $PP_1 \parallel l_1$, then P and P_1 determine the same line p.)

(b) Project the plane π of Fig. 24b to a plane π' so that line q is the special line of π. Then lines UA and UB, VA and VB are carried into parallel lines (Fig. 136); line MN is carried into the diagonal $M'N'$ of parallelogram $M'A'N'B'$ and bisects the second diagonal $A'B'$ in Q'. Hence, for every choice of U and V, line MN is carried into a line $M'N'$ which intersects $A'B'$ in the same point Q'; it follows that all lines MN intersect AB in the same point Q.

Now, let q_1 be another line which intersects AB in the point P. Under our projection, q_1 is carried into a line q_1' parallel to $A'B'$; quadrilateral ABV_1U_1 is carried into trapezoid $A'B'V_1'U_1'$, and line M_1N_1 into line $M_1'N_1'$ which joins the point of intersection of the diagonals to the point of intersection of the opposite sides of the trapezoid (Fig. 136). But then $M_1'N_1'$ intersects the base $A'B'$ of the trapezoid in its midpoint Q' (cf. Problem 2, §1, p. 19). This implies the second assertion of our problem.

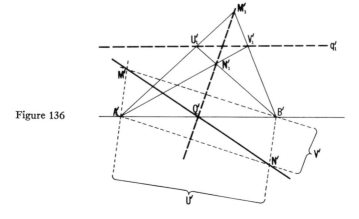

Figure 136

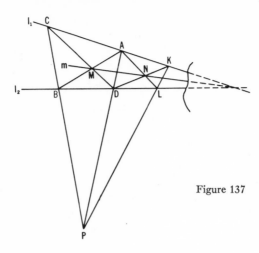

Figure 137

18. (a) Pass through the point M a pair of lines meeting l_1 and l_2 in the points A, C and B, D (Fig. 137). Next, pass a line through the point P of intersection of lines AD and BC, and denote the points where it intersects l_1 and l_2 by K and L. It follows from the theorem of Problem 17 that the line m joining M to the point of intersection of AL and DK passes through the point of intersection of l_1 and l_2.

Note 1. It is of interest to note that if $l_1 \parallel l_2$ (in this case their point of intersection is inaccessible in the sense that it does not exist), then our construction reduces to the construction of Problem 3(b); namely, using straightedge alone, draw through a given point M a line parallel to two given parallel lines. This is not a coincidence but rather a consequence of properties of central projections which make it possible to consider Problem 3(b) a special case of Problem 18(a) (cf. p. 37 ff.). Again, the constructions in Problems 18(b)–(d) yield methods for the construction of parallel lines by means of straightedge alone. We suggest that the reader try to carry out these constructions.

Note 2. The above solution of Problem 18(a) based on the theorem of Problem 17(a) is not the only possible one. A solution based on the theorem of Problem 17(b) is sketched in Fig. 138a. (Here lines l_2 and MN intersect line l_1 in the same point; the numbers next to the lines indicate the order of construction.) Figure 138b represents a solution based on the theorem of Problem 22. (Triangles ABM and $A_1B_1M_1$ are perspective. Incidentally, our first construction can also be justified by means of Desargues's Theorem, since triangles CDK and BAL in Fig. 137 are perspective.) Figure 138c represents a construction based on the theorem of Problem 28(a) (the vertices of hexagon $ABCDEF$ lie alternately on lines m_1 and m_2). This construction can also be justified by the theorem of Problem 28(b) (the sides of hexagon $AMDBNE$ pass alternately through the points F and C). There are other solutions of Problem 18(a). Also, the four constructions indicated above can be justified in many different ways.

Again, the solutions of Problems 18(b)–(d), 19 and 20 given below are not the only possible ones. We suggest that the reader try to find other constructions.

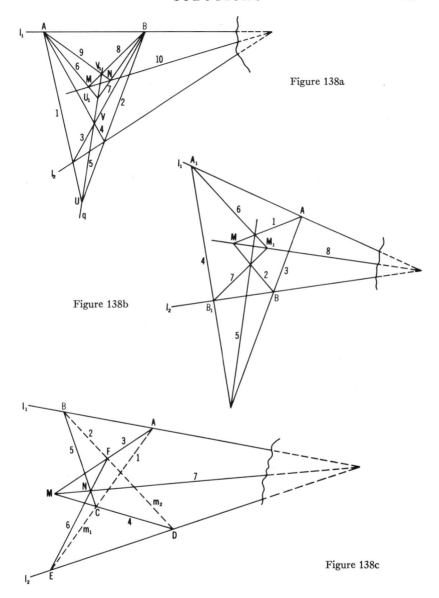

Figure 138a

Figure 138b

Figure 138c

(b) Here is one possible construction: Let A and B be two points on m. Join A, B, and M to the inaccessible points P and Q (cf. solution of part (a)). Let C and D be the points of intersection of AP and BQ, AQ and BP, and let E, F be the points of intersection of MQ and CD, MP and CD (Fig. 139). Join E to P and F to Q, and let N be the point of intersection of FQ and EP. It follows from the theorem of Problem 17(b) that lines MN, PQ and m meet in the same point X. (In Fig. 139, C and D, E and F are two pairs of points of the same line.)

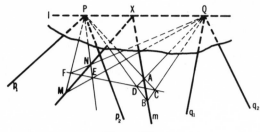

Figure 139

(c) Here is one possible construction: Let lines p_1 and p_2, q_1 and q_2 intersect in the points A, B, C, D (cf. Fig. 140). (If these lines do not intersect within the confines of the drawing we can replace them by other lines that pass through points P and Q; cf. Problem 18(a)). On line AC (or on any other line intersecting BD in the same point E) we select two points A_1 and C_1 so that lines A_1B and C_1D, A_1D and C_1B intersect within the confines of the drawing in points P_1 and Q_1. By the theorem of Problem 17(b) line P_1Q_1 passes through the point F of intersection of lines BD and PQ. It remains to join F to the inaccessible point P (cf. Problem 18(a)).

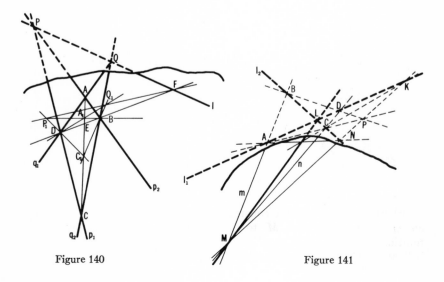

Figure 140   Figure 141

(d) Here is one possible construction: Let m and n be two arbitrary lines through the point M (Fig. 141). We know how to draw lines through the inaccessible points A, B, C, D of intersection of l_1 and l_2 with m and n (Problem 18(b)). We also know how to join A to C and B to D (Problem 18(c)). Now join M to the point P of intersection of AC and BD (Problem 18(a)). Let MP meet l_1 and l_2 in points K and N. By the theorem of Problem 17(a) the point of intersection of lines KC and NA (they can be constructed; cf. Problems 18(b), (c)) lies on the required line.

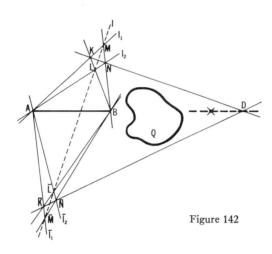

Figure 142

19. Here is one possible construction: Through A draw two lines l_1 and l_2 not passing through the region Q, and through B draw two lines meeting l_1 and l_2 in points K, L and M, N. Denote line ML by l (Fig. 142). Next, pass through A two more lines $\bar{l}_1$ and $\bar{l}_2$ which meet l in points $\bar{M}$ and $\bar{L}$. Let $B\bar{L}$ and $B\bar{M}$ meet l_1 and l_2 in points $\bar{K}$ and $\bar{N}$. It follows from the theorem of Problem 17(b) that the point D of intersection of lines KN and $\bar{K}\bar{N}$ lies on line AB. By repeating this procedure we find another point of line AB to the right of the region Q. The two points enable us to continue the line AB beyond the region Q.

20. Here is one possible solution: Through the point A pass two lines l_1 and l_2 forming a small angle, with B in its interior. Note that the shortness of the straightedge does not prevent us from extending a portion of a line. Next, pass two lines through B which meet l_1 and l_2 in points K_1, K_2 and L_1, L_2. Let P be the point of intersection of K_1L_1 and K_2L_2. Now draw, from P, a number of lines which cut l_1 and l_2 in points K_3, K_4, $\cdots$, K_n and L_3, L_4, $\cdots$, L_n (Fig. 143).

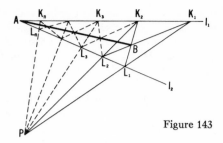

Figure 143

The theorem of Problem 17(a) implies that the points of intersection of K_2L_3 and K_3L_2, K_3L_4 and K_4L_3, $\cdots$ lie on line AB. In this manner it is possible to construct arbitrarily close points of the line AB which can be connected with a short straightedge.

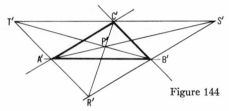

Figure 144

21. (a) Use a central projection to map the plane π of Fig. 28a to another plane π' so that p is the special line of π. Then lines AM and BC are carried into parallel lines $A'M'$ and $B'C'$, lines BN and AC into parallel lines $B'N'$ and $A'C'$, and lines CL and AB into parallel lines $C'L'$ and $A'B'$. Lines AS, BT and CR are carried into the medians $A'S'$, $B'T'$ and $C'R'$ of $\triangle A'B'C'$ (Fig. 144), and so, must intersect in a point P'. It follows that AS, BT and CR intersect in a point P.†

† Note that under a central projection of a plane π to a plane π' a triangle ABC need not go over into a triangle $A'B'C'$. For instance, this is certainly not the case if the line p passes through the interior of the triangle; under a central projection a triangle can go over into rather complicated figures; cf. Fig. 20. However, the three points A, B, C are carried into points A', B', C', and the lines joining the points A, B, C in pairs are carried into lines joining A', B', C' in pairs. It is in this sense that we are to understand the assertion Fig. 28a goes over into Fig. 144. For convenience we do not depict the lines AB, BC, etc., and the lines $A'B'$, $B'C'$, etc., in Figs. 28a and 144, in their entirety, but rather restrict ourselves to certain segments of these lines. However, the solution of our problem is based on the fact that, for example, *line AB* goes over into *line A'B'*. A statement that the segment AB goes over into the segment $A'B'$ might turn out to be false. This remark also applies to the solution of many problems in the sequel.

In addition, there is another more fundamental inaccuracy in our argument. The point P' of Fig. 144 might turn out to lie on the special line of the plane π'. In this case lines AS, BT and CR will not intersect in a point but will be parallel. Inaccuracies of this kind are to be found in most of the problems in the sequel. This issue is discussed on p. 37 ff.

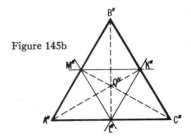

Figure 145b

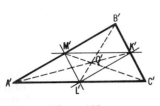

Figure 145a

(b) Use a central projection to map the plane π of Fig. 28b to another plane π' so that RS is the special line of the plane π. In π' we have $K'L' \parallel A'B'$, $K'M' \parallel A'C'$ (Fig. 145a). We now use a parallel projection to map $\triangle A'B'C'$ into an equilateral triangle $A''B''C''$ (Fig. 145b). Then lines $A''K''$ and $B''L''$ intersect on the axis of symmetry $C''D$ of $\triangle A''B''C''$,[T] and lines $A''K''$ and $C''M''$ intersect on the axis of symmetry $B''E$ of our triangle. It follows that the point Q'' of intersection of lines $A''K''$, $C''M''$, $B''L''$ is the point of intersection of the two axes of symmetry, that is, the centroid of the triangle; and lines $L''K''$, $K''M''$ and $M''L''$ are the midlines of the triangle. Hence $L''M'' \parallel B''C''$.

Property B of a parallel projection implies that $L'M' \parallel B'C'$. Property B moreover implies that the point T of intersection of LM and BC also lies on the special line of the plane π, that is, R, S and T are collinear.

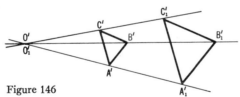

Figure 146

22. We first prove that if lines AA_1, BB_1 and CC_1 are concurrent, then the points P, Q, R of intersection of the lines BC and B_1C_1, CA and C_1A_1, AB and A_1B_1 are collinear. To see this, project the plane π of Fig. 29 to a plane π' so that QR is the special line of π. Then, by Property B of a central projection, we have $A'B' \parallel A_1'B_1'$ and $A'C' \parallel A_1'C_1'$. From $C'A' \parallel C_1'A_1'$ it follows that $O'C'/O'C_1' = O'A'/O'A_1'$, and from $A'B' \parallel A_1'B_1'$ it follows that $O'A'/O'A_1' = O'B'/O'B_1'$; that is, $O'B'/O'B_1' = O'C'/O'C_1'$. Hence lines $B'C'$ and $B_1'C_1'$ are parallel, and the point P of intersection of BC and B_1C_1 lies on the special line of π, i.e., points P, Q, and R are collinear.

We now prove the converse. To this end we project the plane π of Fig. 29 to a plane π' so that the line containing P, Q, R is the special line of π. Under this projection triangles ABC and $A_1B_1C_1$ are carried into similar triangles $A'B'C'$ and $A_1'B_1'C_1'$ whose corresponding sides are parallel (Fig. 146). Let O' be the point of intersection of $A'A_1'$ and

[T] They are interchanged by reflection in $C''D$.

$B'B_1'$, and O_1' the point of intersection of $A'A_1'$ and $C'C_1'$. We have $O'A'/O'A_1' = A'B'/A_1'B_1'$ and $O_1'A'/O_1'A_1' = A'C'/A_1'C_1'$. On the other hand, it follows from the similarity of triangles $A'B'C'$ and $A_1'B_1'C_1'$ that $A'B'/A_1'B_1' = A'C'/A_1'C_1'$. Hence $O'A'/O'A_1' = O_1'A'/O_1'A_1'$, that is, the two points O' and O_1' coincide. Since lines $A'A_1'$, $B'B_1'$, $C'C_1'$ are concurrent, it follows that the same is true of lines AA_1, BB_1, CC_1.

Note that the second assertion in Problem 22 is implied by the first. In fact, let the points P, Q, R of Fig. 29 be collinear. This means that lines PQ, B_1A_1 and BA which join corresponding vertices of triangles PB_1B and QA_1A intersect in the point R. By the first assertion in Problem 22, the points C_1, C and O of intersection of corresponding sides of the triangles are collinear. (Here O is the point of intersection of lines AA_1 and BB_1.) But that means that CC_1 passes through O, i.e., the three lines AA_1, BB_1, and CC_1 are concurrent.

The first assertion in Desargues's Theorem can be derived from the second in an analogous manner.

23. The assertion of the problem is merely another form of Desargues's Theorem (Problem 22; triangles AEH and CFG are perspective).

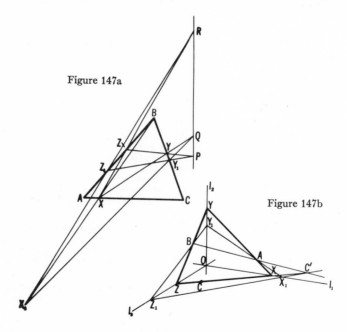

Figure 147a

Figure 147b

24. (a) Pass a line through P, and denote its points of intersection with sides AB and BC of $\triangle ABC$ by Z_1 and Y_1. Denote by X_1 the point where lines QY_1 and RZ_1 meet (Fig. 147a).

Assume now that our problem has been solved, i.e., that the required triangle XYZ has been constructed. Note that in that case triangles $X_1Y_1Z_1$ and XYZ are perspective (the points P, Q, R of intersection of corresponding sides of the two triangles are collinear). It follows that lines XX_1, YY_1, ZZ_1 intersect in a point (cf. Problem 22) and that the point of intersection is B. By joining B to X_1 we obtain, at the point of intersection of BX_1 and AC, the vertex X of our triangle. Now the construction of the remaining vertices presents no difficulty.

(b) We prove first that if an n-gon varies so that its sides pass through n fixed points on a certain line l, and $n - 1$ of its vertices slide along $n - 1$ given lines, then the locus described by the n-th vertex is a line. To see this, project our configuration to a new plane π' so that l is the special line of π, and make use of the result established in Problem 10(b), NML 21 (cf., for example, the solution of Problem 17(a)). Now, the required construction can be carried out in a manner analogous to the construction employed in Problem 10(c), NML 21.

(c) Through A pass a line which intersects l_1 and l_2 in points X_1 and Y_1, respectively. Join the point Z_1 of intersection of lines Y_1B and l_3 to X_1. Assume now that the problem is solved, that is, that triangle XYZ has been constructed (Fig. 147b). Since lines XX_1, YY_1, ZZ_1 intersect at O, triangles XYZ and $X_1Y_1Z_1$ are perspective, and the points of intersection of lines X_1Y_1 and XY (i.e., the point A), Y_1Z_1 and YZ (i.e., the point B), and Z_1X_1 and ZX are collinear. We can now easily find the point C' of intersection of lines ZX and Z_1X_1, since it coincides with the point of intersection of lines Z_1X_1 and AB. The side ZX of the required triangle lies on the line joining the point C' to C.

25. This theorem differs only in formulation from the one stated in Problem 28; the points C, B_1 and the point O_2 of intersection of A_1B and AC_1 are the points of intersection of the diagonals of the quadrilaterals $A_1OO_1C_1$, OO_1BA and A_1C_1BA.

26. Use central projection to map the plane π of Fig. 31 to a plane π' so that the special line of π is the line joining O to the point of intersection of AC and A_1C_1. Under this mapping triangles ABC and $A_1B_1C_1$ are carried into triangles $A'B'C'$ and $A_1'B_1'C_1'$ with $A'A_1' \parallel B'B_1' \parallel C'C_1'$ and $A'C' \parallel A_1'C_1'$. Lines $A'A_1'$, $B'C_1'$ and $C'B_1'$ intersect in a point O_1', and lines $A'C_1'$, $B'B_1'$ and $C'A_1'$ intersect in a point O_2' (Fig. 148a). Denote the parallel lines $A'A_1'$, $B'B_1'$ and $C'C_1'$ by l_1', l_2', l_3'. Since $A'C_1'$ and $C'A_1'$ are the diagonals of parallelogram $A'C'C_1'A_1'$, and since $B'B_1'$ passes through the point of intersection of these diagonals, it follows that the line $B'B_1'$ (i.e., l_2') is equidistant from l_1' and l_3'. We are to show that $A'B_1'$, $B'A_1'$ and $C'C_1'$ intersect in a point. It will then follow that AB_1, BA_1 and CC_1 intersect in a point.

We now use a parallel projection to map the plane π' to a plane π'' so that $\triangle A'C'C_1'$ is carried into a right triangle $A''C''C_1''$.† Then Fig. 148a goes over into Fig. 148b with l_2'' the axis of symmetry of the figure. It follows that lines $A''B_1''$ and $B''A_1''$ intersect in the point O_3'' of the line $C''C_1''$ which is symmetric to O_1'' relative to l_2''. Consequently, lines $A'B_1'$, $B'A_1'$ and $C'C_1'$ of Fig. 148a intersect in a point O_3'. (O_3' is that point of π' which is mapped under our parallel projection onto O_3''.)

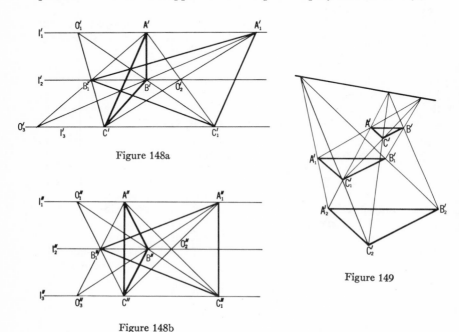

Figure 148a

Figure 149

Figure 148b

27. Project the plane π of the three triangles to a plane π' so that PQR is the special line of π. Under this projection triangles ABC, $A_1B_1C_1$ and $A_2B_2C_2$ go over into pairwise centrally similar triangles $A'B'C'$, $A_1'B_1'C_1'$ and $A_2'B_2'C_2'$ (cf. solution of Problem 22), and the three points of intersection of the lines AA_1, BB_1, CC_1; AA_2, BB_2, CC_2; A_1A_2, B_1B_2, C_1C_2 are carried into the centers of similarity of these triangles. In view of the theorem on three centers of similarity (cf. p. 25, NML 21), these three points are collinear (Fig. 149). Consequently, the preimages of these points under our projection are also collinear.

---

† If we make use of Theorem 1 (p. 45), then we can replace the two projections used in this problem (the central projection followed by the parallel projection) by a single central projection of which we require that it take the quadrilateral ACC_1A_1 into a rectangle (e.g., a square).

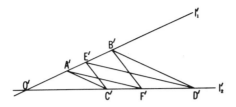

Figure 150

28. Let M, N, P be the points of intersection of the lines AF and ED; EC and BF; AC and BD, in that order; and let O be the point of intersection of AB and CD. We project the plane π of Fig. 33 to a plane π' so that MN is the special line of π. Under this mapping Fig. 33 goes over into Fig. 150, where $A'F' \parallel D'E'$ and $B'F' \parallel C'E'$. Parallelism of the lines $A'F'$ and $D'E'$ implies $O'A'/O'E' = O'F'/O'D'$, and parallelism of the lines $B'F'$ and $C'E'$ implies $O'E'/O'B' = O'C'/O'F'$. Multiplying the two equalities, we get $O'A'/O'B' = O'C'/O'D'$. It follows that lines $A'C'$ and $B'D'$ are parallel, that is, P lies on the special line MN of the plane π. [We leave it to the reader to consider the (simpler) case $l'_1 \parallel l'_2$ (the notation is that of Fig. 150).]

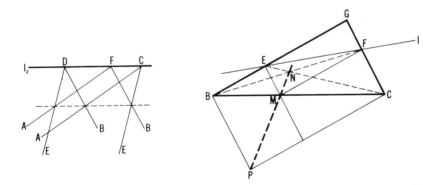

Figure 151a   Figure 151b

29. (i) Let D, F, C be three points on the line l. Pass lines $DB \parallel FB$, $DE \parallel CE$, $FA \parallel CA$ through these points (Fig. 151a. Here A, B and E are points at infinity.) The points of intersection of DE and FA, DB and CA, FB and CE are collinear (why?).

(ii) If line l intersects sides BG and CG of $\triangle BCG$ in E and F (Fig. 151b), then the point N of intersection of the diagonals of quadrilateral $BCEF$ and the vertices P and M of parallelograms $BGCP$ and $EGFM$ are collinear (why?).

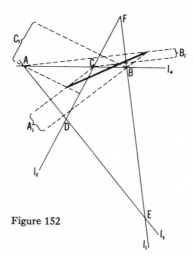

Figure 152

30. Let l_1, l_2, l_3 and l_4 be the four given lines, and let A, B, C, D, E, and F be their points of intersection (cf. Fig. 152).

Consider now 3 of the 4 triangles thus formed, say, the triangles ABE, ACD and BCF. The points of intersection of the altitudes in each of these triangles are the points of intersection of the lines $AB_1 \perp l_1$ and $BA_1 \perp l_3$, $AC_1 \perp l_2$ and $CA_1 \perp l_3$, $BC_1 \perp l_2$ and $CB_1 \perp l_1$. It follows from the result of part (i) of the previous problem that these points are collinear. An analogous statement can be made about any 3 of the 4 triangles. Therefore all 4 points in question are collinear.

31. Since Problem 23 is equivalent to Desargues's Theorem (Problem 22), Problems 31(i) and (ii) are equivalent to certain of the special cases of Desargues's Theorem on p. 30. We leave the required identifications to the reader.

32. (a) Pass through the vertex B of the parallelogram a line $BN' \parallel MD$ (N' is on the diagonal AC, cf. Fig. 153a). Since $NM \parallel N'B$, we have $AN'/AN = AB/AM = n$. Further, the congruence of triangles ADN and CBN' implies that $AN = CN'$. It follows that

$$\frac{AC}{AN} = \frac{AN' + N'C}{AN} = n + 1,$$

which is what we wished to prove.

If Fig. 153a is projected to another plane so that AB is parallel to the special line of the projected plane, then the ratio of segments on the line AB is preserved (cf. p. 36). However, this projection does not preserve the ratio of segments on the diagonal AC. Therefore, in order to obtain a variant of the result just proved, we must reformulate it so as to eliminate the ratio of segments on AC, retaining only the ratio of segments on AB. This is done most simply in the following manner: Pass through point N the line $NM_1 \| DA$ (M_1 is on the side AB). The theorem just proved implies that if $AM = (1/n)AB$, then

$$AM_1 = \frac{1}{n+1} AB.$$

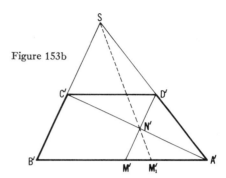

Figure 153b

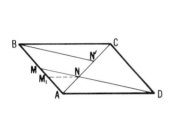

Figure 153a

By now it is clear that our projection leads to the following result: If a point M' divides the base $A'B'$ of a trapezoid $A'B'C'D'$ in the ratio $A'M'/A'B' = 1/n$, then the line SN' which joins the point S of intersection of the (non-parallel) sides of the trapezoid to the point N' of intersection of $D'M'$ with the diagonal $A'C'$ determines a point M_1' on $A'B'$ such that

$$A'M_1' = \frac{1}{n+1} A'B'$$

(Fig. 153b). [Since lines AB and CD are parallel to the special line of the plane, their images under our projection remain parallel. This implies that parallelogram $ABCD$ goes over into a trapezoid $A'B'C'D'$. The parallel lines AD, BC and M_1N go over into lines $A'D'$, $B'C'$ and $M_1'N'$ which intersect in a point S. The ratio of segments on the line AB parallel to the special line of the plane is preserved under a projection.]

(b) Join an arbitrary point S of the plane to the points A and B, and let D and C be the points of intersection of the lines SA and SB with l_1. If N_1 is the point of intersection of DB and AC, then SN_1 intersects AB in a point M_2 such that $AM_2 = \frac{1}{2}AB$ (cf. solution of Problem 2). Further, if DM_2 intersects AC in a point N_2, then SN_2 intersects AB in a point M_3 such that $AM_3 = \frac{1}{3}AB$; if DM_3 intersects AC in a point N_3, then SN_3 intersects AB in a point M_4 such that $AM_4 = \frac{1}{4}AB$, and so on (Fig. 154a, cf. solution of Problem 32(a)).

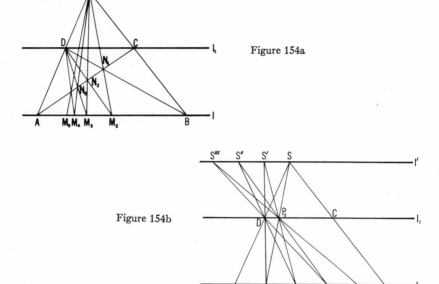

Figure 154a

Figure 154b

[Once the point M_n, with $AM_n = (1/n)AB$, has been determined, it is easy to find the remaining points which divide the segment AB into n equal parts. In fact, draw the line l' through S parallel to l and l_1 (cf. Problem 3(b)). Now, if SM_n intersects DC in a point P_n, M_nD intersects l' in a point S', and $S'P_n$ intersects AB in a point M'_n, then $AM_n = M_nM'_n$ so that $AM'_n = (2/n)AB$, and so on; cf. Fig. 154b, where $n = 5$.]

33. Project the plane π of Fig. 14 to a plane π' so that the line ABE is the special line of the plane π. Then Fig. 14 is carried into Fig. 155. The diagonals CA, DB and FE of the complete quadrilateral go over into the lines $C'A' \parallel F'D'$, $D'B' \parallel F'C'$ and $F'E' \parallel D'C'$. The points of intersection of these lines are denoted by C_1, D_1, F_1 (cf. Fig. 155). Clearly, points C', D' and F' are the midpoints of the sides of triangle $C_1D_1F_1$.

We now determine the images of the midpoints P, Q, R of the diagonals of the complete quadrilateral. The midpoint P of segment CA is the point such that $AP/CP = -1$. If we denote by P_1 the point at infinity of the line CA, then we can write

$$\frac{AP/CP}{AP_1/CP_1} = -1.$$

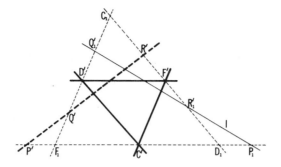

Figure 155

By Property C of a central projection we have

$$\frac{A'P'/C'P'}{A'P_1'/C'P_1'} = -1,$$

where P_1' is the image of the point at infinity P_1, i.e., the point of intersection of $C'A'$ with the special line l of the plane π. We rewrite our equality in the form

$$\frac{C'P_1'/C'P'}{A'P_1'/A'P'} = -1,$$

or, since $A'P_1'/A'P' = 1$ (A' is a point at infinity),

$$\frac{C'P_1'}{C'P'} = -1.$$

It follows that C' is the midpoint of the segment $P'P_1'$, i.e., P' is symmetric to the point P_1' of intersection of the line D_1F_1 with l relative to the midpoint C' of the side D_1F_1 of triangle $C_1D_1F_1$.

Analogously, we can prove that the midpoints Q and R of diagonals DB and FE of the complete quadrilateral are mapped onto points Q' and R' symmetric to the points Q_1' and R_1' of intersection of the special line l with the sides C_1F_1 and C_1D_1 of triangle $C_1D_1F_1$ relative to the midpoints D' and F' of these sides. Thus, the theorem on the complete quadrilateral (stating that the points P, Q and R are collinear) takes the form: *Let P_1', Q_1' and R_1' be the points of intersection of a line l with the sides of a triangle $C_1D_1F_1$. Then the reflections P', Q', R' of P_1', Q_1', R_1' in the midpoints of the corresponding sides of the triangle are collinear.* This theorem is a special case of the theorem of Problem 9(a) (p. 15) and can be used to deduce the theorem on the complete quadrilateral.

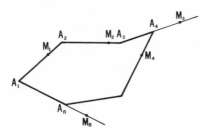

Figure 156

34.. We shall show that the theorems of Menelaus and Ceva are direct consequences of the following theorem, which we prove before solving Problem 34. Let $A_1A_2\cdots A_n$ be an arbitrary polygon, and let M_1, M_2, $\cdots$, M_n be points on the sides of the polygon or on their extensions (Fig. 156). We show that the product

$$(\#)\qquad \frac{A_1M_1}{A_2M_1}\cdot\frac{A_2M_2}{A_3M_2}\cdot\ \cdots\ \cdot\frac{A_nM_n}{A_1M_n}$$

remains unchanged under a central projection. Indeed, if A_1', A_2', $\cdots$, A_n'; M_1', M_2', $\cdots$, M_n' are the images of the points A_1, A_2, $\cdots$, A_n; M_1, M_2, $\cdots$, M_n, under a central projection from a center O, then by formula (*), p. 34,

$$A_1'M_1'/A_2'M_1' = (A_1M_1/A_2M_1)(OA_1'/OA_1)/(OA_2'/OA_2),$$
$$A_2'M_2'/A_3'M_2' = (A_2M_2/A_3M_2)(OA_2'/OA_2)/(OA_3'/OA_3),$$
$$\cdots\cdots\cdots\cdots\cdots\cdots\cdots\cdots\cdots\cdots\cdots\cdots\cdots\cdots\cdots$$
$$A_n'M_n'/A_1'M_n' = (A_nM_n/A_1M_n)(OA_n'/OA_n)/(OA_1'/OA_1).$$

Multiplying these equalities, we get

$$\frac{A_1'M_1'}{A_2'M_1'}\cdot\frac{A_2'M_2'}{A_3'M_2'}\cdot\ \cdots\ \cdot\frac{A_n'M_n'}{A_1'M_n'} = \frac{A_1M_1}{A_2M_1}\cdot\frac{A_2M_2}{A_3M_2}\cdot\ \cdots\ \cdot\frac{A_nM_n}{A_1M_n},$$

which is what we set out to prove.

This theorem can be regarded as a generalization of Property C of a central projection. (It reduces to Property C if the polygon $A_1A_2\cdots A_n$ degenerates into the 2-gon ABA.) We shall now show how the theorems of Menelaus and Ceva follow.

(a) Project the plane π of triangle ABC to a plane π' so that line MN is the special line of π. If points M, N and P lie on a line l, then this line goes over into the line at infinity, and M, N and P go over into the points M', N' and P', which are the points at infinity on $A'B'$, $B'C'$ and $C'A'$. Hence

$$\frac{A'M'}{B'M'} = 1, \quad \frac{B'N'}{C'N'} = 1, \quad \frac{C'P'}{A'P'} = 1 \quad \text{and} \quad \frac{A'M'}{B'M'} \cdot \frac{B'N'}{C'N'} \cdot \frac{C'P'}{A'P'} = 1.$$

But then in view of what was proved above, the value of the product $(AM/BM)(BN/CN)(CP/AP)$ is one.

Conversely, let $(AM/BM)(BN/CN)(CP/AP) = 1$. Since our projection carries M and N into points at infinity M' and N', it follows that $A'M'/B'M' = 1$ and $B'N'/C'N' = 1$. By the result proved above we must have $(A'M'/B'M')(B'N'/C'N')(C'P'/A'P') = 1$, and therefore $C'P'/A'P' = 1$. This means that P' is the point at infinity on the line $A'C'$. But then P must lie on the special line of π. This proves the collinearity of M, N and P.

Remark. Using a similar argument one can prove the following more general theorem: If M_1, M_2, $\cdots$, M_n are the points of intersection of an n-gon $A_1A_2 \cdots A_n$ with a line l, then

$$\frac{A_1M_1}{A_2M_1} \cdot \frac{A_2M_2}{A_3M_2} \cdots \frac{A_nM_n}{A_1M_n} = 1.$$

However, for $n > 3$ this equality does not imply the collinearity of M_1, M_2, $\cdots$, M_n.

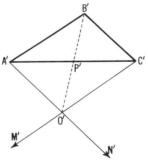

Figure 157

(b) Project the plane π of triangle ABC to a plane π' so that MN is the special line of π. If lines AN, BP and CM intersect in a point O or are parallel, then Fig. 44 in the plane π goes over into Fig. 157, and $A'N' \parallel B'C'$, $C'M' \parallel B'A'$. Hence point P' is the midpoint of $A'C'$ (since it is the point of intersection of the diagonals of the parallelogram $A'B'C'O'$). We thus have $A'M'/B'M' = 1$, $B'N'/C'N' = 1$ (since M' and N' are points at infinity) and $C'P'/A'P' = -1$. It follows that

$$\frac{A'M'}{B'M'} \cdot \frac{B'N'}{C'N'} \cdot \frac{C'P'}{A'P'} = -1,$$

and so, by the result proved above,

$$\frac{AM}{BM}\cdot\frac{BN}{CN}\cdot\frac{CP}{AP} = -1.$$

Conversely, assume that this last equality holds. Since under our projection the points M and N are carried into points at infinity, we have $A'M'/B'M' = 1$ and $B'N'/C'N' = 1$. It follows that $C'P'/A'P' = -1$, that is, point P' is the midpoint of $A'C'$. But then lines $A'N' \parallel B'C'$, $C'M' \parallel B'A'$ and $B'P'$ intersect in a point O' (cf. Fig. 157). Hence lines AN, CM and BP are either concurrent or parallel.

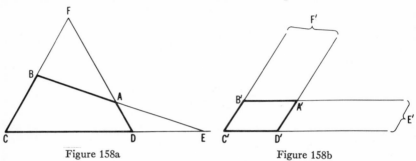

Figure 158a   Figure 158b

35. We must show (cf. Fig. 158) that

$$\frac{AE}{BE}\cdot\frac{BF}{CF}\cdot\frac{CE}{DE}\cdot\frac{DF}{AF} = 1.$$

Note that the expression on the left may be viewed as a special case of the expression ($\#$) on p. 000, where quadrilateral $ABCD$ plays the role of the n-gon $A_1A_2\cdots A_n$ and points E, F, E, F (in that order) play the role of points M_1, M_2, $\cdots$, M_n in Fig. 156. It follows that the expression $(AE/BE)(BF/CF)(CE/DE)(DF/AF)$ is invariant under central projection. Note that a projection of the plane π of Fig. 158a for which EF is the special line carries Fig. 158a into Fig. 158b. Since E', F' are points at infinity we have

$$\frac{A'E'}{B'E'} = \frac{B'F'}{C'F'} = \frac{C'E'}{D'E'} = \frac{D'F'}{A'F'} = 1.$$

Hence

$$\frac{A'E'}{B'E'}\cdot\frac{B'F'}{C'F'}\cdot\frac{C'E'}{D'E'}\cdot\frac{D'F'}{A'F'} = 1 \quad \left(= \frac{AE}{BE}\cdot\frac{BF}{CF}\cdot\frac{CE}{DE}\cdot\frac{DF}{AF} \right).$$

This proves the theorem.

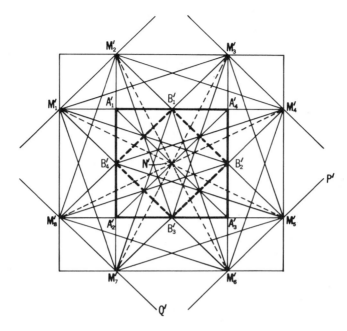

Figure 159

36. Project quadrilateral $A_1A_2A_3A_4$ to a square $A_1'A_2'A_3'A_4'$ (cf. Theorem 1, p. 45). Under such a projection points P and Q are carried into points at infinity corresponding to the directions of the sides of the square; lines PN and QN are carried into the midlines of the square; points B_1, B_2, B_3, and B_4 are carried into the midpoints B_1', B_2', B_3', B_4' of the sides of the square; points M_1, M_2, $\cdots$, M_8 are carried into the points M_1', M_2', $\cdots$, M_8' (Fig. 159). The assertions of our theorem follow from the following rather obvious observations:

(a) Points M_1' and M_5', M_2' and M_6', M_3' and M_7', M_4' and M_8' are symmetric with respect to the center N' of the square. Consequently the lines $M_1'M_5'$, $M_2'M_6'$, $M_3'M_7'$, $M_4'M_8'$ intersect at N'.

(b) Lines $M_2'M_3'$ and $M_6'M_7'$ are parallel to $A_2'A_3'$; lines $M_1'M_8'$ and $M_4'M_5'$ are parallel to $A_1'A_2'$.

(c) Lines $M_1'M_2'$, $M_3'M_8'$, $M_4'M_7'$, and $M_5'M_6'$ are parallel to the diagonal $A_2'A_4'$ of the square, and lines $M_3'M_4'$, $M_2'M_5'$, $M_1'M_6'$ and $M_7'M_8'$ are parallel to the diagonal $A_1'A_3'$ of the square.

(d) $M_1'M_3' \parallel M_5'M_7' \parallel B_4'M_4' \parallel B_2'M_8';$ $M_2'M_4' \parallel M_6'M_8' \parallel B_4'M_5' \parallel B_2'M_1';$

$M_3'M_5' \parallel M_1'M_7' \parallel B_1'M_6' \parallel B_3'M_2';$ $M_4'M_6' \parallel M_2'M_8' \parallel B_1'M_7' \parallel B_3'M_3'.$

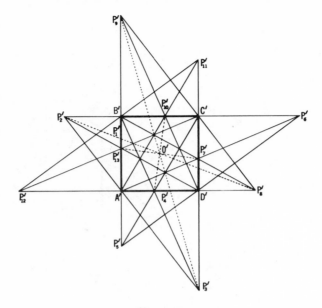

Figure 160

37. Project quadrilateral $ABCD$ to a square $A'B'C'D'$, and let the points P_1, P_2, P_3, $\cdots$ go over into points P_1', P_2', P_3', $\cdots$ (Fig. 160). The positions of these points on the sides of the square yield ratios which we denote by

$$\lambda_1 = \frac{A'P_1'}{B'P_1'}, \qquad \lambda_2 = \frac{B'P_2'}{C'P_2'}, \qquad \lambda_3 = \frac{C'P_3'}{D'P_3'}, \qquad \text{etc.;}$$

we note that they can be negative or positive. From the similarity of triangles $A'D'P_1'$ and $B'P_2'P_1'$ (Fig. 160) it follows that

$$\frac{D'A'}{B'P_2'} = -\frac{A'P_1'}{B'P_1'},$$

and so

$$\frac{C'P_2'}{B'P_2'} = \frac{C'B' + B'P_2'}{B'P_2'} = \frac{C'B'}{B'P_2'} + 1 = \frac{D'A'}{B'P_2'} + 1 = -\frac{A'P_1'}{B'P_1'} + 1.$$

Thus

$$\frac{1}{\lambda_2} = -\lambda_1 + 1,$$

or

(*)
$$\lambda_2 = \frac{1}{1 - \lambda_1}.$$

It is easy to check that formula (*) remains correct if the point P'_1 lies on the extension of the side $A'B'$ beyond the point A' or B'.

Using formula (*) we find:

$$\lambda_2 = \frac{1}{1 - \lambda_1}, \qquad \lambda_3 = \frac{1}{1 - \lambda_2} = 1 - \frac{1}{\lambda_1}, \qquad \lambda_4 = \frac{1}{1 - \lambda_3} = \lambda_1,$$

$$\lambda_5 = \frac{1}{1 - \lambda_4} = \lambda_2, \qquad \lambda_6 = \frac{1}{1 - \lambda_5} = \lambda_3, \qquad \text{etc.,}$$

i.e.,

$$\lambda_1 = \lambda_4 = \lambda_7 = \lambda_{10} = \lambda_{13} = \lambda_{16} = \cdots,$$

$$\lambda_2 = \lambda_5 = \lambda_8 = \lambda_{11} = \lambda_{14} = \lambda_{17} = \cdots = \frac{1}{1 - \lambda_1},$$

$$\lambda_3 = \lambda_6 = \lambda_9 = \lambda_{12} = \lambda_{15} = \lambda_{18} = \cdots = 1 - \frac{1}{\lambda_1}.$$

Now the statements of our theorem follow readily.

(a) $\lambda_1 = \lambda_{13}$ implies that the point P'_{13} coincides with the point P'_1. It follows from the one-to-one nature of a central projection that P_{13} coincides with P_1.

(b) $\lambda_1 = \lambda_7$, $\lambda_2 = \lambda_8$, $\lambda_3 = \lambda_9$, etc., imply that the points P'_1 and P'_7, P'_2 and P'_8, P'_3 and P'_9 are symmetric relative to the center O' of the square, i.e., the lines $P'_1P'_7$, $P'_2P'_8$, $P'_3P'_9$, etc., intersect at O'. Consequently, in view of the properties of a central projection, the lines P_1P_7, P_2P_8, P_3P_9, etc., pass through the point of intersection of the diagonals of the quadrilateral $ABCD$.

(c) The lines $P'_1P'_2$ and $P'_7P'_8$, $P'_2P'_3$ and $P'_8P'_9$, $P'_3P'_4$ and $P'_9P'_{10}$, etc. are symmetric with respect to the center O' of the square (cf. (b) above) and, therefore, parallel. In view of the properties of a central projection, it follows that the lines P_1P_2 and P_7P_8, P_2P_3 and P_8P_9, P_3P_4 and P_9P_{10} intersect in pairs on the line joining the points S and S_1 of intersection of the opposite sides of quadrilateral $ABCD$ (under our projection the line SS_1 is carried into the line at infinity).

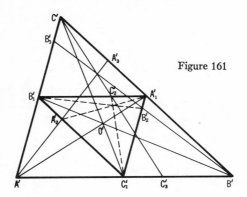

Figure 161

38. Use a central projection to map quadrilateral $ABCO$ to a quadrilateral $A'B'C'O'$ so that O' is the point of intersection of the medians of triangle $A'B'C'$. That this can be done follows from Theorem 1 (p. 45). Under our projection the sides of $\triangle A_1'B_1'C_1'$ are parallel to the sides of $\triangle A'B'C'$ (Fig. 161). Denoting by A_3', B_3', C_3' the points of intersection of lines $A'A_2'$, $B'B_2'$ and $C'C_2'$ with the opposite sides of $\triangle A'B'C'$, we conclude that

$$\frac{A'C_3'}{B'C_3'} = \frac{B_1'C_2'}{A_1'C_2'}, \qquad \frac{B'A_3'}{C'A_3'} = \frac{C_1'A_2'}{B_1'A_2'}, \qquad \frac{C'B_3'}{A'B_3'} = \frac{A_1'B_2'}{C_1'B_2'}.$$

Assume now

$$\frac{A_1'C_2'}{B_1'C_2'} \cdot \frac{B_1'A_2'}{C_1'A_2'} \cdot \frac{C_1'B_2'}{A_1'B_2'} = \pm 1.$$

(In view of the theorems of Ceva and Menelaus, (cf. Problem 34) this assumption means that lines $A_1'A_2'$, $B_1'B_2'$, $C_1'C_2'$ are concurrent or that points A_2', B_2', C_2' are collinear.) It then follows that

$$\frac{A'C_3'}{B'C_3'} \cdot \frac{B'A_3'}{C'A_3'} \cdot \frac{C'B_3'}{A'B_3'} = \pm 1.$$

But, according to the same theorems, this means that lines $A'A_3'$, $B'B_3'$ and $C'C_3'$ are concurrent, or that points A_3', B_3' and C_3' are collinear, according as our product has the value -1 or $+1$.

§3

39. (a) *First Solution* (based on Theorem 1). Let D, E and F be the points of tangency of the inscribed circle S with the triangle ABC (Fig. 162a). The point O of intersection of BE and CF lies inside the circle S. (The line BG, where G is the second point of intersection of

CF with the circle S, intersects the segment EC of line AC. Hence BE intersects the chord FG of S.)

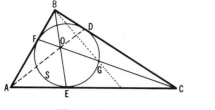

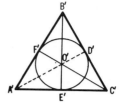

Figure 162a   Figure 162b

Now project our diagram to a plane π' so that S is carried into a circle S' and the point O into the center O' of S'. Under this projection Fig. 162a is carried into Fig. 162b. It is easy to see that lines $B'E'$ and $C'F'$ are angle bisectors as well as altitudes of $\triangle A'B'C'$. It follows that $A'B' = B'C'$ and $C'A' = B'C'$. Hence $A'B'C'$ is an equilateral triangle and so line $A'D'$ passes through O'. The concurrence of $A'D'$, $B'E'$ and $C'F'$ implies the concurrence of AD, BE and CF.

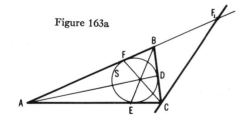

Figure 163a

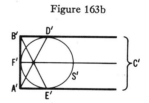

Figure 163b

Second Solution (based on Theorem 1'; the notation is the same as in the previous solution). Find a point F_1 on the extension of AB such that $F_1A/F_1B = -FA/FB$ (Fig. 163a). Line CF_1 lies outside triangle ABC and therefore outside S. We project our diagram to a plane π' so that S is carried into a circle S' and the line CF_1 into the line at infinity of the plane π'. Then Fig. 163a is carried into Fig. 163b, where $A'E' \parallel B'D' \parallel F'C'$. Note that F' is the midpoint of segment $A'B'$. [This is so because, in view of Property C of a central projection,

$$\frac{F_1'A'/F_1'B'}{F'A'/F'B'} = -1, \qquad \frac{F'A'}{B'F'} = \frac{F_1'A'}{F_1'B'};$$

here F_1' is the point at infinity on line $A'B'$ so that $F_1'A'/F_1'B' = 1 = F'A'/B'F'$.] Since $|A'F'| = |B'F'|$, it follows that $F'C'$ is an axis of symmetry of the resulting figure, and, obviously, the point of intersection of the lines $A'D'$ and $B'E'$ lies on $F'C'$. Since $A'D'$, $B'E'$ and $C'F'$ are concurrent, the same is true of AD, BE and CF.

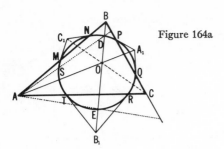

Figure 164a

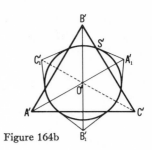

Figure 164b

(b) Observe that the point O of intersection of the lines AA_1 and BB_1 lies inside the circle S. Indeed, AA_1 and BB_1 intersect the chords PQ and TR of S (Fig. 164a). Since lines AD and AE, where D and E are the points of intersection of BB_1 with S, intersect BC outside the segment PQ and on different sides of the segment, it follows that AA_1 intersects chord DE.

Now project Fig. 164a to a plane π' so that S is carried into a circle S' and the point O into the center O' of S'. Figure 164a is then carried into Fig. 164b. Since $A'A_1'$ and $B'B_1'$ pass through the point O', it follows that $A'A_1' \perp B'C'$ and $B'B_1' \perp A'C'$. Hence $A'A_1'$ and $B'B_1'$ are two altitudes of $\triangle A'B'C'$, and O' is their point of intersection. It follows that line $O'C'$ is the third altitude of $\triangle A'B'C'$. Clearly, the perpendicular from the center O' of S' to the side $A'B'$ of $\triangle A'B'C'$ must pass through C_1'. Hence the lines $A'A_1'$, $B'B_1'$ and $C'C_1'$ meet at O'. It follows that AA_1, BB_1 and CC_1 meet at O.

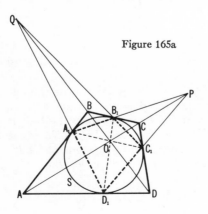

Figure 165a

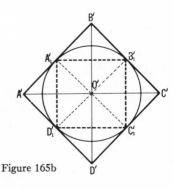

Figure 165b

40. Project Fig. 165a to a plane π' so that S is carried into a circle S', and the point O of intersection of the diagonals of quadrilateral $A_1B_1C_1D_1$ is carried into the center O' of S'. Then Fig. 165a is carried into Fig. 165b, where $A'B' \parallel C'D' \perp A_1'C_1'$ and $B'C' \parallel A'D' \perp B_1'D_1'$.

Consequently, $A'B'C'D'$ is a parallelogram, and since it is circumscribed about a circle it must be a *rhombus*.

(a) It is well known that the point of intersection of the diagonals of a rhombus $A'B'C'D'$ coincides with the center of its inscribed circle. Hence the points of intersection of the diagonals of quadrilaterals $A'B'C'D'$ and $A_1'B_1'C_1'D_1'$ coincide, and the same is true of the points of intersection of the diagonals of quadrilaterals $ABCD$ and $A_1B_1C_1D_1$.

(b) From symmetry considerations it is clear that $A_1'B_1' \parallel D_1'C_1' \parallel A'C'$ and $B_1'C_1' \parallel A_1'D_1' \parallel B'D'$. Hence AC must pass through P, and BD must pass through Q.

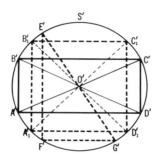

Figure 166

41. Project the diagram of our problem to a new plane π' so that the circle S is taken into a circle S' and the point O into the center O' of S'. Under this projection quadrilateral $ABCD$ is carried into a *rectangle* $A'B'C'D'$ (because the diagonals of $A'B'C'D'$ intersect in the center of the circumscribed circle S'). Hence points P and Q are carried into points at infinity P' and Q' corresponding to the directions of the sides of the rectangle (Fig. 166).

(a) If sides $E'F'$ and $F'G'$ of $\triangle E'F'G'$ inscribed in S' pass through the points at infinity P' and Q', respectively, i.e., if $E'F' \parallel A'B'$ and $F'G' \parallel B'C'$, then side $E'G'$ passes through the center O' of S' (side $E'G'$ lies opposite the right angle $E'F'G'$ inscribed in S'). If side $E'G'$ passes through the center O' and $E'F'$ passes through the point P', that is, if $E'F' \parallel A'B'$, then $F'G' \parallel B'C'$, that is, $F'G'$ passes through the point Q' (since an inscribed angle subtended by a diameter is a right angle). The assertion of part (a) of Problem 41 follows.

(b) If the sides $A_1'B_1'$ and $D_1'C_1'$ of a rectangle $A_1'B_1'C_1'D_1'$ inscribed in circle S' pass through the point P' and side $B_1'C_1'$ passes through Q' (that is, $A_1'B_1' \parallel D_1'C_1' \parallel A'B'$ and $B_1'C_1' \parallel B'C'$), then $A_1'D_1' \parallel B'C' \parallel A'D'$, and diagonals $A_1'C_1'$ and $B_1'D_1'$ meet in the center O' of S'. The assertion of part (b) follows.

(c) If diagonals $A_1'C_1'$ and $B_1'D_1'$ of the inscribed quadrilateral $A_1'B_1'C_1'D_1'$ meet in the center O' of circle S', and if side $A_1'B_1'$ passes through the point P' (i.e., $A_1'B_1' \| A'B'$), then $D_1'C_1' \| A'B'$ and $B_1'C_1' \| A_1'D_1' \| B'C'$. The assertion of part (c) follows.

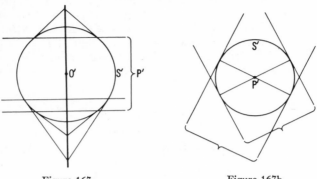

Figure 167a   Figure 167b

42. We consider two cases.

1. *P is an exterior point of S.* Project the diagram of our problem to a plane π' so that circle S goes over into a circle S', and P goes over into a point at infinity P' of π'. Under this projection the required locus goes over into a line; namely, the diameter of S' perpendicular to the direction defined by the point at infinity P' (Fig. 167a). It follows that the required locus is a line.†

2. *P is an interior point of S.* Project the diagram of our problem to a plane π' so that circle S goes over into a circle S', and P goes over into the center P' of S'. Clearly, the required locus is then carried into the line at infinity of π' (Fig. 167b). It follows that the required locus is a line.

Note that if P is a point of S, then the required locus is the tangent to S at P.‡

43. (a) We consider two cases.

1. *P is an exterior point of S* (cf. Fig. 58a). Project the diagram of our problem to a plane π' so that S goes over into a circle S' and P into a point at infinity P' of π'. Then the lines AB and MN go into parallel lines $A'B'$ and $M'N'$ (Fig. 168a). From symmetry considerations it follows that points K' and X' (Fig. 168a) lie on the diameter

† More precisely, the part of a line outside S.

‡ The locus under consideration coincides with the polar of P relative to S (cf. §4, p. 68).

of S' perpendicular to line l', the image of l. Hence the locus of X' is the line through K' perpendicular to l'. Consequently, the locus of X is a line through K.

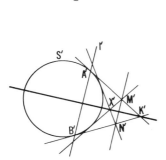

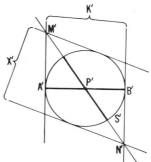

Figure 168a   Figure 168b

2. *P is an interior point of* S. Project the diagram to a plane π' so that S goes into a circle S', and P goes into the center P' of S' (Fig. 168b). Then lines $A'B'$ and $M'N'$ are diameters of S'. Hence the tangents $A'K'$ and $B'K'$ to S' at A' and B' are parallel. Therefore the second tangents to S' from M' and N' are also parallel. We see that in this case the locus of X' is the line at infinity of π'. The point K' is also on that line. Thus the locus of X is a line through K.

It is clear that the conditions of our problem exclude the case when P is on S. (If P coincides with A then M also coincides with A, and there is only a single tangent to S passing through M, namely, the line AK.)

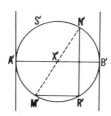

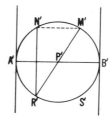

Figure 169a   Figure 169b

(b) If P is on S, the assertion of the problem is clearly true. (Indeed, if P coincides with A, then N also coincides with A, and the fixed point X coincides with A.) We therefore have to consider the following two cases.

1. *P is an exterior point of* S. Project the diagram of our problem to a plane π' so that S goes over into a circle S', and PK goes over into the line at infinity of π' (Fig. 169a). Then AB is carried into a diameter $A'B'$ of S', and lines AK and BK are carried into tangents to the

circle at points A' and B'. It is easy to see that $R'M'$ and $R'N'$ are perpendicular and that, therefore, $M'N'$ is a diameter of S'. Hence, for every choice of the point R', line $M'N'$ passes through the center X' of S'. Our assertion follows.

2. *P is an interior point of S* (cf. Fig. 58b). Project the diagram of our problem to a plane π' so that the circle S is carried into a circle S', and P is carried into the center P' of S' (Fig. 169b). Then AB goes over into a diameter $A'B'$ of S' and K goes over into the point at infinity K' of the diameter perpendicular to $A'B'$. Since $R'N' \perp A'B'$ and $M'N' \perp R'N'$, it follows that $M'N' \parallel A'B'$; that is, for every choice of the point R', lines $M'N'$ and $A'B'$ meet in the point at infinity X' of $A'B'$. The assertion follows.

Figure 170a   Figure 170b

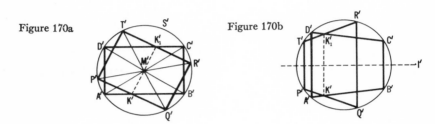

44. (a) Assume that the required quadrilateral $ABCD$ has been constructed. Let M be the given point of intersection of its diagonals, and let AB and CD pass through the given points K and L. Project the diagram of the problem to a plane π' so that the circumscribed circle S goes over into a circle S', and point M goes over into the center M' of S'. Then $ABCD$ goes over into a *rectangle* $A'B'C'D'$.

Now, if $P'Q'R'T'$ is a quadrilateral inscribed in S' whose diagonals meet at the center M' (which implies that $P'Q'R'T'$ is a rectangle) and whose side $P'Q'$ passes through K' then side $R'T'$ must pass through the point K_1' symmetric to K' with respect to M' (Fig. 170a). Thus the sides $R'T'$ of all quadrilaterals inscribed in S' whose diagonals meet at M' and whose sides $P'Q'$ pass through K' pass through the fixed point K_1'. It follows that the sides RT of all quadrilaterals $PQRT$ inscribed in S whose diagonals meet in a point M and whose sides PQ pass through K pass through a fixed point K_1. In order to determine K_1 it suffices to construct two such quadrilaterals. The side CD of the required quadrilateral $ABCD$ is obtained by joining K_1 to L.

If K_1 is different from L and K_1L intersects S, our problem has a unique solution. If K_1L does not intersect S, the problem has no solution. If K_1 coincides with L, our problem has infinitely many solutions.

(b) Let $ABCD$ be the required quadrilateral inscribed in the circle S whose sides BC and DA intersect in a given point M and whose sides AB and CD pass, respectively, through the given points K and L.

Project the plane of the diagram to a plane π' so that S goes into a circle S', and M goes into a point at infinity M' of π'. Then quadrilateral $ABCD$ goes over into a *trapezoid* $A'B'C'D'$ with bases $B'C'$ and $D'A'$ (cf. Fig. 170b). Since the trapezoid is inscribed in a circle its legs are equal.

A quadrilateral $P'Q'R'T'$ inscribed in the circle S' whose sides $Q'R'$ and $T'P'$ meet in the point at infinity M' is an isosceles trapezoid whose axis of symmetry is the diameter l' of S' perpendicular to the direction determined by M'. Hence, if side $P'Q'$ of the quadrilateral passes through some point K', then side $R'T'$ passes through the point K_1' symmetric to K' with respect to l'. It follows that the sides RT of all inscribed quadrilaterals $PQRT$, whose sides QR and PT meet at M and whose sides PQ pass through K, pass through a fixed point K_1. In order to find K_1 it suffices to construct two such quadrilaterals. By joining K_1 to L we find side CD of the required quadrilateral.

If K_1 is different from L our problem has either a unique solution or no solution (depending on whether the line K_1L intersects the circle or not). If K_1 and L coincide then our problem has infinitely many solutions.

45. If O is on S then the problem is meaningless. It remains to consider the following two cases.

1. *O is an exterior point of S.* Project the plane of the diagram onto a plane π' so that the circle S goes over into a circle S', and O goes into a point at infinity O' of π'. Under this projection Fig. 59 is carried into Fig. 171a, where $A'A_1' \parallel B'B_1' \parallel C'C_1'$.

We show that $P'Q' \parallel A'A_1'$. Trapezoid $A'B'B_1'A_1'$ inscribed in S' is isosceles with $A'B' = A_1'B_1'$. Hence arc $A'B'$ = arc $A_1'B_1'$ and $\sphericalangle A'C'B' = \sphericalangle A_1'X'B_1'$. But this implies that the points X', C', P' and Q' lie on a circle. Therefore, $\sphericalangle X'P'Q' = \sphericalangle X'C'Q' = \sphericalangle X'C'A'$. But $\sphericalangle X'C'A' = \sphericalangle X'A_1'A'$, so $\sphericalangle X'P'Q' = \sphericalangle X'A_1'A'$ and, consequently, $P'Q' \parallel A'A_1'$.

In an analogous manner we prove that $Q'R' \parallel B'B_1'$. We thus have $P'Q' \parallel Q'R' \parallel A'A_1'$, which means that P', Q' and R' lie on a line through the point at infinity O'. It follows that points P, Q and R of Fig. 59 lie on a line through O.

2. *O is an interior point of S.* Project Fig. 59 to a plane π' so that S goes over into a circle S' and O goes into the center O' of S' (Fig. 171b). We prove that $P'Q'$ passes through O'. To this end we establish first that

(*)
$$\frac{S_{P'O'A_1'}}{S_{P'O'B'}} = \frac{S_{Q'O'A'}}{S_{Q'O'B_1'}},$$

where S_{XYZ} denotes the area of $\triangle XYZ$.

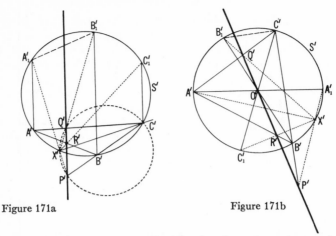

Figure 171a
Figure 171b

Indeed, let XY be a line and denote by h_{XY} the segment of the perpendicular from O' to XY or the length of this segment (the intended meaning will be clear from the context). Then

$$(**) \qquad \frac{S_{P'O'A_1'}}{S_{P'O'B'}} = \frac{P'A_1' \cdot h_{X'A_1'}}{P'B' \cdot h_{B'C'}}, \qquad \frac{S_{Q'O'A'}}{S_{Q'O'B_1'}} = \frac{Q'A' \cdot h_{C'A'}}{Q'B_1' \cdot h_{X'B_1'}}.$$

Note that $h_{X'A_1'}$ is a midline of $\triangle X'A_1'A'$, hence $h_{X'A_1'} = \frac{1}{2}X'A'$. Similarly, $h_{B'C'} = \frac{1}{2}B_1'C'$. Further, it follows from the similarity of triangles $A'Q'X'$ and $B_1'Q'C'$ that

$$\frac{A'X'}{B_1'C'} = \frac{Q'A'}{Q'B_1'}, \quad \text{and so} \quad \frac{h_{X'A_1'}}{h_{B'C'}} = \frac{X'A'}{B_1'C'} = \frac{Q'A'}{Q'B_1'}.$$

Also, by an analogous argument we obtain

$$\frac{h_{C'A'}}{h_{X'B_1'}} = \frac{P'A_1'}{P'B'}.$$

Substituting these relations in the equalities (**) we get the relation (*).

Now, denote by Q_1' the point of intersection of line $P'O'$ with side $A'C'$ of $\triangle A'B'C'$. Also, let h_1, h_2, h_3 and h_4 be the lengths of the perpendiculars from the points A_1', B', A' and B_1' to the line $P'O'Q_1'$. Since $O'A' = O'A_1'$, it follows that $h_1 = h_3$ and, similarly, $h_2 = h_4$. Hence

$$\frac{S_{P'O'A_1'}}{S_{Q_1'O'A'}} = \frac{P'O'}{Q_1'O'}, \qquad \frac{S_{P'O'B'}}{S_{Q_1'O'B_1'}} = \frac{P'O'}{Q_1'O'},$$

and therefore

$$\frac{S_{P'O'A_1'}}{S_{Q_1'O'A'}} = \frac{S_{P'O'B'}}{S_{Q_1'O'B_1'}},$$

or

(***)
$$\frac{S_{P'O'A_1'}}{S_{P'O'B'}} = \frac{S_{Q_1'O'A'}}{S_{Q_1'O'B_1'}}.$$

Comparing equalities (***) and (*) we get

$$\frac{S_{Q_1'O'A'}}{S_{Q_1'O'B_1'}} = \frac{S_{Q'O'A'}}{S_{Q'O'B_1'}}.$$

It follows that points Q_1' and Q' coincide.

A similar argument shows that R' lies on line $O'P'$. Thus, P', Q' and R' lie on a line through O'. The assertion of the problem follows.

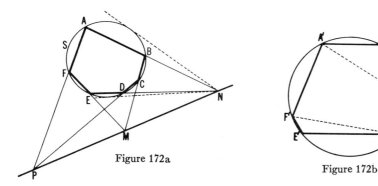

Figure 172a

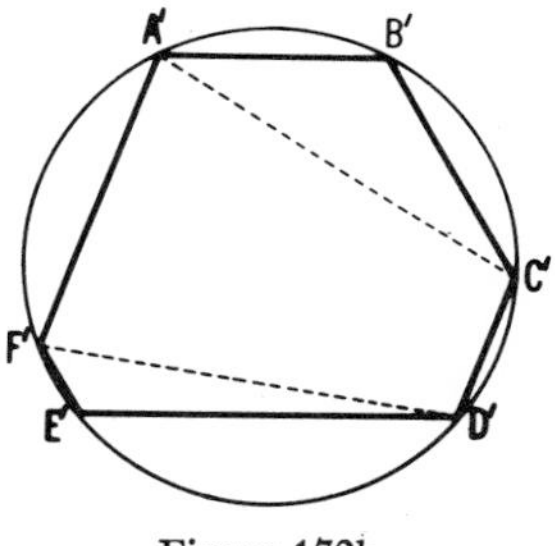

Figure 172b

46. Let M, N and P be the points of intersection of the opposite sides of the inscribed hexagon $ABCDEF$ (see Fig. 60 and Fig. 172a). Since the tangents to S from N touch S in points of the arcs AB and DE, it follows that NM does not intersect S. Hence we can project Fig. 172a to a plane π' so that S goes over into a circle S'; and NM goes into the line at infinity of π'. Figure 172a is then carried into Fig. 172b where $A'B' \parallel E'D'$ and $B'C' \parallel E'F'$. Consequently,

$$\angle A'B'C' = \angle D'E'F', \quad \text{i.e.,} \quad \text{arc } A'B'C' = \text{arc } D'E'F'.$$

It follows that

$$\angle F'A'C' + \angle D'C'A'$$
$$= \tfrac{1}{2}(\text{arc } C'D' + \text{arc } D'E'F') + \tfrac{1}{2}(\text{arc } F'A' + \text{arc } D'E'F')$$
$$= \tfrac{1}{2}(\text{arc } C'D' + \text{arc } D'E'F' + \text{arc } F'A' + \text{arc } A'B'C') = 180°.$$

Hence $A'F' \parallel C'D'$, that is, lines $A'F'$ and $D'C'$ intersect in a point at infinity. Thus, the points P', M' and N' of intersection of the opposite sides of hexagon $A'B'C'D'E'F'$ are collinear—they lie on the line at infinity of the plane π'. Consequently, points P, M and N in Fig. 172a are also collinear.

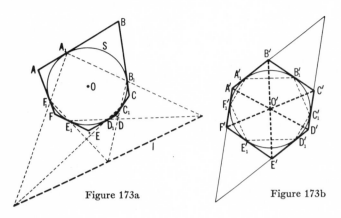

Figure 173a   Figure 173b

47. The hexagon $A_1B_1C_1D_1E_1F_1$ of Fig. 173a is inscribed in the circle S and so satisfies the requirements of Pascal's Theorem (Problem 46). We project Fig. 173a to a plane π' so that S goes into a circle S', and the line l containing the points of intersection of the opposite sides of the hexagon $A_1B_1C_1D_1E_1F_1$ goes into the line at infinity of π'. Under this projection $A_1B_1C_1D_1E_1F_1$ is carried into a hexagon $A_1'B_1'C_1'D_1'E_1'F_1'$ whose opposite sides are parallel (Fig. 173b). Consider now the tangents $A'B'$, $A'F'$, $D'C'$, $D'E'$ to S'. Since $A_1'F_1' \parallel C_1'D_1'$, it follows that the quadrilateral determined by these tangents has $A'D'$ as an axis of symmetry. This axis passes through the center O' of S' and is perpendicular to $A_1'F_1'$ and $C_1'D_1'$. In an entirely analogous manner we can prove that lines $B'E'$ and $C'F'$ pass through O'. It follows that lines AD, BE and CF are concurrent.

48. Consider the pentagon $ABCDE$ inscribed in the given circle S (B, C, D and E are arbitrary points of the circle). It follows from Pascal's Theorem that the point K of intersection of the tangent to S at A with the side CD lies on the line determined by the points L and M of intersection of lines AB and DE, AE and BC, respectively (cf. Figs. 174 and 62a). Hence K can be constructed by straightedge alone (since it is the point of intersection of CD and LM). The line joining A to K is the required tangent.

Remark. Note that in this construction one can confine oneself to an arbitrarily small arc of the circle containing A (the points C, D, E and F can be chosen on that arc). This fact will be of use to us in the sequel.

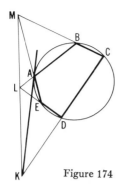

Figure 174

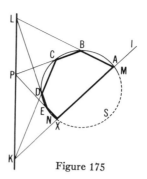

Figure 175

49. Consider the hexagon $ABCDEX$ inscribed in the circle S, where A and X are the points of intersection of line l with S, and B, C, D and E are arbitrary points of the arc MN (Fig. 175). In view of Pascal's Theorem (cf. Problem 46), the points K, L and P of intersection of lines AX (i.e., line l) and CD, AB and DE, BC and EX are collinear. Hence, using straightedge alone, we can first find P (as the point of intersection of BC and KL and then X (as the point of intersection of PE and l).

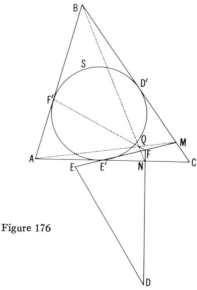

Figure 176

50. Consider the (degenerate) hexagon $AF'BMFN$ (Fig. 65). In view of Brianchon's Theorem it follows that line FF' passes through the point of intersection of lines AM and BN, i.e. through Q (Fig. 176). By considering the appropriate hexagons we show analogously that lines DD' and EE' also pass through Q.

§4

51. If A lies *outside* the circle S $(d > 1)$, and AC, AD are the tangents from A to S, then the polar a of A coincides with CD, and $a \perp OA$ (cf. p. 69). Let P be the point of intersection of CD and OA (Fig. 177a). Since triangles OCA and OPC are similar, $OA/OC = OC/OP$, or $OP = OC^2/OA = 1/d$, which is what we wanted to prove.

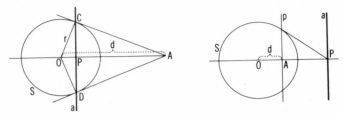

Figure 177a   Figure 177b

If A is *on* S $(d = 1)$, then our theorem is obvious. If A is *inside* S $(d < 1)$, p is a line through A perpendicular to OA, and P is the pole of p, then P lies on the line OA outside S (Fig. 177b). As above we deduce that $OA = 1/OP$, or $OP = 1/OA = 1/d$. The polar a of A is the perpendicular through P to OA (cf. Theorem 2, p. 69). Hence OP is the distance from O to a; but this distance is just $1/d$.

Note. In the same way, we can show that, if the radius of S is r, then the distance from the polar a of A to O is r^2/d.

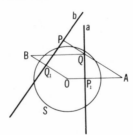

Figure 178

52. Let P_1 be the point of intersection of OA and a, and let Q_1 be the point of intersection of OB and b (Fig. 178). Consider the right trapezoids $OAPQ_1$ and $OBQP_1$ with $\angle AOQ_1 = \angle BOP_1$. By Problem 51, $OA \cdot OP_1 = OB \cdot OQ_1 = r^2$ (r is the radius of S), so that $OA/OB = OQ_1/OP_1$. It follows that the trapezoids are similar. ($OAPQ_1$ is obtained from $OBQP_1$ by means of a dilation with coefficient $k = OA/OB = OQ_1/OP_1$ and center O, followed by a reflection in the bisector of the angle AOB.) Hence $OA/AP = OB/BQ$ (OA and OB, AP and BQ are pairs of corresponding sides of the trapezoids), which is what we set out to prove.

53. (a) Let P and Q be the points of intersection of the opposite sides of the quadrilateral inscribed in S, and let R be the point of intersection of its diagonals. It follows from Theorem 1 that R is the pole of PQ (cf. Fig. 73a). This implies our theorem (cf. p. 71).

(b) Let A_1, B_1, C_1, D_1 be the points of tangency of the sides of the quadrilateral $ABCD$ circumscribed about S (Fig. 57). Then points of intersection of the diagonals of quadrilaterals $ABCD$ and $A_1B_1C_1D_1$ coincide (cf. Problem 40(a), §3). Also, the lines joining the points of intersection of the opposite sides of the quadrilaterals coincide (the method of proof is analogous to that used in Problem 40(a)). Now our result follows from part (a).

54. The points of tangency of the two tangents from A to the circle S coincide with the points of intersection of S with the polar a of A (cf. p. 69). Now a can be easily constructed using straightedge alone (cf. Fig. 66b). To construct the tangents, join A to the points of intersection of a with S.

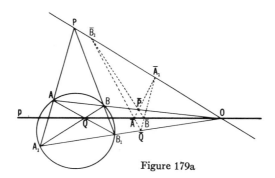

Figure 179a

55. Let ABB_1A_1 be a quadrilateral inscribed in a circle S. Let sides AA_1 and BB_1 intersect in P, sides AB and A_1B_1 in O, and diagonals AB_1 and BA_1 in Q. Then the polar p of P is the line OQ (Fig. 179a). It follows that p is the polar of P with respect to the pair of lines AB and A_1B_1 (cf. Problem 17(a), §2). Hence p is the polar of any point of the line OP with respect to the lines AB and A_1B_1 (cf. Problem 17(a)). It is easy to prove that A_1B_1 *is the polar of any point of* AB *with respect to the lines* OP *and* p. [For proof, project the four lines AB, A_1B_1, OP and p of the plane π to a new plane π' so that OP is the special line of π. Then AB and A_1B_1 are carried into parallel lines $A'B'$ and $A_1'B_1'$, OP is carried into the line at infinity $O'P'$ of the plane π', and p is carried into the midline p' of the strip determined by $A'B'$ and $A_1'B_1'$ (Fig. 179b). By definition of the polar of a point with respect to a pair of lines, $A_1'B_1'$ is the polar of any point P' on line $A'B'$ with respect to lines p' and $O'P'$ (cf. solution of Problem 17(a)). But then A_1B_1 is the polar of the preimage P on line AB with respect to the lines p and OP.] Hence, given the lines OP, p and AB, we construct line A_1B_1 by means of straightedge alone. Namely, we draw two lines $\bar{P}\bar{A}\bar{A}_1$ and $\bar{P}\bar{B}\bar{B}_1$ which intersect in $\bar{P}$ on line AB ($\bar{A}$ and $\bar{B}$ are on p, while $\bar{A}_1$ and $\bar{B}_1$ are on OP), and join the point $\bar{Q}$ of intersection of lines $\bar{A}\bar{B}_1$ and $\bar{B}\bar{A}_1$ to the point O of intersection of lines p and AB.

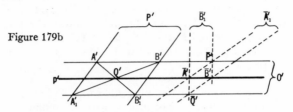

Figure 179b

We return now to the solution of our problem. Let p be an arbitrary line which meets l in some point O and intersects the given arc in the points M and N. (The points of intersection of p with the given arc may coincide with the endpoints of the arc. All we require is that line p not be parallel to l and that the arc MN be less than a semicircle.) The pole P of p with respect to S is the point of intersection of the tangents to S at M and N, and can be constructed by straightedge alone (cf. e.g. Problem 48, in particular, the remark at the end of the solution to that problem; one can also make use of Theorem 1, p. 66). Now suppose that l intersects S in points A and B (which we are to determine). Lines PA and PB intersect S in two more points A_1 and B_1 (Fig. 180). As we have shown above, given the lines AB (i.e., l) and p, we can construct A_1B_1 by means of straightedge alone. Note that if l is outside the angle MOP (in which case l intersects S but does not intersect the arc MN), then A_1B_1 passes through the interior of the angle MOP and, consequently, either does not intersect S (in this case l does not intersect S, and the points A and B do not exist), or intersects arc MN in points A_1 and B_1. The points of intersection of PA_1 and PB_1 with l are the required points.

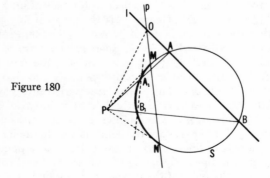

Figure 180

We leave it to the reader to consider in detail the case where A_1 and B_1 coincide, i.e., line A_1B_1 is tangent to S at the point A_1. In this case l is tangent to S at the point A of intersection of lines PA_1 and l; p is the polar of P with respect to the lines OA and OA_1.

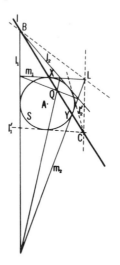

Figure 181

56. Line l_2 in Fig. 72b is a tangent from B to the circle S with center A and radius a. Hence by means of a parallel ruler we can draw from an arbitrary point B two tangents l_1 and l_2 to S without drawing S (Fig. 181; naturally, point B has to be outside S). Now, let B be a point of l, let L be the pole of l with respect to S, and let m_1 and m_2 be the tangents to S from L. The point Q of intersection of the diagonals of the quadrilateral formed by the lines l_1, l_2, m_1 and m_2 lies on l (cf. Problem 40, §3). It follows that BQ (i.e., l) is the polar of L with respect to the lines l_1 and l_2, and that BL is the polar of Q with respect to l_1 and l_2 (cf. Problem 17(a), §2). But then BL is the polar of every point of l with respect to l_1 and l_2 (cf. Problem 17(a)). Since l is given and l_1 and l_2 can be constructed, the line BL can be constructed by means of straightedge alone.

In an analogous manner we can find the line CL, where C is another point of l in the exterior of S. Then L is the point of intersection of BL and CL. The tangents m_1 and m_2 from L to S, which can be constructed by means of a parallel ruler, intersect l in the required points X and Y.

[If l does not intersect S, then L lies in the interior of S, and there are no tangents from L to S.]

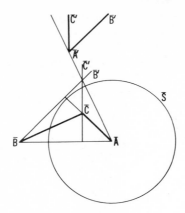

Figure 182

57. Let a be the polar of A with respect to the circle S. If we use a central projection to project S to a circle $\bar{S}$ and A to a point $\bar{A}$, then the line a is carried into the polar $\bar{a}$ of $\bar{A}$ with respect to $\bar{S}$. Similarly, the pole B of a line b with respect to S is carried under the projection into the pole $\bar{B}$ of the line $\bar{b}$ with respect to $\bar{S}$, where $\bar{b}$ is the image of b. We consider now various possible locations of the triangles ABC and $A'B'C'$ relative to S.

1. Suppose at least one of the vertices of $\triangle ABC$, say A, is in the interior of S. We project the plane π of our diagram to a plane π' so that S is carried into a circle $\bar{S}$, and A is carried into the center $\bar{A}$ of $\bar{S}$. Under this projection our diagram is carried into the diagram of Fig. 182, where $\bar{A}'$ is the pole of $\bar{B}\bar{C}$; the poles $\bar{B}'$ and $\bar{C}'$ of lines AC and AB are carried into the poles of diameters $\bar{A}\bar{C}$ and $\bar{A}\bar{B}$ of $\bar{S}$, that is, they are carried into points at infinity $\bar{B}'$ and $\bar{C}'$ corresponding to directions perpendicular to $\bar{A}\bar{C}$ and $\bar{A}\bar{B}$ (cf. Figs. 182 and 67b). It follows that $\bar{B}\bar{B}'$ and $\bar{C}\bar{C}'$ are altitudes of $\triangle \bar{A}\bar{B}\bar{C}$. Since $\bar{A}\bar{A}'$ is the third altitude of $\triangle \bar{A}\bar{B}\bar{C}$ (the pole $\bar{A}'$ of $\bar{B}\bar{C}$ lies on the perpendicular from the center $\bar{A}$ of $\bar{S}$ to the line $\bar{B}\bar{C}$), lines $\bar{A}\bar{A}'$, $\bar{B}\bar{B}'$ and $\bar{C}\bar{C}'$ are concurrent. Consequently AA', BB' and CC' are concurrent.

2. Suppose at least one of the sides of the triangle ABC does not intersect S. In this case the corresponding vertex of $\triangle A'B'C'$ is in the interior of S, and we can apply the argument used in case 1 to $\triangle A'B'C'$.

3. Finally, suppose all the vertices of $\triangle ABC$ are in the exterior of S and none of its sides lies entirely in the exterior of S. In this case our theorem reduces to the theorem of Problem 39(b).

58. Let A', B', C' be the poles of the sides of $\triangle ABC$, and let A_1', B_1' and C_1' be the poles of the sides of $\triangle A_1B_1C_1$ relative to the circle S (Fig. 183). In view of Theorem 2, $B'C'$ is the polar of A, and the point K' of intersection of $B'C'$ and $B_1'C_1'$ is the pole of AA_1. Similarly, the points L' and M' of intersection of lines $A'C'$ and $A_1'C_1'$, $A'B'$ and $A_1'B_1'$ are the poles of lines BB_1 and CC_1. Hence $K'L'$ is the polar of the point O of intersection of AA_1 and BB_1. Since, by assumption, CC_1 passes through O, the pole M' of CC_1 lies on line $K'L'$. Thus points K', L' and M' are collinear and, so, in view of Desargues's Theorem (Problem 22, §2), lines $A'A_1'$, $B'B_1'$ and $C'C_1'$ are concurrent, which is what we set out to prove.

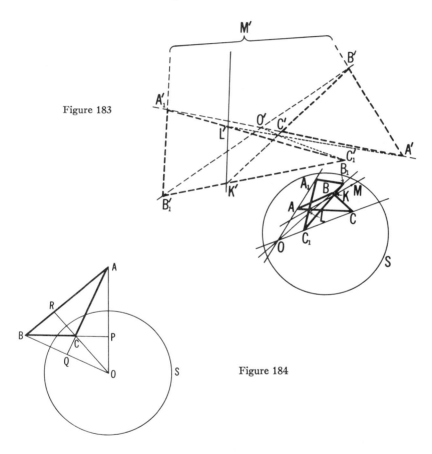

Figure 183

Figure 184

59. Consider a triangle ABC which is self polar with respect to a circle S with center O (Fig. 184). Since the polar BC of A is perpendicular to OA, O lies on the altitude AP of $\triangle ABC$. Similarly, O also lies on the remaining two altitudes BQ and CR. Hence O is the orthocenter of $\triangle ABC$. Further, since each of the pairs of points A and P, B and Q, C and R lies on one side of O, $\triangle ABC$ is obtuse. The uniqueness of the circle S relative to which an obtuse triangle T is self polar follows from the fact that its center O is the point of intersection of the altitudes of T, and its radius r is determined by the relation $r^2 = OA \cdot OP = OB \cdot OQ = OC \cdot OR$ (cf. Problem 51). [The equality of the last 3 products follows from the similarity of triangles OAQ and OBP, OAR and OCP. It can easily be checked that $r = 2R \sqrt{\cos A \cos B \cos C}$, where R is the radius of the circle circumscribed about $\triangle ABC$.]

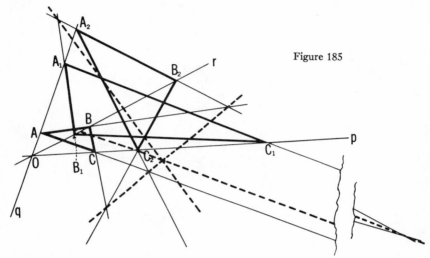

Figure 185

60. Under a polarity the theorems of Problems 17(a) and 17(b) go over into each other (and, consequently, it is sufficient to prove only one of them). The theorems of Problems 21(a) and 21(b) also go over into each other. The theorem of Problem 22 and its converse go over into each other. Here application of a polarity does not lead to any new results since the two statements are equivalent (cf. the remark following the solution of Problem 22). The theorem of Problem 23 also goes over into an equivalent theorem (since this theorem is really the same as that of Problem 22; see the solution of Problem 23). Similarly, application of polarities to the theorems of Problems 25 and 26 does not lead to new results; under a polarity these theorems go over into themselves (except that in the new formulations obtained by dualizing the theorems stated in §2, the term "perspective triangles" means triangles perspective from a line rather than from a point; that this change is harmless follows from Desargues's Theorem which establishes the equivalence of the two notions).

The theorem of Problem 27 goes over under a polarity into the following: If three triangles ABC, $A_1B_1C_1$ and $A_2B_2C_2$ are located in the plane so that points A, A_1, A_2 lie on a line q, B, B_1, B_2 lie on a line r,

C, C_1, C_2 lie on a line p, and if the lines q, r, p are concurrent (Fig. 185), then the three lines which, by Desargues's Theorem contain the points of intersection of the corresponding sides of triangles ABC and $A_1B_1C_1$, ABC and $A_2B_2C_2$, $A_1B_1C_1$ and $A_2B_2C_2$ are concurrent; in other words, *if the centers of perspectivity of three pairwise perspective triangles coincide, then their axes of perspectivity are concurrent.*

The theorem in Problem 28 goes over into an equivalent theorem (which the reader should try to formulate). One way of seeing this is to note that the two alternative formulations of Problem 28 following its statement are dual to each other.

61. This problem is the dual of Problem 24(b), §2; therefore one way of solving it is to apply a polar transformation (with respect to a circle S) to the n lines and n points. Lines l_1, l_2, $\cdots$, l_n go over into n collinear points L_1, L_2, $\cdots$, L_n, and the points M_1, M_2, $\cdots$, M_n go over into lines m_1, m_2, $\cdots$, m_n. Now, we know (Problem 24(b)) how to inscribe an n-gon $B_1B_2\cdots B_n$ in the n-gon formed by the lines m_1, m_2, $\cdots$, m_n such that its sides pass through the points L_1, L_2, $\cdots$, L_n. The required n-gon $A_1A_2\cdots A_n$ is then obtained from the n-gon $B_1B_2\cdots B_n$ by the polarity with respect to S.

This problem can also be solved in another way which does not require construction of the auxiliary n-gon $B_1B_2\cdots B_n$. Namely, when solving Problem 24(b), we proved that if $n-1$ vertices of an n-gon lie on $n-1$ fixed lines, and its sides pass through n fixed collinear points, then its n-th vertex lies on a definite line l. This line can be found by constructing two such n-gons. The principle of duality permits us to conclude that *if $n-1$ sides of an n-gon pass through $n-1$ points M_1, M_2, $\cdots$, M_{n-1}, and its vertices lie on n concurrent lines l_1, l_2, $\cdots$, l_n, then its n-th side passes through a fixed point M* (M is either an ordinary point or a point at infinity). The point M can be found by constructing two such n-gons. By joining M and M_n we obtain the side A_nA_1 of the required n-gon $A_1A_2\cdots A_n$. Determination of the remaining sides of the polygon presents no difficulties. If M is an ordinary point and does not coincide with M_n, then the problem has a unique solution. If M coincides with M_n, the problem is indeterminate. If the point M_n is a point at infinity, then the problem has a unique solution if the direction determined by M_n is not parallel to l_1 or to l_n, and no solution otherwise.

62. Let $A_1A_2A_3A_4$ be a quadrilateral, and let b_1, b_2, b_3, b_4 be the lines joining its vertices to the points P and Q in which diagonals p and q of the quadrilateral intersect the line n determined by the points of intersection of the opposite sides. Let m_1, m_2, m_3, m_4, m_5, m_6, m_7, m_8 be the lines joining the vertices of quadrilateral $A_1A_2A_3A_4$ to the vertices of the circumscribed quadrilateral $B_1B_2B_3B_4$ formed by the lines b_1, b_2, b_3, b_4 (see Fig. 186). The theorems in Problem 36(a)–(d) imply, by the duality principle, that:

(a) The points of intersection of m_1 and m_5, m_2 and m_6, m_3 and m_7, m_4 and m_8 lie on n.

(b) The points of intersection of m_2 and m_3, m_6 and m_7 lie on q, and the points of intersection of m_1 and m_8, m_4 and m_5 lie on p.

(c) The points of intersection of m_1 and m_2, m_3 and m_8, m_4 and m_7, m_5 and m_6 lie on the line joining the point of intersection of diagonals A_1A_3, A_2A_4 with the point of intersection of sides A_1A_4 and A_2A_3; the points of intersection of m_1 and m_6, m_7 and m_8, m_3 and m_4, and m_2 and m_5 lie on the line joining the point of intersection of diagonals A_1A_3 and A_2A_4 with the point of intersection of sides A_1A_2 and A_3A_4.

(d) The points of intersection of m_1 and m_3, m_5 and m_7, b_4 and m_2, b_2 and m_6; m_2 and m_4, m_6 and m_8, b_4 and m_3, b_2 and m_7; m_3 and m_5, m_1 and m_7, b_1 and m_4, b_3 and m_8; m_4 and m_6, m_2 and m_8, b_1 and m_5, b_3 and m_1 lie on four lines passing through the point of intersection of the diagonals.

The theorems in Problems 37(a)–(c) imply, by the duality principle, the following theorems. Let $ABCD$ be a quadrilateral, 1 a line passing through the vertex A, 2 the line joining B to the point of intersection of lines CD and 1, 3 the line joining C to the point of intersection of lines DA and 2, 4 the line joining D to the point of intersection of lines AB and 3, etc. (Fig. 187). Then:

(a) The line 13, obtained by going around all the vertices of the quadrilateral three times, coincides with the initial line 1 (it is clear that this theorem is equivalent to that in Problem 37(a)).

(b) The points of intersection of lines 1 and 7, 2 and 8, 3 and 9, etc., lie on the line joining the points of intersection of opposite sides of the quadrilateral.

(c) The lines joining the points of intersection of lines 1 and 2, 7 and 8; 2 and 3, 8 and 9; 3 and 4, 9 and 10; etc., pass through the point of intersection of the diagonals of the quadrilateral.

The theorem in Problem 38(b) goes over into the following theorem. *Join the points of intersection of a line o with the sides of a triangle ABC to the opposite vertices. Let $A_1B_1C_1$ be the triangle determined by these three lines. Let O be an arbitrary point, let a_1, b_1, c_1 be the lines joining the vertices of $\triangle A_1B_1C_1$ to the point O, and let A_2, B_2, C_2 be the points of intersection of lines a_1, b_1, c_1 with the corresponding sides of $\triangle ABC$* (Fig. 188). *Then lines AA_2, BB_2, and CC_2 intersect in a point.*

63. Under a polarity the theorem in Problem 39(a) goes over into the following theorem. *The points of intersection of the sides of a triangle ABC with the corresponding sides of the triangle determined by the points of tangency E, F, G of the sides of $\triangle ABC$ and its inscribed circle are collinear* (Fig. 189).

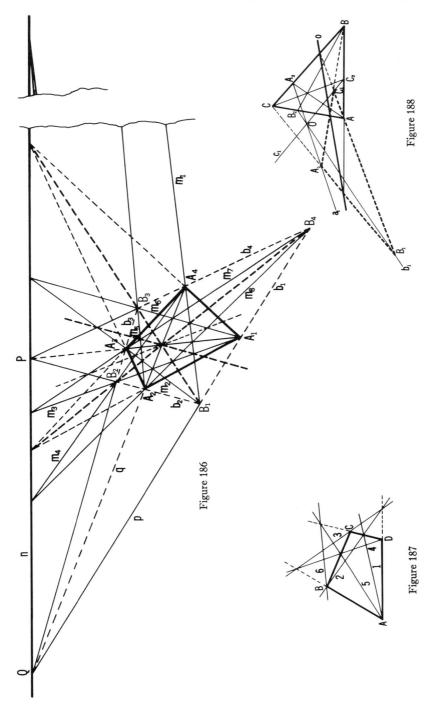

Figure 186

Figure 187

Figure 188

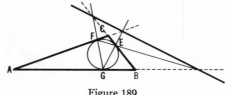

Figure 189

The theorem in Problem 39(b) goes over into the following theorem. Let ABC be a triangle, and let S be a circle which intersects AB, BC and AC. Let a_1, b_1 and c_1 be the lines determined by the points of contact of the tangents to S from A, B and C, respectively (Fig. 190). Then the points of intersection of a_1, b_1 and c_1 with the corresponding sides of $\triangle ABC$ are collinear.†

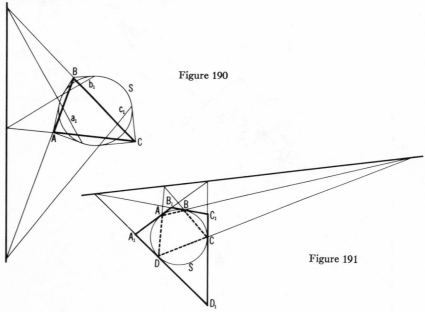

Figure 190

Figure 191

The theorem of Problem 40(a) goes over into the following theorem. Let $A_1B_1C_1D_1$ be a quadrilateral circumscribed about a circle S, and let A, B, C, D be the points of tangency of its sides with S (Fig. 191). Then the points of intersection of opposite sides of the quadrilateral $ABCD$ lie on the line joining the points of intersection of opposite sides of $A_1B_1C_1D_1$. Under a polarity the theorem of Problem 40(b) goes over into itself.

† In view of Desargues's Theorem, the theorems obtained by means of polarities from those in Problems 39(a) and (b) are equivalent to the results stated in these problems.

The theorems of Problems 41(a)–(c) go over into the following theorems. Let l be the line joining the points of intersection of opposite sides of a quadrilateral $ABCD$ circumscribed about a circle S, and let m and n be the lines determined by the diagonals of the quadrilateral. Then:

(a) If two vertices of a triangle circumscribed about S lie on two of the three lines l, m, n, then the third vertex lies on the third of these lines.

(b) There are infinitely many quadrilaterals circumscribed about S whose diagonals lie on the lines m and n. The lines joining the points of intersection of opposite sides of all such quadrilaterals coincide with l.

(c) There are infinitely many quadrilaterals circumscribed about S such that one diagonal lies on m, and the line joining the points of intersection of opposite sides is l. The second diagonal of such a quadrilateral lies on n.

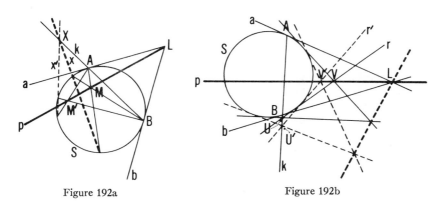

Figure 192a   Figure 192b

The theorems of Problems 43(a) and (b) go over into the following theorems. We are given a circle S, a point L outside S and a line p passing through L; k denotes the line joining the points of contact A and B of the tangents from L to S. Then:

(a) If M is a point varying on p, then the second points of intersection of each pair of lines joining M to the points A and B with the circle S determine a line x, and all of these lines meet k in a fixed point X (Fig. 192a).

(b) If a tangent r to the circle S intersects p and k in points V and U, then the point of intersection of the second tangents to S from U and V lies on a fixed line passing through L (Fig. 192b).

The theorem of Problem 45 goes over into the following theorem. Let a and a_1, b and b_1, c and c_1 be tangents to a circle S from points K, L, M on a line o, and let x be any tangent to S. Then the lines joining the vertices of the triangle formed by a, b, c (shaded in Fig. 193) to the corresponding points of intersection of x and the lines a_1, b_1, c_1 meet in a point on o.

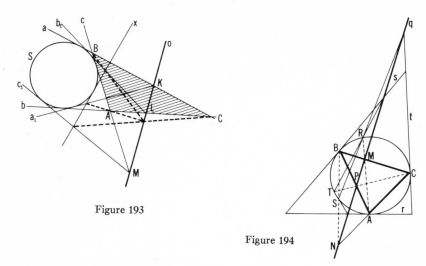

Figure 193

Figure 194

A polarity takes the theorems of Problems 46 and 47 into one another. The theorem of Problem 50 goes into the following theorem. Let r, s, t be tangents to the circle circumscribed about a triangle ABC at the vertices A, B, C, and let M, N, P be three points on the sides BC, CA and AB lying on a line q. We denote the second points of intersection of the lines AM, BN and CP with the circumscribed circle by R, S and T, respectively. Then the points of intersection of the lines RS and t, ST and r, TR and s lie on q (Fig. 194).

64. Under a polar transformation the theorem of Problem 42 goes into the following proposition: Let p be a line and S a circle. Each pair of tangents to S from a point on p determines a chord. All of these chords pass through the same point (Fig. 195).

65. This problem is dual to Problem 44 of the preceding section (the case when the line does not intersect S corresponds to Problem 44(a), and the case when it does intersect S corresponds to Problem 44(b)). Hence this problem can be solved as follows: A polarity with respect to the given circle brings us to Problem 44. After solving that problem we obtain a quadrilateral from which the required quadrilateral is obtained by a polarity. In the present case, however, we need not first solve Problem 44 whose solution is based on the proposition which goes over under a polarity into the following: If the vertices A and C of a quadrilateral $ABCD$ circumscribed about a given circle lie on a line l, and the vertex B lies on a line l_1, then the vertex D lies on a certain fixed line m. With the aid of this proposition our problem is easily solved (cf. the solutions of Problems 44(a) and (b)).

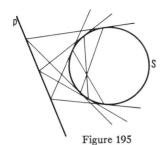

Figure 195

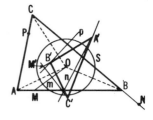

Figure 196

66. Let M, N and P be three points located on sides AB, BC, and CA of a triangle ABC or on their extensions (Fig. 196). As a result of a polar transformation, $\triangle ABC$ goes into a triangle $A'B'C'$ whose sides are the polars a, b, c of the points A, B, C, and the points M, N and P go into lines m, n and p passing through points C', A' and B'. Let M', N' and P' be the points in which m, n and p intersect the sides of $\triangle A'B'C'$. We shall try to relate the expressions

$$\frac{AM}{BM}\cdot\frac{BN}{CN}\cdot\frac{CP}{AP} \quad \text{and} \quad \frac{A'M'}{B'M'}\cdot\frac{B'N'}{C'N'}\cdot\frac{C'P'}{A'P'}.$$

We observe that the ratio $A'M'/B'M'$ is equal to the quotient $(A'M'/C'M')/(B'M'/C'M')$. By the law of sines we have

$$\left|\frac{A'M'}{C'M'}\right| = \frac{\sin \angle A'C'M'}{\sin \angle C'A'M'}, \quad \text{and} \quad \left|\frac{B'M'}{C'M'}\right| = \frac{\sin \angle B'C'M'}{\sin \angle C'B'M'}.$$

It follows that $A'M'/B'M'$ is equal in absolute value to

$$\frac{\sin \angle A'C'M'}{\sin \angle C'A'M'} \Big/ \frac{\sin \angle B'C'M'}{\sin \angle C'B'M'} = \frac{\sin \angle C'B'M'}{\sin \angle C'A'M'} \Big/ \frac{\sin \angle B'C'M'}{\sin \angle A'C'M'}.$$

We know that the polar of A is perpendicular to OA, where O is the center of the circle S of the polar transformation (cf. p. 69). Hence $C'B' \perp OA$, $C'A' \perp OB$, $A'B' \perp OC$ and, consequently,

$$\sin \angle C'B'M' = \sin \angle AOC, \quad \sin \angle C'A'M' = \sin \angle BOC$$

(angles $C'B'M'$ and AOC as well as $C'A'M'$ and BOC have mutually perpendicular sides, hence are equal or supplementary and so have equal sines). Thus

$$\frac{\sin \angle C'B'M'}{\sin \angle C'A'M'} = \frac{\sin \angle AOC}{\sin \angle BOC}.$$

Since $C'M' \perp OM$ we have, similarly,

$$\frac{\sin \sphericalangle B'C'M'}{\sin \sphericalangle A'C'M'} = \frac{\sin \sphericalangle AOM}{\sin \sphericalangle BOM}.$$

We now transform the latter expression. To this end we compute in two ways the areas of triangles AOM and BOM and form their ratio:

$$\frac{S_{AOM}}{S_{BOM}} = \left| \frac{\frac{1}{2}AO \cdot OM \cdot \sin \sphericalangle AOM}{\frac{1}{2}BO \cdot OM \cdot \sin \sphericalangle BOM} \right| = \left| \frac{\frac{1}{2}AM \cdot h_{AB}}{\frac{1}{2}BM \cdot h_{AB}} \right|$$

(here h_{AB} is the common altitude of the triangles AOM and BOM). From the latter equality we obtain readily

$$\frac{\sin \sphericalangle AOM}{\sin \sphericalangle BOM} = \left| \frac{OB}{OA} \cdot \frac{AM}{BM} \right|.$$

Hence the ratio $A'M'/B'M'$ is equal in absolute value to

$$\frac{\sin \sphericalangle AOC}{\sin \sphericalangle BOC} \bigg/ \left(\frac{OB}{OA} \cdot \frac{AM}{BM} \right) = \frac{1}{AM/BM} \cdot \left(\frac{\sin \sphericalangle AOC}{\sin \sphericalangle BOC} \frac{OA}{OB} \right).$$

A similar argument shows that the ratios $B'N'/C'N'$ and $C'P'/A'P'$ are equal in absolute value to

$$\frac{1}{BN/CN} \cdot \frac{\sin \sphericalangle BOA}{\sin \sphericalangle COA} \frac{OB}{OC} \quad \text{and} \quad \frac{1}{CP/AP} \cdot \frac{\sin \sphericalangle COB}{\sin \sphericalangle AOB} \frac{OC}{OA},$$

respectively. Multiplication of these three expressions shows that *the absolute values of the expressions*

$$\frac{AM}{BM} \cdot \frac{BN}{CN} \cdot \frac{CP}{AP} \quad \text{and} \quad \frac{A'M'}{B'M'} \cdot \frac{B'N'}{C'N'} \cdot \frac{C'P'}{A'P'}$$

are reciprocal.

It remains to relate the signs of these expressions. We assume, for simplicity, that the center O of S lies in the interior of $\triangle ABC$. We have $OA \perp B'C'$, $OB \perp A'C'$ and $OM \perp C'M'$. This implies that if OM is between OA and OB, then $C'M'$ is in the exterior of the angle $A'C'B'$, and if OM is in the exterior of the angle AOB, then $C'M'$ is between $C'A'$ and $C'B'$ (cf. the disposition of the lines in Fig. 196). It follows that the ratios AM/BM and $A'M'/B'M'$ have opposite signs. In much the same way we show that the ratios BN/CN and $B'N'/C'N'$, CP/AP and $C'P'/A'P'$ have opposite signs. This justifies the conclusion that *the expressions*

$$\frac{AM}{BM} \cdot \frac{BN}{CN} \cdot \frac{CP}{AP} \quad and \quad \frac{A'M'}{B'M'} \cdot \frac{B'N'}{C'N'} \cdot \frac{C'P'}{A'P'}$$

have opposite signs.† All in all, we have

(*) $$\frac{A'M'}{B'M'} \cdot \frac{B'N'}{C'N'} \cdot \frac{C'P'}{A'P'} = - \frac{1}{\dfrac{AM}{BM} \cdot \dfrac{BN}{CN} \cdot \dfrac{CP}{AP}}.$$

In view of property A of a polarity, lines $A'N'$, $B'P'$ and $C'M'$ intersect in a point (or are parallel) if and only if points M, N and P are collinear. This fact and formula (*) imply that under a polarity the theorems of Ceva and Menelaus go over into one another. It follows that we need only prove one of them.

67. Let ABC and $A_1B_1C_1$ be two triangles perspective from the point O of intersection of AA_1, BB_1 and CC_1 (see p. 30). Consider the polarity Π relative to a circle S with center O. In view of property B of a polarity, Π takes triangles ABC and $A_1B_1C_1$ into triangles whose sides are parallel in pairs. Such triangles are connected by a translation or a central similarity (cf. pp. 18–19 of NML 8 and p. 21 of NML 18). But then the lines joining corresponding vertices of these triangles are concurrent or parallel. Now property A of polar transformation permits us to conclude that the points of intersection of corresponding sides of triangles ABC and $A_1B_1C_1$ are collinear.

The second part of Desargues's Theorem, which asserts that if two triangles are perspective from a line than they are perspective from a point, follows from the first part by the principle of duality. (To show this we apply to the diagram associated with the first part of the theorem a polarity with respect to an *arbitrary* circle; cf. Problem 60.)

68. We apply the polarity with respect to the circle S. Sides BC, CA, AB of $\triangle ABC$ go over into points A', B', C' on S, and the circumscribed $\triangle ABC$ goes over into the inscribed $\triangle A'B'C'$ (that is, the sides of $\triangle ABC$ go into the vertices of $\triangle A'B'C'$ and conversely). The tangent l goes over into a point L on S, points M, N and P go over into lines LA', LB' and LC', points M_1, N_1 and P_1 go over into lines m_1, n_1 and p_1 passing through A', B' and C' and perpendicular to $A'L$, $B'L$ and $C'L$; the latter conclusion follows from property C of polar transformations (Fig. 197). The theorem formulated in the problem goes over into the following theorem: *The lines m_1, n_1 and p_1 intersect in a point of S.* It suffices to prove one of these two theorems.

---

† It can be shown that this conclusion holds also when the center of S is outside $\triangle ABC$. We leave it to the reader to discuss all possible cases.

That lines m_1, n_1 and p_1 intersect in a point of S is quite clear, however. In fact, $m_1 \perp A'L$ implies that m_1 intersects S in the point L_1
diametrically opposite to L. Similarly, lines n_1 and p_1 must also pass
through L_1. [We note that since L and L_1 are diametrically opposite
points of S, it follows that $l_1 \parallel l$ in Fig. 83; cf. property B of a polarity.]

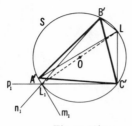

Figure 197

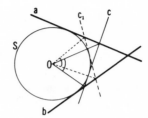

Figure 198

69. *The segments determined by two tangents a and b to a circle S on
a variable third tangent c subtend a fixed angle at the center of S* (Fig. 198;
cf. Fig. 81b).

70. Under a polarity relative to a circle S, an inscribed triangle ABC
goes over into a circumscribed triangle $A'B'C'$, a point L of S goes
over into a tangent l, and the foot P of the perpendicular from L to
AB goes over into the line $C'P'$, where P' is a point of l such that
$\angle C'OP' = 90°$, that is P' is the point of intersection of l and the line
through O parallel to the bisector of the exterior angle at the vertex C'
(OC' is the bisector of the interior angle, Fig. 199). We therefore arrive
at the following theorem: *The lines joining the vertices of a triangle $A'B'C'$
to the points of intersection of a tangent l to its inscribed circle S with the
lines passing through the center O of S and parallel to the bisectors of the
exterior angles at these vertices are concurrent* (Fig. 199).

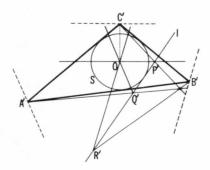

Figure 199

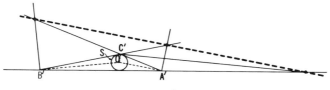

Figure 200

71. Under a polarity relative to the circumscribed circle S a triangle ABC goes into a triangle $A'B'C'$ circumscribed about S; the midpoints of the sides of $\triangle ABC$ go over into lines passing through A', B', C' and perpendicular to the angle bisectors OA', OB' and OC' (O is the center of S), that is, into the bisectors of the exterior angles of $\triangle A'B'C'$, and the medians of $\triangle ABC$ go into the points of intersection of the bisectors of the exterior angles of $\triangle A'B'C'$ with its opposite sides (Fig. 200). We are therefore led to the following theorem: *The points of intersection of the bisectors of the exterior angles of a triangle with its opposite sides are collinear.*

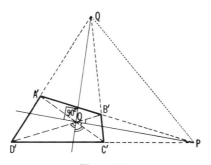

Figure 201

72. Under a polarity relative to a circle S a parallelogram $ABCD$ goes over into a quadrilateral $A'B'C'D'$ whose diagonals intersect at the center O of S (cf. property B of polar transformation). To the diagonals AC and BD of the parallelogram $ABCD$ there correspond the points P and Q of intersection of opposite sides of the quadrilateral $A'B'C'D'$. If the diagonals of the parallelogram are mutually perpendicular (that is, if the parallelogram is a rhombus), then the segment PQ subtends a right angle at O (Fig. 201; cf. property C of a polarity). Under a polarity the theorem formulated in the problem goes over into the following theorem: *If the segment joining the points P and Q of intersection of the opposite sides of a quadrilateral $A'B'C'D'$ subtends a right angle at the point of intersection O of its diagonals, then OP and OQ bisect the angles formed by the diagonals of the quadrilateral.*

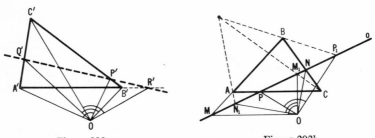

Figure 202a   Figure 202b

73. (a) Under a polarity relative to a circle S with center O, a triangle ABC goes into a triangle $A'B'C'$, and the altitudes of $\triangle ABC$ go into points P', Q' and R' on the sides of $\triangle A'B'C'$ such that $\angle A'OP' = \angle B'OQ' = \angle C'OR' = 90°$ (Fig. 202a; cf. property C of polar transformation). We are thus led to the following theorem: *Let O be a point in the plane of a triangle ABC. Then the points of intersection of the lines through O perpendicular to OA, OB and OC with the corresponding sides of the triangle are collinear.*

Note. Application of a polarity to Fig. 202a leads to the following interesting theorem: *Let o be a line and O a point in the plane of a triangle ABC, let M, N and P be the points of intersection of the line o with the sides AB, BC and CA of the triangle, and let M_1, N_1 and P_1 be three points on o such that $\angle MOM_1 = \angle NON_1 = \angle POP_1 = 90°$. Then lines AN_1, BP_1 and CM_1 are concurrent* (Fig. 202b).

In turn, one can apply to this theorem a polarity (relative to any circle with center $O_1 \neq O$) and thus obtain a new (rather complicated) theorem, etc.

(b) Let l be the bisector of one of the angles formed by lines m and n. Under a polarity relative to a circle S with center O the lines m, n and l go over into collinear points M, N and L such that the segments ML and NL subtend at O equal or supplementary angles (property C of a polarity); in other words, L is the point of intersection of MN with the bisector of one of the two angles formed by the lines OM and ON. Since we do not know which of these two angle bisectors contains L, we consider both bisectors of the angles formed by the lines m and n. These go over into the points of intersection of MN with the angle bisectors of the two adjacent angles formed by OM and ON. It is therefore convenient to consider also the angle bisectors of the exterior angles of $\triangle ABC$, and to formulate the theorem on the points of intersection of the angle bisectors as follows: The six angle bisectors of the interior and exterior angles of a triangle ABC intersect, three at a time, in four points. Under a polarity this theorem goes over into the following theorem: *Let A, B, C and O be four points, no three of which are collinear. The points of intersection of the six bisectors of the angles formed by the lines OA and OB, OB and OC, OC and OA with the corresponding sides of the triangle ABC lie, three at a time, on four lines* (Fig. 203a).

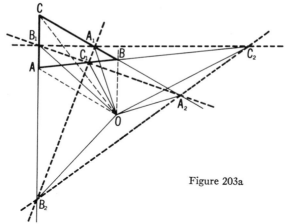

Figure 203a

Note. Application of a polarity to Fig. 203a leads to the following theorem: *Let o be a line and O a point in the plane of a triangle ABC, let M, N and P be the points of intersection of o with sides AB, BC and CA, and let M_1 and M_2, N_1 and N_2, P_1 and P_2 be the points of intersection of o with the bisectors of the angles formed by ON and OP, OP and OM, OM and ON. Then the six lines AN_1, AN_2, BP_1, BP_2, CM_1 and CM_2 intersect, three at a time, in four points* (Fig. 203b; cf. the note following the previous problem).

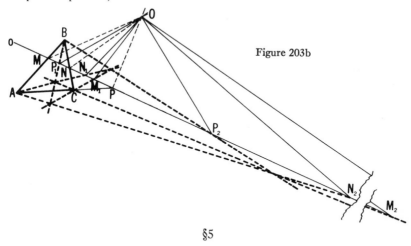

Figure 203b

§5

75. Of the three versions of Pappus's Theorem stated in Problem 28, p. 33, we prove version (a). We denote the points on lines l_1 and l_2 by A, C, E and B, D, F, respectively; the points of intersection of lines AB and ED, CD and AF, EF and CB by K, M, L; the points of intersection of AB and CD, CB and ED, l_1 and l_2 by G, H and O; the point of intersection of KL and CD by M' (Fig.

204; the notations used here differ from those used in Problem 28, but they make it easy to compare the present solution with the solution of Problem 80). [It may happen that certain points are at infinity.] We must show that M' coincides with M. Projection of CD from the center A to the line l_2 carries C, G, D and M into O, B, D and F. Projection of l_2 from the center E to the line CB carries O, B, D and F into C, B, H and L. Projection of CB from the center K back to the line CD carries the points C, B, H and L into the points C, G, D and M'. The product of these three successive projections is a projective transformation of the line CD which carries the points C, G, D and M into the points C, G, D and M'. In view of a fundamental property of projective transformations (see pp. 89–90) *a projective transformation of a line which leaves three of its points fixed* (in our case the points C, G and D) *is the identity transformation*. It follows that the points M and M' coincide.

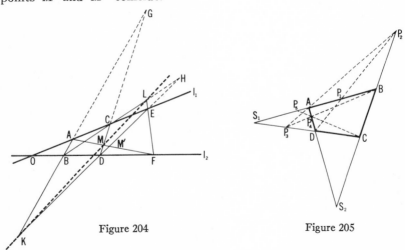

Figure 204   Figure 205

76. We denote the points of intersection of the opposite sides of quadrilateral $ABCD$ by S_1 and S_2 (Fig. 205). Projection of AB from the center D to the line BC carries S_1, A, B into C, S_2, B. Projection of BC from the center A to DC carries C, S_2, B into C, D, S_1. Projection of DC from the center B to DA carries C, D, S_1 into S_2, D, A. Projection of DA from the center C to AB carries S_2, D, A into B, S_1, A. The product of these four projections is a projective transformation of the line AB which carries S_1, A, B into B, S_1, A. The square of this transformation carries S_1, A, B into A, B, S_1. Its cube carries S_1, A, B into S_1, A, B, and so must be the identity transformation. It follows that after going around the sides of the quadrilateral three times we invariably return to the starting point; in particular, the points P_1 and P_{13} on the side AB coincide.

77. (a) This problem is a special case of the previous problem.

(b) We denote the points of intersection of the extensions of the sides of the hexagon by B_1, B_2, B_3, B_4, B_5 and B_6 (Fig. 206a), and the points at infinity corresponding to the directions A_1A_2, A_2A_3 and A_3A_4 by ∞_1, ∞_2 and ∞_3. Projection of the line A_1A_2 from the center A_6 to the line A_2A_3 carries A_1, A_2, B_6, ∞_1 into B_1, A_2, ∞_2, A_3. Projection of A_2A_3 from the center A_1 to A_3A_4 carries B_1, A_2, ∞_2, A_3 into ∞_3, B_2, A_4, A_3. Using appropriate projections we go, successively, from the points ∞_3, B_2, A_4, A_3 on the line A_3A_4 to the points A_5, ∞_1, A_4, B_3 on A_4A_5; to the points A_5, A_6, B_4, ∞_2 on A_5A_6; to the points B_5, A_6, ∞_3, A_1 on A_6A_1; to the points ∞_1, B_6, A_2, A_1 on the initial line A_1A_2. The product of these six projections defines a projective transformation of A_1A_2 which carries A_1, A_2, B_6, ∞_1 into ∞_1, B_6, A_2, A_1. The square of this transformation carries A_1, A_2, B_6, ∞_1 into A_1, A_2, B_6, ∞_1 and so is the identity transformation on the line A_1A_2 (to justify this conclusion it would be sufficient to know that the transformation in question leaves *three* points fixed; cf. solution to Problem 76).

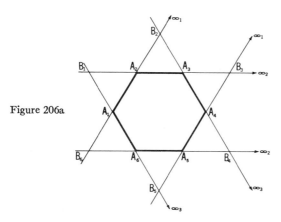

Figure 206a

(c) We denote the points of intersection of the extensions of the sides of the decagon by B_1, B_2, $\cdots$, B_{10}; C_1, C_2, $\cdots$, C_{10} as shown in Figure 206b, and the points at infinity on the lines A_1A_2, A_2A_3, etc., by ∞_{12}, ∞_{23}, etc. Projection from the center A_{10} carries the points A_1, A_2, B_{10} on line A_1A_2 into the points B_1, A_2, C_{10} on A_2A_3. Successive projections from centers A_1, A_2, $\cdots$, A_9 take these points into C_1, B_2, ∞_{34} on line A_3A_4; then into ∞_{45}, C_2, A_5 on line A_4A_5; then into A_6, ∞_{56}, A_5 on line A_5A_6; then into A_6, A_7, B_5 on line A_6A_7; then into B_6, A_7, C_5 on line A_7A_8; then into C_6, B_7, ∞_{89} on line A_8A_9; then into $\infty_{9,10}$, C_7, A_{10} on line A_9A_{10}; then into A_1, $\infty_{10,1}$, A_{10} on line $A_{10}A_1$; then into A_1, A_2, B_{10} on the original line A_1A_2. The product of these ten projections defines a projective transformation of the line A_1A_2 which leaves the three points A_1, A_2, B_{10} fixed, and must therefore be the identity transformation of that line (cf. solution of part (b)).

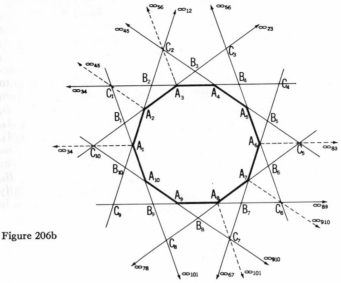

Figure 206b

78. (a) Projection of the circle S to the line AB from M carries the points A, B, N, P on the circle into A, B, O, E on the line. Projection of S to AB from Q carries the same four points into A, B, F, O. It follows that the cross-ratios of the quadruples of points A, B; O, E and A, B; F, O are equal, i.e.

$$\frac{AO/BO}{AE/BE} = \frac{AF/BF}{AO/BO} = \frac{BO/AO}{BF/AF}.$$

This implies the equality of the cross-ratios of the quadruples A, B; O, E and B, A; O, F. We now reflect the quadruple A, B, O, E in the center O of chord AB, and this carries our quadruple into B, A, O, F_1, where F_1 is symmetric to E with respect to O. But then the cross-ratios of the quadruples B, A; O, F and B, A; O, F_1 are equal, which implies that $F = F_1$, as we set out to prove.

Note. Another solution of this problem makes use of Theorem 1 in §3 (p. 54). Specifically, we project Fig. 93 to a plane π' so that the circle S goes into a circle S', and the point O into the center O' of S'. Then, using property C of a central projection (cf. p. 35) it is easy to show the equality of the cross-ratios of the quadruples A, B; O, E and B, A; O, F.

(b) This is a generalization of part (a). The proof, similar to that of part (a), is left to the reader.

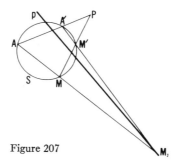

Figure 207

79. Let P be a point and S a circle. By the *projection of S onto itself from P* we mean the transformation which carries a point M on S into the second intersection point M' of PM and S (Fig. 207). This transformation is projective. Indeed, let A and A' be a pair of corresponding points, and M and M' another. By Theorem 1 of §4 (p. 66), the point M_1 of intersection of AM and $A'M'$ lies on a fixed line p, the polar of P relative to S. This shows that the transformation which sends M into M' can be realized by first projecting S from A to the line p (this projection sends M into M_1; Fig. 207) and then projecting p to the circle S from the point A' (this sends M_1 into M'). Hence the transformation from M to M' is projective, as asserted.

Now we prove the theorems of Problems 41(a)–(c).

(a) We consider the following sequence of projective transformations of the circle: first we project the circle onto itself from P, then from Q, and finally from O. It is easy to see that the effect of these transformations on the vertices of the inscribed quadrilateral is as follows: $A \to B \to C \to A$, $B \to A \to D \to B$, $C \to D \to A \to C$, and $D \to C \to B \to D$. This shows that the resulting projective transformation† has four fixed points and so is the identity (cf. the solutions of Problems 76–77; to justify our conclusion it would have sufficed to produce *three* points of the circle left fixed by our transformation). It follows that if projection of the circle S onto itself from P carries a point E of S into F, and projection from Q carries F into G, then projection from O carries G into E. But this means that if two sides EF and FG of an inscribed triangle pass through P and Q, then the side EG passes through O.

In much the same way we show that the sequence of projections of the circle onto itself with centers O, P, Q yields the identity transformation (for it leaves the vertices of the quadrilateral $ABCD$ fixed). It follows that if two sides of an inscribed triangle pass through O and P, then the third side passes through Q.

† The product of projective transformations of a circle (or a line) is a projective transformation (for, clearly, such a product does not affect the cross-ratio of four points).

(b) Consider the sequence of projections of the circle S onto itself from the points P, Q, again P and again Q. The vertices of the quadrilateral $ABCD$ transform as follows: $A \rightarrow B \rightarrow C \rightarrow D \rightarrow A$, $B \rightarrow A \rightarrow D \rightarrow C \rightarrow B$, $C \rightarrow D \rightarrow A \rightarrow B \rightarrow C$ and $D \rightarrow C \rightarrow B \rightarrow A \rightarrow D$. It follows that the resulting transformation is the identity so that, if projection of the circle S onto itself from P takes A_1 into B_1, projection from Q takes B_1 into C_1 and projection from P takes C_1 into D_1, then projection from Q takes D_1 into A_1. But this means that if sides A_1B_1 and C_1D_1 of a quadrilateral $A_1B_1C_1D_1$ inscribed in the circle pass through point P, and side B_1C_1 passes through Q, then side D_1A_1 also passes through Q.

The point O of intersection of the diagonals of the quadrilateral $ABCD$ is the center of a projection of the circle onto itself equivalent to the sequence of projections of the circle onto itself from P and Q. The point of intersection of the diagonals of the constructed quadrilateral $A_1B_1C_1D_1$ also has the same property and must therefore coincide with O.

(c) The proof is entirely analogous to the proof of Problem 41(b) and is left to the reader.

80. We denote the points of intersection of AB and DE, BC and EF, CD and FA, CD and KL, by K, L, M, M' and the points of intersection of AB and CD, BC and DE by G and H (Fig. 208). We must show that M and M' coincide. Projection of CD from A to the circle S carries the points G, C, D and M into the points B, C, D and F. Projection of these points from E to the line BC carries them into B, C, H, L. Projection of the latter points from K to the line CD carries them into G, C, D, M'. But then M and M' coincide (cf. the solution of Problem 75).

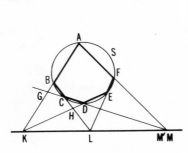

Figure 208

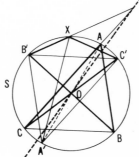

Figure 209

81. (a) Consider the hexagon $ABB'XC'C$ (Fig. 209; note the order of the vertices!). By Pascal's Theorem the points of intersection of the sides AB and XC', AC and XB', BB' and CC' (the point O) are collinear. A similar argument shows that the points of intersection of AB and XC', BC and XA' and the point O are collinear. The assertion of the problem follows.

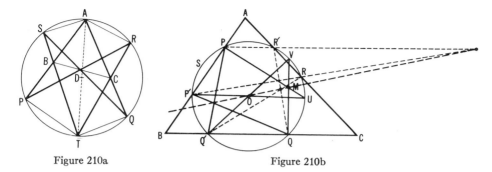

Figure 210a   Figure 210b

(b) Consider the hexagon $APRTSQ$ (note the order of the vertices!) inscribed in the circle with diameter AT (Fig. 210a). By Pascal's Theorem the points of intersection of sides AP and ST, AQ and RT, RP and QS are collinear, which is what we wanted to prove.

(c) Let U and V be the points of intersection of PM and $P'O$, QM and $Q'O$ (Fig. 210b). Since $\sphericalangle P'PM = \sphericalangle Q'QM = 90°$, points U and V lie on S (they are diametrically opposite to P' and Q'). Now we consider the hexagon $P'QVQ'PU$ (note the order of the vertices!) inscribed in S. By Pascal's Theorem, the points of intersection of sides QV and PU, $Q'V$ and $P'U$, $P'Q$ and $Q'P$ of the hexagon, that is points M, O and the point of intersection of $P'Q$ and $Q'P$, are collinear. A similar argument shows that the points of intersection of $P'R$ and PR', $Q'R$ and QR' lie on line MO.

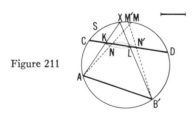

Figure 211

82. (a) We consider the following projective transformation of the circle S: A point M of S is projected from A to the line CD. The resulting point N on CD is translated by $NN' = a$ along line CD (this is a projective transformation of line CD), and finally, the point N' is projected from B to the point M' on S (Fig. 211). The required point X is a fixed point of the above projective transformation. To determine it we have to find the images, under our transformation, of three arbitrary points on the circle S. The problem can have two, one or no solutions.

(b) The solution differs from the solution of problem (a) only in that in place of the translation by a along line CD, we must use the half turn about the given point E (which is also a projective transformation of CD).

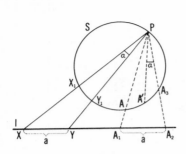

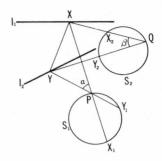

Figure 212a   Figure 212b

83. (a) Let S be a circle passing through P, and suppose that the required lines PX and PY intersect S in the points X_1 and Y_1 (Fig. 212a). We consider the following projective transformation of S: The circle is projected from P to the line l, then l is translated a distance a along itself, then l is projected from P back to S, and finally, S is rotated about its center through an angle 2α. The sense of rotation is chosen so that the point of intersection of PM and l (M on S) is induced to move in a direction opposite to that of the above translation. It is clear that the effect of our transformation† on the point X_1 is $X_1 \to X \to Y \to Y_1 \to X_1$ (bear in mind that arc $X_1Y_1 = 2 \sphericalangle X_1PY_1 = 2\alpha$), so that X_1 is a fixed point. Now we choose three points A, B, C on S, and construct their images A', B', C' under the transformation (cf. Fig. 212a: A_1 is the point of intersection of PA and l, $A_1A_2 = a$, A_3 is the point of intersection of PA_2 and S, arc $A_3A' = 2\alpha$; B' and C' are constructed similarly). The point X_1 can be constructed as a fixed point of the projective transformation of the circle S which carries A, B, C into A', B', C'.

The problem can have two, one or no solutions.

(b) We draw circles S_1 and S_2 passing through the points P and Q, respectively. Let PX and PY intersect S_1 in points X_1 and Y_1, and let QX and QY intersect S_2 in points X_2 and Y_2 (Fig. 212b). We consider the following projective transformation of S_1: S_1 is projected from P to l_1, then l_1 is projected from Q to the circle S_2, then S_2 is rotated about its center through the angle 2β, then S_2 is projected from Q to l_2; then l_2 is projected from P to S_1; and finally S_1 is rotated about its center through the angle 2α. The effect of our transformation on the point X_1 is $X_1 \to X \to X_2 \to Y_2 \to Y \to Y_1 \to X_1$, so that X_1 is a fixed point. Now we choose three points A_1, B_1, C_1 on S_1 and construct their images A_1', B_1', C_1' under our transformation. The

---

† Observe that our transformation is a projective transformation; for, the individual transformations leave the cross-ratio unchanged.

point X_1 can then be determined as a fixed point of the projective transformation of S_1 carrying A_1, B_1, C_1 into A_1', B_1', C_1'.

Since S_1 can be rotated through 2α in two ways, the problem can have up to four solutions.

84. (a) We carry out, in succession, n projections of the circle onto itself from the points M_1, M_2, $\cdots$, M_n (cf. the beginning of the solution of Problem 79). Then, the vertex A_1 of polygon $A_1A_2\cdots A_n$ (cf. Fig. 99a) goes over successively into A_2, A_3, $\cdots$, A_n and, finally, A_1, so that A_1 is a fixed point of the product of these projections. Now we find the images A', B', C' of three points A, B, C of the circle under our transformation, and determine A_1 as a fixed point of the projective transformation of the circle which carries the three points A, B, C into the three points A', B', C'. Determination of the remaining vertices of the n-gon presents no difficulties. The problem can have two, one or no solutions. In the particular case when the product of the n projections is the identity transformation, the problem may turn out to be indeterminate (in connection with such special cases cf. Problems 41(a) and (b) of §3 as well as the solution of Problem 41(a) of NML 8). It is of interest to note that this construction, just as the construction in Problem 84(b), can be effected with straightedge alone.

If any of the points M_1, M_2, $\cdots$, M_n are points at infinity, that is, if we are given the directions of some of the sides of the required n-gon instead of points through which they pass, then the corresponding projections of the circle onto itself are replaced by reflections in diameters perpendicular to the given directions of the sides (cf. the solution of Problem 41(a) of NML 8 where all the points M_1, M_2, $\cdots$, M_n are points at infinity).

(b) Under the polar transformation with respect to the given circle S, the lines l_1, l_2, $\cdots$, l_n go into points L_1, L_2, $\cdots$, L_n. Now we construct a polygon $A_1'A_2'\cdots A_n'$ inscribed in S whose sides pass through L_1, L_2, $\cdots$, L_n (cf. part (a)). Property A of a polar transformation (cf. p. 79) implies that the polygon whose sides a_1, a_2, $\cdots$, a_n are the polars of A_1', A_2', $\cdots$, A_n' fulfills the requirements of the problem.

85. (a) We denote by α the central angle corresponding to the chord of the circle S of given length AB. Further, let l be a line defining the direction of side BC, and let M be a point on AC (Fig. 213a). We consider the following projective transformation of the circle: S is rotated about its center through an angle α, then it is reflected in the diameter perpendicular to l, then it is projected onto itself from M (cf. the beginning of Problem 79). It is clear that A is a fixed point of this transformation (we have: $A \to B \to C \to A$). Thus A can be determined as a fixed point of a known projective transformation (cf. the solutions of Problems 82–84). The problem can have two solutions, one solution or no solutions (it is not difficult to show that our projective transformation cannot be the identity transformation).

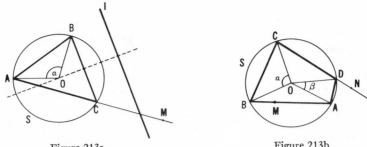

Figure 213a   Figure 213b

(b) Let M and N be the given points on the sides AB and CD of the required quadrilateral, and let α and β be the central angles of the circle corresponding to the known chords BC and AD (Fig. 213b). We consider the following projective transformation of the circle: S is projected onto itself from the point M, then it is rotated about its center through the angle α, then it is projected onto itself from the point N, and finally it is rotated about its center through the angle β. It is clear that A is a fixed point of our transformation (we have: $A \rightarrow B \rightarrow C \rightarrow D \rightarrow A$) and this is the key to its construction. The problem can have two, one or no solutions, and can be indeterminate in exceptional cases.

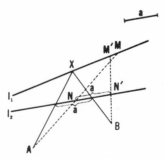

Figure 214

86. (a) We consider the following projective transformation of the line l_1: A point M on l_1 is projected from A to the line l_2, then the resulting point N on l_2 is translated a distance $NN' = a$ along l_2, and finally, N' is projected from B to the point M' on l_1 (Fig. 214). The required point X is a fixed point of this projective transformation, and as such can be determined (cf. the solution of Problem 82(a)). The problem can have two, one or no solutions.

(b) The solution differs from that of part (a) only in that we replace the translation through a distance a along l_2 by a half turn about E of l_2 (cf. the solution of Problem 82(b)).

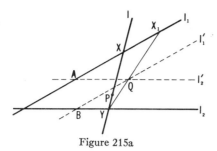

Figure 215a   Figure 215b

87. (a) Let X and Y denote the points of intersection of the required line with l_1 and l_2 (Fig. 215a). We project l_1 from P to l_2, then we bring l_2 into coincidence with l_1 so that, in particular, B coincides with A, and finally we subject l_2 to the central similarity with center A and coefficient m/n. The resulting transformation of l_1 is projective, since it is the product of a projection and a central similarity. X is a fixed point of this transformation (we have: $X \rightarrow Y \rightarrow X$), and so can be determined (cf. the solutions of Problems 82–85). Since the central similarity can have the coefficient $-m/n$, the problem has up to four solutions. In the special case when our projective transformation reduces to the identity, the problem is indeterminate. (This will happen if the lines l_1 and l_2 and the points A and B correspond under the central similarity with center P and coefficient $\pm m/n$.)

(b) We assume that $l_1 \nparallel l_2$, and project l_1 to l_2 from P. This projection carries the required point X on l_1 into a point Y on l_2. Next we project l_2 back to l_1 from the point Q of intersection of the lines $l_1' \parallel l_1$ and $l_2' \parallel l_2$ passing through B and A (Fig. 215a). Let this projection carry the point Y on l_2 to a point X_1 on l_1. The similarity of the triangles AQX_1 and BYQ yields the relation $AX_1/AQ = BQ/BY$, that is,

$$AX_1 \cdot BY = AQ \cdot BQ = p^2,$$

where p can be determined. If we now apply to l_1 the dilatation with center A and coefficient k^2/p^2, then the point X_1 will go into a point X' such that

$$AX' = \frac{k^2}{p^2} AX_1 = \frac{k^2}{p^2} \cdot \frac{p^2}{BY} = \frac{k^2}{BY} = AX,$$

that is, X' coincides with X. This shows that X is a fixed point of our projective transformation of l_1 and, as such, it can be determined. Since the central similarity can have the coefficient $-k^2/p^2$, the problem can have up to four solutions (our projective transformation cannot reduce to the identity).

If $l_1 \| l_2$, and B_1 is the point of intersection of PA with l_2, then

$$B_1Y = \frac{PB_1}{PA} \cdot AX.$$

Hence the condition $AX \cdot BY = k^2$ is equivalent to the condition

$$BY \cdot B_1Y = \frac{PB_1}{PA} \cdot k^2$$

(Fig. 215b). Since, in addition to the product $BY \cdot B_1Y$ of the segments BY and B_1Y, we are also given their sum (or difference) BB_1, these segments can be readily constructed.

Note. Instead of stipulating that the required line pass through a given point P, we could stipulate that it have a preassigned direction. Then in the solution we need only replace the central projection with center P by a parallel projection.

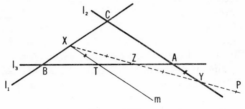

Figure 216

88. Let l_1, l_2, l_3 intersect in pairs in the points A, B, C, and let X, Y, Z be the points of intersection of the required line l with l_1, l_2, l_3. By assumption, $XZ = ZY$ (Fig. 216). Let T be the point of intersection of l_3 with the line $m \| l_2$ passing through X; clearly, $XT = AY$. The similarity of triangles XTB and CAB implies that $XB/XT = CB/CA$. But then $BX/YA = CB/CA$, and the right hand side is known. This reduces our problem to that of passing a line through a point P which intersects two given lines l_1 and l_2 in points X and Y such that the ratio BX/YA has a given value, that is to Problem 87(a). We leave it to the reader to consider the case when two of the lines l_1, l_2, l_3 are parallel, and the case when all three are parallel.

89. We consider the following projective transformation of the line l_1: We project l_1 to l_2 from P, then we translate l_2 parallel to itself by the distance a_2, then we project l_2 to l_1 from P, and then we translate l_1 parallel to itself by the distance a_1. It is clear that the required point X_1 is a fixed point of this transformation ($X_1 \rightarrow X_2 \rightarrow Y_2 \rightarrow Y_1 \rightarrow X_1$, Fig. 217), and can therefore be constructed (cf. the solutions of the preceding problems). Since translation along a line can be carried out in two directions, the problem can have up to four solutions. In the exceptional case when our transformation turns out to be the identity, the problem may be indeterminate (this will happen if the lines l_1 and l_2 correspond under the central similarity with center P and coefficient $\pm a_1/a_2$).

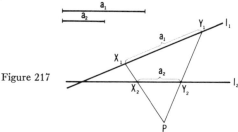

Figure 217

90. We project l_1 to l_2 from M_1, then l_2 to l_3 from M_2, then l_3 to l_4 from M_3, etc., finally l_n to l_1 from M_n (cf. Fig. 101). The fixed points of the resulting projective transformation of l_1 are vertices of the required n-gon (cf. the solution of Problem 84(a)). The problem can have two, one or no solutions. In exceptional cases when the projective transformation of the line l_1 is the identity, the problem is indeterminate.

If for some of the sides of the required n-gon we are given the direction of the side in question instead of one of its points, then the corresponding central projection must be replaced by a parallel projection.

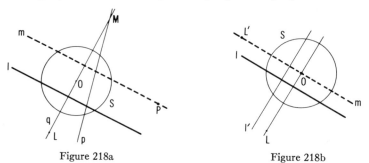

Figure 218a　　　　　　　　　　　Figure 218b

91. (a) The position of the required line m (cf. Fig. 218a) is determined by P and the point at infinity on l. It follows that the pole M of m with respect to the given circle S is the point of intersection of the polar p of P and the polar q of the point at infinity on l. The line p is easy to construct by means of a straightedge alone (cf. p. 69). The line q must pass through the pole L of the given line l which can be constructed by straightedge alone, and through the pole of the line at infinity, that is, through the center O of the circle S. This shows that M can be determined by straightedge alone. Once M is known, its polar m with respect to S can be constructed by straightedge alone.

It is clear that this construction is not possible when l passes through O. But in that case the intersection of l and S determines a segment with known midpoint O, and the line through P parallel to l can be constructed as in the solution of Problem 3(b) of §1. Our construction is not possible in still another case, namely, when P coincides with O. In that case we proceed as follows: We construct the pole L of the given line l relative to S; line OL is perpendicular to l. Next we draw a line l' parallel to OL and construct the pole L' of l' relative to S. Then OL' is the required line, for it is perpendicular to l' and therefore parallel to l (Fig. 218b).

(b) We pass through M a line parallel to AB, and through B a line parallel to AM. Let N be the point of intersection of these lines. It is clear that MN is the required segment.

(c) Let L be the pole of l with respect to S. The line OL is perpendicular to l. To find the required perpendicular we need only pass through P a line parallel to OL. This construction is not possible if l passes through the center O of S, but then we can construct a line l' parallel to l and drop a perpendicular from P to l'.

92. Draw a segment BC whose length is that of the given radius. Through A pass a line parallel to BC and lay off on it segments MA and AN equal to the segment BC (cf. Problem 91(b)). The segment MN is a diameter of the required circle. Now we pass a line through M, and drop a perpendicular from N to that line (cf. Problem 91(c)). The foot of this perpendicular is a point on the required circle. By varying the line through M we can obtain arbitrarily many points on the required circle (Fig. 219).

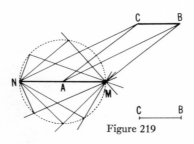

Figure 219

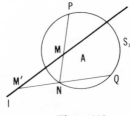

Figure 220

93. Let P and Q be two points on S_1, (Fig. 220). We project the line l from P to S_1 and then project S_1 from Q back to l. It is clear that the points of intersection of S_1 and l are fixed under the resulting projective transformation of l.† An easy way of finding the images of three points R, S, T on l is to project three points $\bar{R}$, $\bar{S}$, $\bar{T}$ of S_1 to l first from P to the points R, S, T, and then from Q to the points R', S', T' (to construct five points P, Q, $\bar{R}$, $\bar{S}$, $\bar{T}$ of the circle S_1 we use the method of Problem 92). Thus our problem reduces to that of determining by straightedge the fixed points of a projective transforma-

† This transformation is projective, for it preserves cross-ratios (cf. p. 92).

tion of l determined by the images R', S', T' of three given points R, S, T on l. Given a circle S in the plane this problem can be solved using straightedge alone (cf. p. 96).

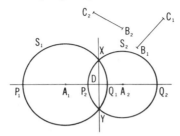

Figure 221

94. We shall first find the points P_1, Q_1 and P_2, Q_2 of intersection of the line of centers A_1A_2 with S_1 and S_2 (Fig. 221; cf. Problem 93). It is clear that if the segments P_1Q_1 and P_2Q_2 lie one outside the other or one inside the other, then S_1 and S_2 do not intersect. It remains to consider the case when P_2 lies inside the segment P_1Q_1, and Q_1 lies inside the segment P_2Q_2.

We now determine the point D of intersection of the line of centers A_1A_2 and the common chord XY of S_1 and S_2 (X and Y are the required points of intersection of the circles). To this end we consider the projective transformation of the line A_1A_2 which carries a typical point R into the point R' such that $\measuredangle RXR' = 90°$. This transformation is projective, since it can be obtained as follows: A_1A_2 is projected from the point X to any circle S passing through X, then S is rotated about its center through 180°, and then S is projected from X to A_1A_2 (cf. the solution of Problem 83(a)). This transformation sends P_1 into Q_1, Q_1 into P_1, and P_2 into Q_2, and so we know the images of three points on l. Using straightedge alone we can easily determine the image of a preassigned point M on l under our projective transformation; in fact, we can realize the transformation by projecting l to some other line l_1, then projecting l_1 to another line l_2, and then projecting l_2 back to l (cf. Fig. 89).† In particular, the point D can be found as the image of the point at infinity on l (this requires construction of a line parallel to l, and this construction can be carried out by straightedge alone, cf. Problem 91(a)). The line XY is the perpendicular at D to A_1A_2. As such it can be constructed following the solution of Problem 91(c). The required points X and Y are then determined as the points of intersection of the line XY with one of the circles S_1 or S_2 (cf. Problem 93).

† We could also project P_1, Q_1, P_2, Q_2 and M from any point O on S to the points $\bar{P}_1$, $\bar{Q}_1$, $\bar{P}_2$, $\bar{Q}_2$ and $\bar{M}$ of S; then, using the construction in Fig. 98, find the point $\bar{M}'$ which is the image of $\bar{M}$ under the projective transformation of S which carries $\bar{P}_1$, $\bar{Q}_1$ and $\bar{P}_2$ into $\bar{Q}_1$, $\bar{P}_1$ and $\bar{Q}_2$, and finally project $\bar{M}'$ from O back to l.

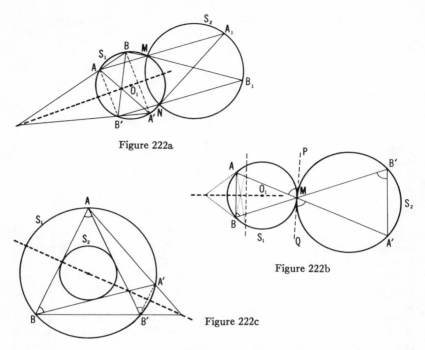

Figure 222a

Figure 222b

Figure 222c

95. (a) Let M and N be the points of intersection of the circles S_1 and S_2 (Fig. 222a). We project two points A and B of S_1 from M to S_2, then project the resulting points A_1 and B_1 from N to S_1 and obtain points A', B' on S_1. We have arc AB = arc $A'B'$ (for $\angle AMB = \angle A'NB'$; these angles are equal to angles A_1MB_1 and A_1NB_1 inscribed in arc A_1B_1, of S_2). It follows that $AB' \parallel BA'$, so that the line joining the points of intersection of AB and $A'B'$, AA' and BB' is a diameter of S_1 (this is clear from considerations of symmetry; we can also argue that the line in question is the polar of the point at infinity at which lines AB' and BA' meet). In the same way we can find another diameter of S_1. The center of S_1 is then the point of intersection of these two diameters.

(b) Let M be the point of tangency of S_1 and S_2 (Fig. 222b). We project two points A and B of S_1 from M to S_2 and obtain two points A' and B'. The chords AB and $A'B'$ are parallel (if PQ is the common tangent of S_1 and S_2, then $\angle ABM = \angle AMP$ since their common measure is half the arc AM; similarly, $\angle A'B'M = \angle A'MQ$, so that $\angle ABM = \angle A'B'M$). Now, using straightedge only, we can construct a chord of S_1 parallel to AB (cf. Problem 3(b) of §1), and so find a diameter of S_1 (cf. the solution of part (a)). A similar construction yields another diameter, and the intersection of these two diameters is the required center of S_1.

(c) From a point A of the larger circle S_1 we draw tangents AB and AB' to the second circle S_2 (cf. Problem 54, §4), and from the point B of intersection of the first tangent with S_1 we draw the second tangent BA' to S_2 (Fig. 222c). Clearly, $\angle BAB' = \angle ABA'$ (by symmetry), $\angle ABA' = \angle A'B'A$ (since they subtend the same arc). It follows that $\angle BAB' = \angle A'B'A$, and therefore $AB \parallel A'B'$. But then the points of intersection of AA' and BB', AB' and BA' lie on a diameter of S_1 (cf. the solution of part (a)). Similarly we can find another diameter of S_1 and so determine its center.

Supplement

96. Let PAQ and RAS be two hyperbolic vertical angles, and let $\bar{P}\bar{Q}\bar{R}\bar{S}$ be the quadrilateral whose sides are the tangents to circle Σ at P, Q, R, S (Fig. 223). Lines $\bar{P}A$ and $\bar{R}A$ (more accurately, the segments of these lines contained in the interior of the disk **K**) are bisectors of the angles PAQ and RAS. Since the bisectors of these angles form a single line, the diagonal $\bar{P}\bar{R}$ of $\bar{P}\bar{Q}\bar{R}\bar{S}$ passes through the point of intersection of the diagonals of $PQRS$. But this is just the assertion of the theorem in Problem 40(a) in §3. The fact that the bisectors of vertical angles form a single line is very easily proved in Euclidean as well as in hyperbolic geometry (it is implied by the equality

$$\delta_{\bar{P}AP} + \delta_{PAS} + \delta_{SA\bar{R}} = \delta_{\bar{R}AR} + \delta_{RAQ} + \delta_{QA\bar{P}}).$$

In this way we obtain a new and simple solution of Problem 40(a).

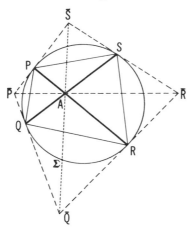

Figure 223

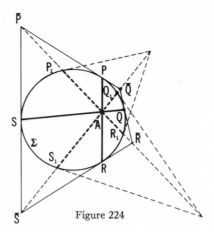

Figure 224

97. Let $\bar{P}\bar{Q}\bar{R}\bar{S}$ be a quadrilateral circumscribed about circle Σ; let P, Q, R, S be its points of tangency with Σ, and let P_1R_1 and Q_1S_1 be the chords determined by Σ on the diagonals $\bar{P}\bar{R}$ and $\bar{Q}\bar{S}$ (they are the bisectors of the hyperbolic angles PAQ and QAR, where A is the point of intersection of PR and QS; cf. the preceding problem). Then *the tangents to Σ at P_1 and R_1 intersect on the line $\bar{Q}\bar{S}$, and the tangents to Σ at Q_1 and S_1 intersect on the line $\bar{P}\bar{R}$* (Fig. 224).

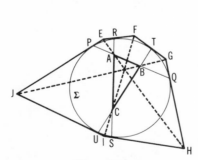

Figure 225a

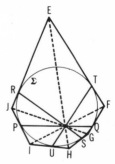

Figure 225b

98. Let ABC be a triangle determined by hyperbolic lines PQ, RS and TU, and let $EFGHIJ$ be a hexagon circumscribed about Σ whose sides touch Σ at the points P, R, T, Q, S, U (Fig. 225). Then the bisectors of the angles of $\triangle ABC$ are the lines EH, FI and GJ (cf. Problem 96). To say that the angle bisectors of a triangle are concurrent means that the lines EH, FI and GJ are concurrent; but this is just the assertion of Brianchon's Theorem.

Note. Our solution shows only that Brianchon's Theorem implies the concurrence of the angle bisectors in a noneuclidean triangle. The converse assertion—that the concurrence of the angle bisectors in a noneuclidean triangle implies Brianchon's Theorem—is, strictly speaking, false. The point is that the lines PQ, RS and TU in Fig. 225a may be concurrent (Fig. 225b). In this (admittedly exceptional) case we have no triangle ABC, and Brianchon's Theorem is a consequence not of the theorem on the concurrence of the angle bisectors in a triangle, but of the simpler theorem on bisectors of vertical angles (cf. Fig. 225b with Fig. 223).

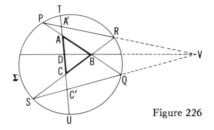

Figure 226

99. Let PQ, RS and TU be noneuclidean lines which determine a triangle ABC, let V be the point of intersection of PR and SQ, and let A', C' and D be the points in which the lines VP, VS and VB intersect TU (Fig. 226). Then

$$d_{AB} = \log\left(\frac{AQ/BQ}{AP/BP}\right), \qquad d_{BC} = \log\left(\frac{BS/CS}{BR/CR}\right),$$

$$d_{AC} = \log\left(\frac{AU/CU}{AT/CT}\right).$$

We must show that

$$\log\left(\frac{AQ/BQ}{AP/BP}\right) + \log\left(\frac{BS/CS}{BR/CR}\right) > \log\left(\frac{AU/CU}{AT/CT}\right),$$

that is, that

$$\left(\frac{AQ/BQ}{AP/BP}\right)\left(\frac{BS/CS}{BR/CR}\right) > \left(\frac{AU/CU}{AT/CT}\right).$$

We have that $(AQ/BQ)/(AP/BP) = (AC'/DC')/(AA'/DA')$, because the points A, D; C', A' are obtained from A, B; Q, P when PQ is projected to UT from the center V. Again, $(BS/CS)/(BR/CR) = (DC'/CC')/(DA'/CA')$, because the points D, C; C', A' are obtained from B, C; S, R when RS is projected to UT from V. It follows that

$$\left(\frac{AQ/BQ}{AP/BP}\right)\left(\frac{BS/CS}{BR/CR}\right) = \left(\frac{AC'/DC'}{AA'/DA'}\right)\left(\frac{DC'/CC'}{DA'/CA'}\right) = \frac{AC'/CC'}{AA'/CA'}.$$

Since $\dfrac{AC'}{CC'} > \dfrac{AU}{CU}$ $\left(\text{for } \dfrac{AC'}{CC'} - \dfrac{AU}{CU} = \dfrac{AC'\cdot CU - CC'\cdot AU}{CC'\cdot CU} = \right.$

$\left.\dfrac{AC'(CC'+C'U)-CC'(AC'+C'U)}{CC'\cdot CU} = \dfrac{C'U(AC'-CC')}{CC'\cdot CU} = \dfrac{C'U\cdot AC}{CC'\cdot CU} > 0\right),$

and $\dfrac{AA'}{CA'} < \dfrac{AT}{CT}$ $\left(\text{for } \dfrac{AA'}{CA'} - \dfrac{AT}{CT} = \dfrac{AA'\cdot CT - CA'\cdot AT}{CA'\cdot CT} = \right.$

$\left.\dfrac{AA'(CA'+A'T)-CA'(AA'+A'T)}{CA'\cdot CT} = \dfrac{A'T(AA'-CA')}{CA'\cdot CT} = \dfrac{A'T\cdot CA}{CA'\cdot CT} < 0\right),$

we conclude that

$$\left(\frac{AQ/BQ}{AP/BP}\right)\left(\frac{BS/CS}{BR/CR}\right) = \frac{AC'/CC'}{AA'/CA'} > \frac{AU/CU}{AT/CT},$$

which is what we set out to prove.

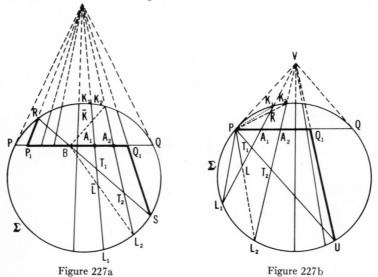

Figure 227a   Figure 227b

100. (a) The second assertion of the problem follows directly from Fig. 227a. It remains to show that the distances from points of RS to the line PQ increase beyond all bounds as these points move away from B. In terms of Fig. 227a we first show that

$$d_{A_1T_1} < d_{A_2T_2} \qquad \text{or} \qquad \frac{A_1L_1/T_1L_1}{A_1K_1/T_1K_1} < \frac{A_2L_2/T_2L_2}{A_2K_2/T_2K_2}.$$

Now

$$\frac{A_2L_2/T_2L_2}{A_2K_2/T_2K_2} = \frac{A_1\bar{L}/T_1\bar{L}}{A_1\bar{K}/T_1\bar{K}}$$

(since the points A_1, T_1; $\bar{K}$, $\bar{L}$ are obtained from A_2, T_2; K_2, L_2 by projection from the center B), and

$$\frac{A_1L_1}{T_1L_1} < \frac{A_1\bar{L}}{T_1\bar{L}}, \qquad \frac{A_1K_1}{T_1K_1} > \frac{A_1\bar{K}}{T_1\bar{K}}$$

(cf. the solution of the preceding problem). Hence

$$\frac{A_1L_1/T_1L_1}{A_1K_1/T_1K_1} < \frac{A_1\bar{L}/T_1\bar{L}}{A_1\bar{K}/T_1\bar{K}} = \frac{A_2L_2/T_2L_2}{A_2K_2/T_2K_2},$$

which is what we wished to prove. The distance from the points of the line RS to the line PQ increases beyond all bounds, for the rays P_1R and Q_1S are infinite; cf. p. 108.

(b) The second assertion of the problem follows directly from Fig. 227b. We now show that the distances from the points of UP to the line QP increase in the direction PU. In terms of the notation in Fig. 227b we must show that

$$d_{T_1A_1} < d_{T_2A_2} \qquad \text{or} \qquad \frac{T_1K_1/A_1K_1}{T_1L_1/A_1L_1} < \frac{T_2K_2/A_2K_2}{T_2L_2/A_2L_2}.$$

Now,

$$\frac{T_2K_2/A_2K_2}{T_2L_2/A_2L_2} = \frac{T_1\bar{K}/A_1\bar{K}}{T_1\bar{L}/A_1\bar{L}}$$

(points T_1, A_1; $\bar{K}$, $\bar{L}$ are obtained from points T_2, A_2; K_2, L_2 by projection from P), and

$$\frac{T_1K_1}{A_1K_1} < \frac{T_1\bar{K}}{A_1\bar{K}}, \qquad \frac{T_1L_1}{A_1L_1} > \frac{T_1\bar{L}}{A_1\bar{L}}$$

(cf. solution of Problem 99). Hence

$$\frac{T_1K_1/A_1K_1}{T_1L_1/A_1L_1} < \frac{T_1\bar{K}/A_1\bar{K}}{T_1\bar{L}/A_1\bar{L}} = \frac{T_2K_2/A_2K_2}{T_2L_2/A_2L_2},$$

which is what we wished to prove.

The distances from the points of the line PU to PQ increase beyond all bounds in the direction PU, for the ray Q_1U is infinite (cf. p. 108).

On the other hand, the distances from the points of PU to the line PQ decrease beyond all bounds in the direction UP, for the ratio A_1K_1/T_1K_1 tends to one as the point A_1 tends to P. (To see this observe that

$$\frac{A_1K_1}{T_1K_1} = \frac{S_{PA_1K_1}}{S_{PT_1K_1}} = \frac{\frac{1}{2}PA_1 \cdot PK_1 \cdot \sin \measuredangle A_1PK_1}{\frac{1}{2}PT_1 \cdot PK_1 \cdot \sin \measuredangle T_1PK_1} = \frac{PA_1}{PT_1} \cdot \frac{\sin \measuredangle A_1PK_1}{\sin \measuredangle T_1PK_1}$$

$$= \frac{\sin \measuredangle PT_1A_1}{\sin \measuredangle PA_1T_1} \cdot \frac{\sin \measuredangle A_1PK_1}{\sin \measuredangle T_1PK_1} = \frac{\sin \measuredangle PT_1A_1}{\sin \measuredangle T_1PK_1} \cdot \frac{\sin \measuredangle A_1PK_1}{\sin \measuredangle PA_1T_1}.$$

If $A_1 \to P$, then

$$\measuredangle PT_1A_1 = \measuredangle UT_1L_1 \to 180° - \measuredangle UPV, \quad \measuredangle T_1PK_1 \to \measuredangle UPV,$$

$$\frac{\sin \measuredangle PT_1A_1}{\sin \measuredangle T_1PK_1} \to 1 \text{ and } \measuredangle A_1PK_1 \to \measuredangle QPV, \measuredangle PA_1T_1 = \measuredangle QA_1K_1 \to \measuredangle QPV,$$

$$\frac{\sin \measuredangle A_1PK_1}{\sin \measuredangle PA_1T_1} \to 1.) \quad \text{The ratio } A_1L_1/T_1L_1 \text{ tends to one (proof analogous}$$

to that just given). Hence

$$\frac{A_1K_1/T_1K_1}{A_1L_1/T_1L_1} \to 1, \quad \text{that is,} \quad d_{A_1T_1} = \log\left(\frac{A_1K_1/T_1K_1}{A_1L_1/T_1L_1}\right) \to 0.$$

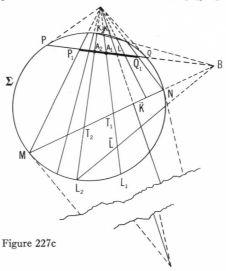

Figure 227c

(c) The common perpendicular of two lines in the hyperbolic plane is the line joining the points of intersection of the tangents to the circle Σ at P and Q, M and N (Fig. 227c), that is, the poles of the lines PQ and MN with respect to Σ (cf. the beginning of §4). This line is the polar of the point B of intersection of PQ and MN (cf. Theorem 2 of §4, p. 69); it intersects Σ if and only if B is exterior to Σ. This implies the first assertion of the problem. The last assertion follows directly from Fig. 227c. It remains to show that the distances of the points of MN from the line PQ increase beyond all bounds as these points move away from the foot of the common perpendicular of MN and PQ. In terms of the notation of Fig. 227c we must first show that

$$d_{T_1 A_1} < d_{T_2 A_2}, \quad \text{or} \quad \frac{T_1 K_1 / A_1 K_1}{T_1 L_1 / A_1 L_1} < \frac{T_2 K_2 / A_2 K_2}{T_2 L_2 / A_2 L_2}.$$

Now

$$\frac{T_2 K_2 / A_2 K_2}{T_2 L_2 / A_2 L_2} = \frac{T_1 \bar{K} / A_1 \bar{K}}{T_1 \bar{L} / A_1 \bar{L}}$$

(points A_1, T_1; $\bar{K}$, $\bar{L}$ are obtained from A_2, T_2; K_2, L_2 by projection from B), and

$$\frac{T_1 K_1}{A_1 K_1} < \frac{T_1 \bar{K}}{A_1 \bar{K}}, \qquad \frac{T_1 L_1}{A_1 L_1} > \frac{T_1 \bar{L}}{A_1 \bar{L}}$$

(cf. with solution of Problem 99). Hence

$$\frac{T_1 K_1 / A_1 K_1}{T_1 L_1 / A_1 L_1} < \frac{T_1 \bar{K} / A_1 \bar{K}}{T_1 \bar{L} / A_1 \bar{L}} = \frac{T_2 K_2 / A_2 K_2}{T_2 L_2 / A_2 L_2},$$

which is what we wished to prove.

The distances of the points of the line MN to the line PQ increase beyond all bounds, for the rays $P_1 M$ and $Q_1 N$ are infinite (cf. p. 108).

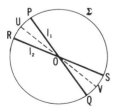

Figure 228a

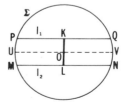

Figure 228b

101. (a) First let l_1 and l_2 be two intersecting lines in the hyperbolic plane. We move their point of intersection by means of a hyperbolic motion to the center O of the disk $\mathbf{K}$ (Fig. 228a). It is easy to see that the (simultaneously Euclidean and hyperbolic) bisector UV of the angle POR formed by these lines is their hyperbolic axis of symmetry. In fact (Euclidean) reflection in the line UV carries PQ into RS; but this is also a hyperbolic reflection in the line UV, for the Euclidean perpendiculars to the diameter UV of the disk $\mathbf{K}$ are also hyperbolic perpendiculars to UV.

Now we consider two ultraparallel lines l_1 and l_2. We move the midpoint of their common perpendicular KL (cf. Problem 100(c)) to the center O of the disk $\mathbf{K}$ by means of a hyperbolic motion (Fig. 228b). Then l_1 and l_2 are perpendicular to KL in the Euclidean sense, and the segments OK and OL are congruent in the Euclidean sense (cf. p. 109). The Euclidean and hyperbolic perpendicular UV to line KL at O is the (Euclidean and hyperbolic) axis of symmetry of l_1 and l_2.

It is somewhat more difficult to show the existence of an axis of symmetry for parallel lines PQ and PT. In this case we draw the line TQ parallel to PT and PQ, and then the line PU parallel to PQ and PT and perpendicular to QT (Fig. 229a). Line PU is the required axis of symmetry of lines PQ and PT; for proof we need only take PU into a diameter of $\mathbf{K}$ by means of a suitable hyperbolic motion (Fig. 229b).

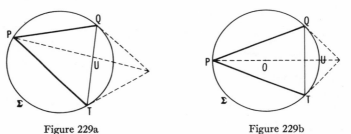

Figure 229a   Figure 229b

(b) Reflection in l carries l_1 into a line l_1' passing through A_2 (for l_1 passes through A_1) and belonging to the same pencil as l_1 and l. Since such a line is obviously unique, it follows that l_1' coincides with l_2.

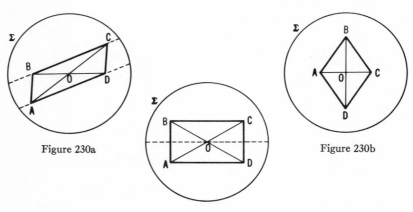

Figure 230a   Figure 230b

Figure 230c

102. Let $ABCD$ be a hyperbolic parallelogram. We move the point of intersection of its diagonals to the center of the disk **K** by means of a hyperbolic motion. Since the hyperbolic lengths of the segments OA, OC (and of the segments OB, OD) are equal, it follows that their Euclidean lengths are also equal (cf. p. 109). This enables us to conclude that the quadrilateral $ABCD$ is a Euclidean parallelogram (Fig. 230a).

(a) $d_{AB} = d_{CD}$, for the segments AB and CD are related by a hyperbolic motion, namely, the half turn about the center O of **K**. The proof that $d_{AD} = d_{BC}$ is similar to that just given.

(b) $\delta_A = \delta_C$, for the angles A and C are related by a hyperbolic motion, namely, a half turn about O. In the same manner we prove that $\delta_B = \delta_D$.

(c) If the diagonals AC and BD are perpendicular in the hyperbolic sense, then they are also perpendicular in the Euclidean sense. It follows that $ABCD$ is a Euclidean rhombus (Fig. 230b). In that case $d_{AB} = d_{AD}$, for the segments AB and AD are related by a hyperbolic motion, namely, reflection in the line AC; $\delta_{BAC} = \delta_{DAC}$, for the angles BAC and DAC are related by the same hyperbolic motion.

(d) If $d_{OA} = d_{OB}$, then the segments OA and OB are congruent in the Euclidean sense (cf. p. 109), and so $ABCD$ is a Euclidean rectangle (Fig. 230c). In that case $\delta_A = \delta_B$, for the angles A and B are related by a noneuclidean motion, namely reflection in the diameter of the disk **K** perpendicular (in the Euclidean and hyperbolic sense) to AB and DC.

(e) Cf. parts (c) and (d).

Note. We suggest that the reader prove the theorems in Problems (a)–(e) as problems in *Euclidean geometry* without using the parallel axiom; this would automatically prove that these theorems are true in hyperbolic geometry.

103. No. They are ultraparallel (cf. Fig. 230a).

104. Let H be the point of intersection of the altitudes AK and BL of an acute triangle ABC. [These altitudes intersect, for both of them pass through the interior of $\triangle ABC$; in fact, if the altitude from A intersected the extension of side BC beyond C, then angle C would be obtuse in view of the theorem about an exterior angle of a triangle which remains valid in hyperbolic geometry (see Fig. 231a).] We move the point H to the center O of **K** by means of a hyperbolic motion (Fig. 231b). We have $AK \perp BC$, $BL \perp AC$ in the ordinary (Euclidean) sense of perpendicularity. It follows that O is the point of intersection of the Euclidean altitudes of $\triangle ABC$, so that $CO \perp AB$. The fact that AB is perpendicular to the diameter CO of **K** in the Euclidean sense implies that CO is a hyperbolic altitude of $\triangle ABC$. This, in turn, implies that the three (hyperbolic) altitudes of an acute triangle ABC are concurrent.

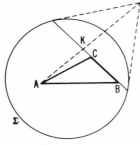

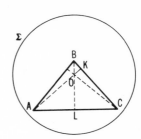

Figure 231a   Figure 231b

Matters are different in the case of an obtuse triangle. If two altitudes AK and BL of an obtuse triangle ABC intersect in a point H, then the third altitude also passes through that point; this is proved as above. Now assume that the altitudes AK and BL of an obtuse triangle ABC (with obtuse angle C) are parallel. We move the vertex C to the center of $\mathbf{K}$ by means of a hyperbolic motion (Fig. 232a). Then $AK \perp BC$ and $BL \perp AC$ in the Euclidean sense. It follows that point P of Σ where AK and BL meet is the point of intersection of the Euclidean altitudes of $\triangle ABC$, and $CP \perp AB$ in the Euclidean sense; but then CP is also a hyperbolic altitude of $\triangle ABC$. To sum up: *if two altitudes AK and BL of an obtuse triangle ABC are parallel, then all three altitudes AK, BL and CM are parallel* (we leave it to the reader to state the corresponding Euclidean theorem pertaining to the chords of $\mathbf{K}$).

Figure 232a

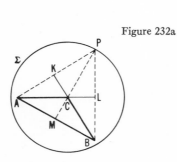

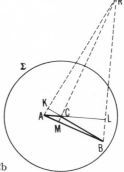

Figure 232b

Finally assume that the altitudes AK and BL of a triangle ABC are ultraparallel. We move C to the center of $\mathbf{K}$ by means of a hyperbolic motion (Fig. 232b). Then $AK \perp BC$ and $BL \perp AC$ in the Euclidean sense. The point R of intersection of lines AK and BL (which is outside $\mathbf{K}$!) is the point of intersection of the Euclidean altitudes of $\triangle ABC$, so that $CR \perp AB$ in the Euclidean sense. It follows that CR is also a hyperbolic altitude of $\triangle ABC$. To sum up: *if the altitudes AK and BL of an obtuse triangle ABC are ultraparallel, then all three altitudes AK, BL and CM are ultraparallel* (cf. pp. 121–122).

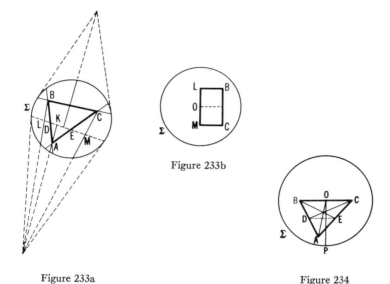

Figure 233b

Figure 233a   Figure 234

105. We prove first that *the line DE joining the midpoints of the sides AB and AC of a hyperbolic triangle ABC and the perpendicular bisector of the side BC are perpendicular.* We draw perpendiculars AK, BL and CM from the vertices of the triangle to the midline DE (Fig. 233a). The congruence criterion for right triangles (which remains true in hyperbolic geometry; cf. p. 115) implies that the triangles ADK and BDL, AEK and CEM are congruent, so that $d_{BL} = d_{AK} = d_{MC}$. We move the midpoint of segment LM to the center O of the disk **K** by means of a hyperbolic motion (Fig. 233b). Then $OL = OM$, $BL \perp LM$, and $CM \perp LM$ (in the Euclidean sense). Now the equality $d_{LB} = d_{MC}$ implies that the segments LB and MC are congruent in the Euclidean sense (otherwise reflection in a diameter of **K** perpendicular to LM, which is a hyperbolic motion, would carry one of these segments into a part of the other), so that the quadrilateral $LMCB$ is a Euclidean rectangle. The Euclidean perpendicular at O to line LM is also perpendicular to it in the hyperbolic sense. At the same time it is the perpendicular bisector of BC in the Euclidean and hyperbolic sense. This implies our assertion.

Now we bring the midpoint of side BC of an arbitrary triangle ABC into coincidence with the center O of **K** (Fig. 234). The (Euclidean) perpendicular OP to BC is also perpendicular to it in the hyperbolic sense. The midline DE of the triangle which is perpendicular to OP in the hyperbolic sense is perpendicular to it in the Euclidean sense as well. It follows that quadrilateral· $BCED$ is a Euclidean trapezoid. In view of the theorem of Problem 2, §1, medians AO, BE and CD of $\triangle ABC$ are concurrent.

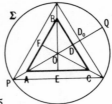

Figure 235

106. The proposition is false. To see this, it suffices to consider an equilateral triangle with center at the center O of the disk **K** (Fig. 235). The Euclidean medians of this triangle are also its hyperbolic medians. Moreover, $d_{OA} \neq 2d_{OD}$, for if the hyperbolic length of a side of $\triangle ABC$ increases indefinitely (i.e., its vertices approach the circle Σ), then

$$d_{OD} \to d_{OD_0} = \log\left(\frac{OQ/D_0Q}{OP/D_0P}\right) = \log\left(\frac{2}{2/3}\right) = \log 3,$$

$$d_{OA} \to d_{OP} = \infty.$$

Note. The argument just given shows that even for an equilateral triangle the ratio OA/OD in which the point of intersection of the medians divides the median AD is not constant, but depends on the length of the side of the triangle (this is connected with the fact that in hyperbolic geometry noncongruent equilateral triangles are dissimilar; cf. text following Problem 110).

107. If the perpendicular bisectors of two sides of a triangle intersect in a point O, then the third one also passes through O; the proof of this fact does not differ from the usual proof (cf. the proof of the concurrence of the angle bisectors in a hyperbolic triangle, p. 117). Assume now that the perpendicular bisectors KL and MN to the sides AB and BC are ultraparallel, that is, have a common perpendicular PQ (Fig. 236a). Then, as we are about to show, the third perpendicular bisector is also perpendicular to PQ (that RS intersects PQ can be seen directly from Fig. 236a). Drop perpendiculars AA_1, BB_1 and CC_1 to line PQ. The right triangles AKL and BKL are congruent (congruent legs test), so $AL = BL$, $\delta_{ALK} = \delta_{BLK}$, $\delta_{ALA_1} = \delta_{BLB_1}$. It follows that the right triangles ALA_1 and BLB_1 are congruent (hypotenuse and acute angle test). Hence $AA_1 = BB_1$. A similar argument shows that $BB_1 = CC_1$. But then $AA_1 = CC_1$. Further, the right triangles ARS and CRS are congruent (congruent legs test), so that $AS = CS$ and $\delta_{ASR} = \delta_{CSR}$. Also, the right triangles ASA_1 and CSC_1 are congruent (congruent leg and hypotenuse test), so that $\delta_{ASA_1} = \delta_{CSC_1}$. Now we have

$$\delta_{RSA_1} = \delta_{RSA} + \delta_{ASA_1} = \delta_{RSC} + \delta_{CSC_1} = \delta_{RSC_1},$$

which means that RS is perpendicular to PQ.

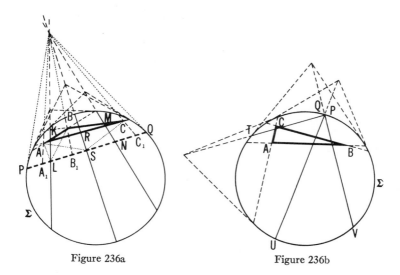

Figure 236a   Figure 236b

Finally consider the case where the perpendicular bisectors UP and VP to sides AB and BC are parallel (see Fig. 236b). Then the third perpendicular bisector QT is parallel to UP and VP (for if, say, lines UP and QT were ultraparallel, then, as was shown above, UP and VP would be ultraparallel). It is clear from Fig. 236b that QT and UV cannot coincide. It follows that in this case, too, lines UP, VP and QT belong to the same pencil.

Figure 237

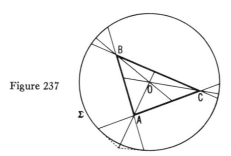

108. (a) We move the point of intersection of the angle bisectors of $\triangle ABC$ (cf. p. 117) to the center O of $\mathbf{K}$ (Fig. 237). Then the angles OAB, OAC, OBA, OBC, OCA and OCB are acute in the Euclidean and hyperbolic sense. Hence $\delta_A < \measuredangle A$, $\delta_B < \measuredangle B$, $\delta_C < \measuredangle C$ (cf. final remark in fine print on p. 114). Hence

$$\delta_A + \delta_B + \delta_C < \measuredangle A + \measuredangle B + \measuredangle C = 180°,$$

which is what we set out to prove.

(b) We prove, first of all, that *every n-gon can be split into* $n - 2$ *triangles by means of nonintersecting diagonals.* Since every noneuclidean polygon is a Euclidean polygon contained in the interior of the disk **K**, it suffices to prove this assertion for Euclidean polygons. (The proof is obvious for convex polygons; cf. Fig. 238a).

We shall show that every n-gon **M** $(n > 3)$ can be split into two smaller polygons. Let A be a vertex of **M**, and let AB and AC be the sides issuing from A. Consider all segments with endpoints A interior to **M** (Figs. 238b, c). If one of these segments happens to be a diagonal AK of the polygon **M** (Fig. 238b), then this diagonal splits **M** into two smaller parts. If the segments in question do not contain a diagonal, that is, if their endpoints belong to one side of **M** (Fig. 238c), then diagonal BC cuts all of these segments and so lies entirely in the interior of **M**; but then BC splits **M** into two smaller polygons.

We see that the process just described enables us to split **M** into triangles. If splitting **M** into triangles requires the use of k diagonals, then the number of triangles is $k + 1$. These $k + 1$ triangles have $3(k + 1)$ sides, of which n are the sides of **M** and $2k$ are diagonals (every diagonal is a common side of two triangles). Hence

$$3(k + 1) = n + 2k, \qquad k = n - 3,$$

and this implies that **M** splits into $k + 1 = n - 2$ triangles. Since the sum of the angles of each of the $n - 2$ triangles is less than 180° (cf. part (a)), it follows that the sum of the angles of the n-gon is less than $180°(n - 2)$, which is what we wished to prove.

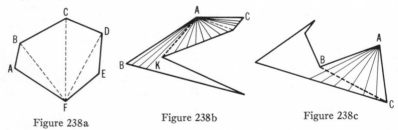

| Figure 238a | Figure 238b | Figure 238c |

109. Let $S(\mathbf{M})$ be a non-negative number associated with a polygon **M**. If $S(\mathbf{M})$ is to be the area of the polygon **M**, then it is natural to require that it satisfy the following conditions:†

1. *If the polygons* $\mathbf{M}_1$ *and* $\mathbf{M}_2$ *are congruent then* $S(\mathbf{M}_1) = S(\mathbf{M}_2)$.

2. *If* **M** *is the union of two disjoint polygons* $\mathbf{M}_1$ *and* $\mathbf{M}_2$ (i.e., if **M** is split into two polygonal parts $\mathbf{M}_1$ and $\mathbf{M}_2$ with no common interior points), *then* $S(\mathbf{M}) = S(\mathbf{M}_1) + S(\mathbf{M}_2)$.

3. *For some polygon* $\mathbf{M}_0$, *we have* $S(\mathbf{M}_0) = 1$.‡

† Conversely, if $S(\mathbf{M})$ satisfies conditions 1.–3., it is the area associated with **M**.
‡ This condition defines a "unit" of area.

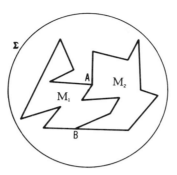

Figure 239

It is clear that the angular defect of a hyperbolic polygon (cf. p. 124) satisfies the first requirement. We shall show that it satisfies the second requirement as well. Indeed, suppose a polygon **M** is split by means of a polygonal line AB into a k-gon **M**$_1$ and an l-gon **M**$_2$ (Fig. 239). We shall show that the angular defect of **M** is the sum of the angular defects of **M**$_1$ and **M**$_2$. Assume that the polygonal line AB has m links (that is, it has, in addition to A and B, $m-1$ internal vertices). Suppose, for definiteness, that A coincides with a vertex of **M**, and B lies on a side of **M** (all other cases are entirely analogous to this one). We have

$$k + l = n + 2m + 1;$$

for, the sum of k vertices of **M**$_1$ and l vertices of **M**$_2$ includes n vertices of **M** and $2m+1$ superfluous vertices (each of the internal vertices of the polygonal line AB and its vertex B enter twice into the sum $k+l$ and not at all into n; the vertex A enters twice into the sum $k+l$ and once into n). Further, if we denote by **A**$_1$, **A**$_2$ and **A** the sums of the angles of the polygons **M**$_1$, **M**$_2$ and **M**, then

$$\mathbf{A}_1 + \mathbf{A}_2 = \mathbf{A} + (2m-1)180°;$$

for, the sum **A**$_1$ + **A**$_2$ contains, in addition to the angles in **A**, $m-1$ $360°$ angles at the interior vertices of the polygonal line AB and one $180°$ angle at its vertex B. Now

$$[(k-2)180° - \mathbf{A}_1] + [(l-2)180° - \mathbf{A}_2]$$
$$= (k+l-4)180° - (\mathbf{A}_1 + \mathbf{A}_2)$$
$$= (n+2m-3)180° - \mathbf{A} - (2m-1)180° = (n-2)180° - \mathbf{A},$$

which is what we wished to prove.

Since the angular defect of a polygon satisfies requirements 1. and 2., it must be proportional to the area function on polygons (if the angular defect of M_0 is $1/k$, then the angular defect of any polygon is equal to its area divided by k).[T]

Note 1. The argument above shows that the area of a hyperbolic triangle cannot be arbitrarily large (for the angular defect cannot exceed 180°). The triangles of maximal area (equal to $k\,180°$, where k is the proportionality constant of Problem 109) are the "triangles" whose sides are pairwise parallel (Fig. 240a; in Fig. 240b the same triangle is represented schematically as in Figs. 115 and 118 of the text).

Note 2. The proof of the fact that the angular defect of a polygon is proportional to its area is valid in Euclidean geometry; here, however, the proportionality factor is zero (the angular defect of an n-gon in Euclidean geometry is zero since the sum of its angles is $(n-2)180°$). It follows that the preceding discussion is of no value in Euclidean geometry; here derivation of the area of a polygon follows a much more complicated path. Even the formula for the area of a triangle given in terms of the magnitudes of its sides and angles is far more complicated than its hyperbolic counterpart; as regards an n-gon, for $n > 3$ there is no transparent general formula in Euclidean geometry which expresses the area of the n-gon in terms of its sides and angles.

It is of interest to note that the proof given above carries over to *spherical geometry* (where a polygon is a portion of the sphere bounded by arcs of great circles; such circles play the same role in spherical geometry as do lines in the plane). The angular defect of a spherical n-gon is always negative, as can be anticipated from the fact that there are spherical triangles with three right angles. It follows that here the proportionality constant (between angular defect and area) is negative. We can say that *the area of a spherical n-gon is proportional to the difference between the sum of its angles and* $180°(n-2)$ (this difference is called *angular excess* of a spherical n-gon). See also pp. 343, 344 of the supplement to Chapter II.[TT]

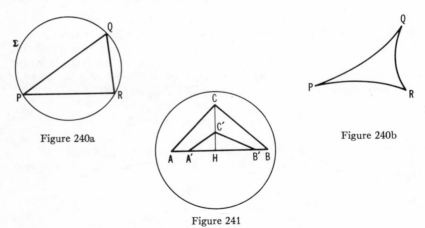

Figure 240a

Figure 241

Figure 240b

[T] This is not obvious. For a proof of this famous theorem of Bolyai see, e.g., p. 345 ff of E. D. Moise, *Elementary Geometry from an Advanced Standpoint*, Addison-Wesley Publishing Co., Reading, 1963.

[TT] Reference to untranslated Russian material.

110. Let ABC and $A'B'C'$ be two hyperbolic triangles with pairwise congruent angles, and let C and C' be the largest angles of these triangles. The altitudes CH and $C'H'$ pass through the interiors of the respective triangles (for the angles A, A' and B, B' are acute in view of the theorem of Problem 108(a); further see the beginning of the solution of Problem 104). If we knew that $AH = A'H'$, we could deduce that the right triangles AHC and $A'H'C'$ are congruent (hypotenuse and acute angle test). This would imply the equality $CH = C'H'$ and the congruence of the right triangles BHC and $B'H'C'$ (hypotenuse and acute angle test). The required congruence of triangles ABC and $A'B'C'$ would follow. Thus we need only show that the assumption $AH \neq A'H'$ leads to a contradiction. Suppose, for definiteness, that $AH > A'H'$. We move both triangles (by a hyperbolic motion) so that points H and H' coincide with the center of **K**, and line AB coincides with line $A'B'$ (Fig. 241). Since $AH > A'H'$ and $\delta_A = \delta_{A'}$, it follows that $\sphericalangle A > \sphericalangle A'$ (cf. p. 115). But then $HC > HC'$ and $\sphericalangle HCA < \sphericalangle HC'A'$. The latter implies that $\delta_{HCA} < \delta_{HC'A'}$. If we had $HB' > HB$, then we could show in a similar manner that $HC' > HC$, which contradicts the inequality $HC > HC'$ obtained above. Hence $HB > HB'$ and, as above, $\delta_{HCB} < \delta_{HC'B'}$. But then

$$\delta_C = \delta_{HCA} + \delta_{HCB} < \delta_{HC'A'} + \delta_{HC'B'} = \delta_{C'},$$

which contradicts the equality $\delta_{C'} = \delta_C$.

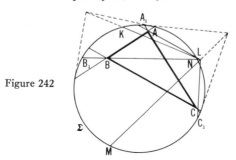

Figure 242

111. Draw the perpendicular bisectors KL and MN of sides AB and AC of $\triangle ABC$, and the lines AA_1, BB_1 and CC_1 which pass through the vertices of $\triangle ABC$ and belong to the same pencil as lines KL and MN (depending on whether KL and MN intersect, are ultraparallel or parallel, the lines AA_1, BB_1 and CC_1 pass through their point of intersection, are perpendicular to their common perpendicular, or are parallel to them; Fig. 242). In view of the theorem of Problem 101(b), KL is the axis of symmetry of the lines AA_1 and BB_1, and MN is the axis of symmetry of the lines AA_1 and CC_1. This implies that all vertices of $\triangle ABC$ lie on the circle (or equidistant curve, or horocycle) obtained by choosing on each line l of the pencil determined by KL and MN the point symmetric to A with respect to the axis of symmetry of AA_1 and l (see pp. 126–129).

It is easy to see that all the possibilities envisaged in the preceding discussion can actually occur; after all, it is possible to inscribe arbitrarily many triangles in a circle, equidistant curve or horocycle. [It is likewise easy to see that these possibilities are mutually exclusive. If it is possible to circumscribe a circle about $\triangle ABC$, then there exists a point O equidistant from its vertices, and lines KL and MN must intersect at O. Similarly, it is possible to show that if one can circumscribe an equidistant curve about $\triangle ABC$, then KL and MN must have a common perpendicular, and finally, if it is possible to circumscribe a horocycle about $\triangle ABC$, then KL and MN must be parallel.]

112. Consider two hyperbolic circles S_1 and S_2 with radii r_1 and r_2, a regular hexagon $A_1A_2A_3A_4A_5A_6$ circumscribed about S_1 and a regular hexagon $B_1B_2B_3B_4B_5B_6$ inscribed in S_2.† Let s_1 and s_2 denote the hyperbolic circumferences of the circles, and p_1 and p_2 the perimeters of the hexagons. Then

$$\frac{s_1}{r_1} < \frac{p_1}{r_1}, \qquad \frac{s_2}{r_2} > \frac{p_2}{r_2}.$$

Hence, if we could choose r_1 and r_2 so that $p_1/r_1 < p_2/r_2$, then it would follow that $s_1/r_1 < s_2/r_2$, and this would prove the assertion of the problem.

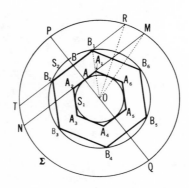

Figure 243

† The definition of a regular hexagon in hyperbolic geometry is the same as the Euclidean definition. We note that in hyperbolic geometry it is not always possible to circumscribe a regular hexagon about a circle, and this fact restricts the magnitude of r_1.

If the centers of S_1 and S_2 coincide with the center O of **K**, then these two curves are Euclidean circles (Fig. 243). Let their Euclidean radii be a_1 and a_2 (the radius of the disk **K** is taken to have unit length). Then

$$r_1 = \log\left(\frac{OP}{AP} \Big/ \frac{OQ}{AQ}\right) = \log\frac{AQ}{AP} = \log\frac{1+a_1}{1-a_1}, \qquad r_2 = \log\frac{1+a_2}{1-a_2},$$

$$AA_1 = a_1\sqrt{3}/3, \qquad b_1 = AM = \sqrt{1-a_1^2},$$

$$d_{AA_1} = \log\left(\frac{AM}{A_1M} \Big/ \frac{AN}{A_1N}\right) = \log\frac{A_1N}{A_1M} = \log\frac{b_1 + a_1\sqrt{3}/3}{b_1 - a_1\sqrt{3}/3}, \qquad p_1 = 12d_{AA_1},$$

and

$$BB_1 = a_2/2, \qquad OB = a_2\sqrt{3}/2, \qquad b_2 = BR = \sqrt{1 - 3a_2^2/4},$$

$$d_{BB_1} = \log\left(\frac{BR}{B_1R} \Big/ \frac{BT}{B_1T}\right) = \log\frac{B_1T}{B_2T} = \log\frac{b_2 + a_2/2}{b_2 - a_2/2}, \qquad p_2 = 12d_{BB_1}.$$

In particular, if $a_1 = 0.1$, $a_2 = 0.9$ then

$$r_1 = \log(1.1/0.9) \approx 0.08715, \qquad r_2 = \log(1.9/0.1) \approx 1.27875,$$

$$a_1\sqrt{3}/3 \approx 0.05774, \qquad b_1 \approx 0.99499,$$

$$d_{AA_1} \approx \log(1.05273/0.93725) \approx 0.05046, \qquad p_1 \approx 0.6055,$$

$$b_2 \approx 0.6265, \qquad d_{BB_1} \approx \log(1.0765/0.1765) \approx 0.78627, \qquad p_2 \approx 9.435.$$

Hence

$$\frac{s_1}{r_1} < \frac{p_1}{r_1} < 7 \qquad \text{and} \qquad \frac{s_2}{r_2} > \frac{p_2}{r_2} > 7.$$

Note. It can be shown that in hyperbolic geometry, the ratio s/r of the circumference s of a circle to its radius r increases with r. Specifically, if $r \to 0$, then $s/r \to \pi = 3.14159\cdots$, and if $r \to \infty$, then $s/r \to \infty$.